GEOMETRY

Plane and Solid

THE LAIDLAW MATHEMATICS SERIES

ALGEBRA—First Course

GEOMETRY—Plane and Solid

ALGEBRA—Second Course

TRIGONOMETRY and Advanced Topics

GENERAL MATHEMATICS—Book One

GENERAL MATHEMATICS—Book Two

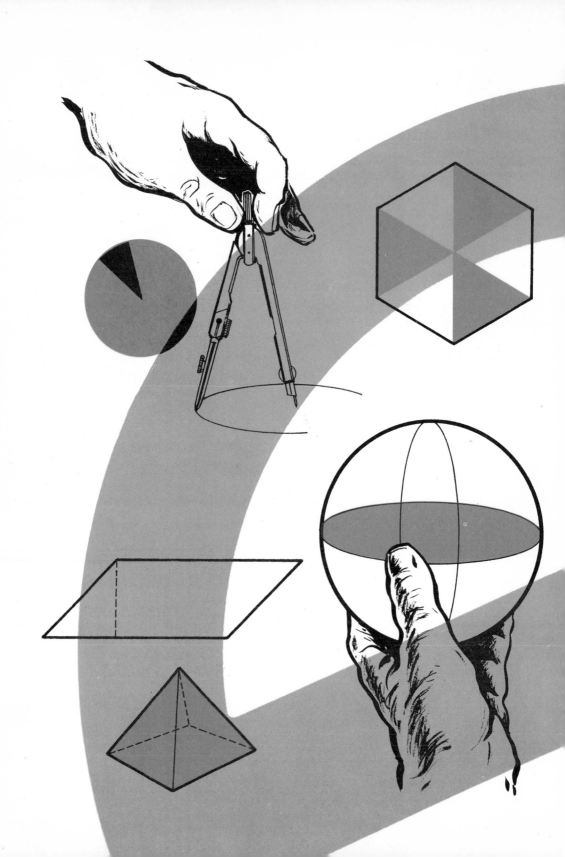

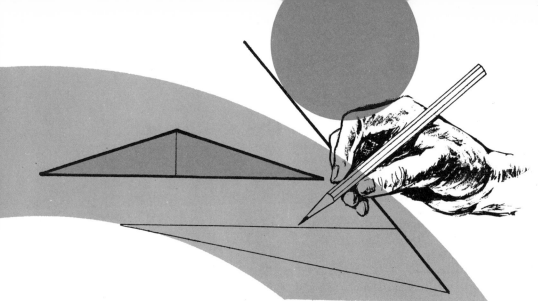

GEOMETRY

Plane and Solid

Kenneth E. Brown
Specialist in Mathematics
United States Office of Education

Gaylord C. Montgomery
Chairman, Mathematics Department
John Burroughs School
St. Louis, Missouri

LAIDLAW BROTHERS • PUBLISHERS

River Forest, Illinois

Summit, New Jersey   Palo Alto, California   Dallas, Texas   Atlanta, Georgia

ART DIRECTOR: Raymon Naylor

COVER DESIGNOR: George Armstrong, Jr.

PHOTOGRAPHS:

Culver Pictures, Inc.: 436.
Philip Gendreau: 24, 28, 46, 159, 172, 260, 343, 361 (G. A. Douglas), 403, 479, 521, 547.
Monkmeyer Press Photo Service: 96, 202 (P. Palmer).
Photo Researchers, Inc.: 370 (M. Baur), 461 (H. Taylor).
Wide World Photos: 312.

PREFACE

Geometry—Plane and Solid is designed to be a clear, teachable, yet challenging text fulfilling the generally accepted objectives of teaching geometry. Essentially these objectives are

(*1*) to develop an understanding of the meaning and nature of proof.

(*2*) to teach the process of deductive reasoning in mathematical and non-mathematical situations.

(*3*) to develop an understanding of plane and space relationships.

(*4*) to provide opportunities for original and creative thinking.

(*5*) to develop an appreciation of the power of mathematics.

(*6*) to extend and strengthen mathematics vocabulary.

To help achieve these objectives, the recommendations of The College Entrance Examination Board, The Commission of Mathematics, and the Reports of the Curriculum Committee of the National Council of Teachers of Mathematics were examined and considered in selecting and organizing the contents of this book.

Development

Throughout the text geometry is developed as a postulational, "if-then," system of reasoning. Considerable emphasis is given to the nature of proof as a sequence of related statements directed toward establishing the validity of a conclusion. Each conclusion is justified by reference to recognized and acceptable assumptions, definitions, undefined terms, previously proved theorems, or a combination of these reasons. The students are made aware that each theorem can be traced back to its fundamental assumptions.

Many of the early original proofs are nonmathematical and pertain to familiar situations. The first mathematical proofs are almost an immediate consequence of an assumption. Then many original, more sophisticated proofs are included requiring knowledge of a variety of theorems, power of analysis, insight, and reasoning.

At the end of each chapter the concepts of Plane Geometry are extended to Solid Geometry. In this way the essentials of Solid Geometry may be included or omitted at the discretion of the teacher. Chapters on Trigonometry and Coordinate Geometry have been provided to be used entirely or in part.

Discovery

The developmental exercises, which are an integral part of the text, lead the student to the discovery of the proofs of new principles presented in the lesson. They encourage the student to analyze the conditions stated and to think about the assumptions and theorems which are related to these conditions. Numerous complete proofs are given to furnish the student with models that he can follow. Other proofs are partially complete to provide essential experiences in sustained thinking. The student's understanding of the principles discussed in the developmental exercises is then reinforced in the exercises that follow

Provisions For Individual Differences

Special provisions have been made for all ranges of ability. The abundance of developmental exercises and model proofs will particularly benefit the slow student. For the more-able student each chapter includes "Extend Your Horizon." In general, the odd-numbered exercises are less difficult than the even-numbered exercises, and within each group the exercises are arranged in order of increasing difficulty.

Visual Aids

Color is used functionally to indicate points of emphasis. Two vertical parallel color lines are used to indicate informational material to be learned. All theorems, corollaries, and summary statements are marked in this way. Two horizontal parallel color lines are used to indicate exercise material. The developmental exercises which are marked with both vertical and horizontal lines provide both material to be learned and exercise material.

Review

Each chapter ends with a chapter summary, review exercises, and a chapter test. The chapter summary is a concise outline of the chapter with references to the pages where a discussion of the material may be found. The review exercises and chapter test enable the student to readily check his progress and the completeness of his vocabulary. Independent chapter tests with which the teacher may check the progress of the student are provided in the teacher's manual.

The Authors

CONTENTS

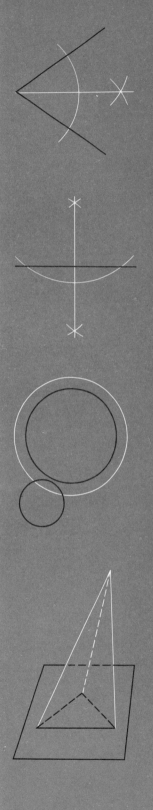

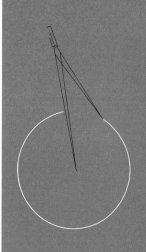

Chapter 6   Indirect Proof and Inequalities   295

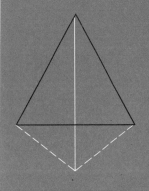

Chapter 7   Locus   335

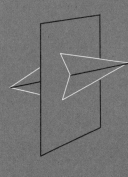

Contents_____11

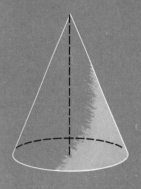

Chapter 11   Numerical Trigonometry   509

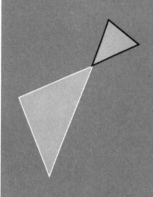

Chapter 12   Coordinate Geometry   533

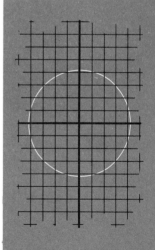

Chapter 1

WHAT IS GEOMETRY?

When man first recognized form, shape, and pattern, *geometry* came into existence. The early pottery of all countries showed a crude attempt at geometric ornamentation using simple circles and lines. As the civilizations developed, the designs showed greater balance and symmetry.

The Egyptians extended the uses of geometry to *measurement*. When the Nile River overflowed, erasing landmarks and boundary lines, it was necessary to measure the land to determine new boundary lines. In developing surveying methods, the Egyptians recognized many constant relationships between the sides and angles of certain figures. They used these relationships in measuring similar areas and in constructing the pyramids, sphinxes, and obelisks. The Egyptians based this applied geometry on observation and experience. They made no attempt to prove that the techniques or relationships were valid.

This practical geometry stimulated the interest of Greek scholars. They took the important step of *proving* the relationships, raising geometry from an intuitive tool to a *logically developed science*. Many famous scholars, including Thales, Pythagoras, Hippocrates, and Plato, contributed to this development. They emphasized the importance of a rigorous method of reasoning. Plato, perhaps trying to insure that his students were capable of sound reasoning, had inscribed over the door of the Academy at Athens, "Let no one enter here who is ignorant of geometry." About the year 300 B. C. Euclid, the Father of Geometry, included the proofs accumulated to that time in a series of books called the *Elements*. The geometry you are about to study is fundamentally the same as the geometry developed by the Greeks. It emphasizes the importance of logical reasoning.

In a logical system of forming conclusions, as developed in geometry, each proof is a link in a chain of proofs. It depends on the previous proofs and can be used to establish later proofs. At the base of the entire system are (*1*) undefined terms, (*2*) definitions, and (*3*) assumptions.

UNDEFINED TERMS

Harold Osburn was stopped by the Highway Patrol for driving 65 miles per hour. Was he exceeding the speed limit? Before his guilt or innocence can be established many terms must be understood. What is meant by *driving?* What is meant by *the speed limit?* In many states there exists a *reasonable and prudent* speed law rather than an absolute maximum speed law. Thus, in these states the terms *reasonable* and *prudent* must be understood.

If you consult a dictionary to define *reasonable*, you will find that you are led, in a circular fashion, back to *reasonable*.

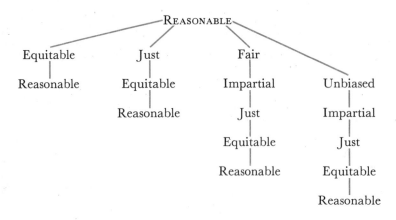

However, if you consult the dictionary for the meaning of *driving*, and each new word that occurs in the definition, you will find a long and perhaps endless list of definitions. The definition of *drive* is *to cause to turn, move, point,* or *follow a course.*

To cause is *to bring about; to bring about* is *to accomplish; to accomplish* is *to effect; to effect* is *to make; to make* is *to compel.* If you assume that you know the meaning of *to compel* you can stop there. If not, you must continue the chain of definitions until you do find a word that you assume you know. This word is considered an *undefined term* since you accepted it without definition.

Thus you see that an attempt to define every word will:

(*1*) lead you back to the original word, or

(*2*) produce an endless chain of definitions.

These difficulties may be eliminated by accepting certain key words as undefined, and keeping these as few as possible. In geometry, the undefined terms will include *between, straight, point, line, surface,* and *congruent.*

A **point** *may be described as a* **position.** No one can actually see a point because it has no dimensions. Usually a dot is used to represent a point. It is identified by a capital letter as in Figure 1, and is read "Point *A*."

• *A*

Fig. 1

A **line** *may be described as a* **set of points.** It has only one dimension—*length.* In Euclidean Geometry a line extends indefinitely in two opposite directions. If *A* and *B* are any two points on a line, then the set of points consisting of *A* and *B* and all the points between *A* and *B* is called a *line segment.* When no misunderstanding will result, a line segment is sometimes referred to as a *line.* For example, to draw a line two inches long really means that a line segment two inches long is to be represented. A line segment is represented by a mark drawn along a straightedge or ruler. It is identified by capital letters at its endpoints or by a single lower-case letter. The line segment in Figure 2 is called "*Line AB*" or "*Line l.*" Points *A* and *B* are points on line *l.* Line *l* is also said to contain points *A* and *B.* Two lines are said to be equal if they have the same measure. A *broken line* is made up of line segments connected so that successive line segments have an endpoint in common.

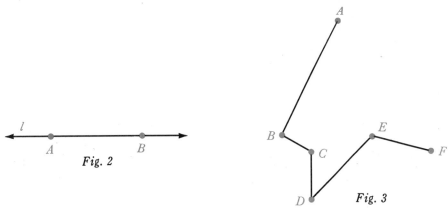

Fig. 2

Fig. 3

Exercises

1. Draw a line segment and identify it in two ways.

2. Name 5 points on this line and 10 line segments.

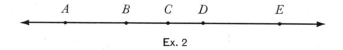

Ex. 2

3. Using the line in Exercise **1** identify a point on the line. Name another point on the line. How many points are on the line?

4. Draw two line segments so they have one point in common.

5. Draw two line segments so they have every point in common.

6. Is it possible to draw two line segments so they have two points in common? Why or why not?

DEFINITIONS

The *definition* of a word is an explanation of the meaning of the word. Be alert to distinguish between definitions and descriptions. If an attempt is made to define "desk" as an article of furniture having a flat top resting on legs, the desk is not distinguished from a table. Unless people understand and agree as to the meanings of words and phrases used in a discussion, it is difficult to arrive at similar conclusions. The properties necessary for an acceptable definition are listed below.

An acceptable definition must

(*1*) be expressed in words or phrases previously defined or which have been accepted as undefined.

(*2*) name the term (or phrases) being defined.

(*3*) place the term in its smallest (or nearest) class.

(*4*) state all the characteristics which make it different from other members of its class.

(*5*) be true when its form is reversed, i.e., if its subject and predicate are interchanged.

(*6*) include no unnecessary information.

▌Developmental Exercises

DE—1. Examine the following statement in terms of the requirements for an acceptable definition: *A plane is a surface such that a straight line joining any two points of the plane lies entirely in the surface.*

Solution

In this definition

● the words used are readily understood.

● the term to be defined is named.

● it is placed in its nearest class (*surface*).

● it is distinguished from all others in the class (*such that a straight line joining any two points lies entirely in the surface*).

● the form may be reversed (*any surface such that a straight line joining any two points lies entirely in the surface is a plane*).

● there is no unnecessary information.

Since all the requirements have been met, the definition is acceptable.

To help you determine if the term is placed in its nearest class, you may wish to make a sketch of the relationships between the possible classes. For example, consider the completion of the statement "A wren is a ?." Some of the classes which you may consider are *animal*, *bird*, and *perching bird*. All members of each class may be represented by a circle. Since all birds are animals, the circle representing *all birds* is completely within the circle representing *all animals*. Likewise, since all perching birds are birds, the circle representing *perching birds* is completely within the circle representing *all birds*. The wren is in all three of these classes, thus it goes in the innermost circle, *all perching birds*. The nearest class is always this innermost circle.

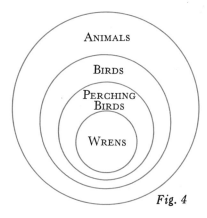

Fig. 4

DE—2. Examine the following statement in terms of the requirements for an acceptable definition: *George Washington was a human being.*

Solution

● The words used are understood.
● The term being defined is named (*George Washington*).
● The nearest class is not named.
● The nearest class is *presidents* not *human beings.*
● It states no characteristics which makes him different from others in his class.
● It is not reversible (*any human being is George Washington*).
● There is no unnecessary information.

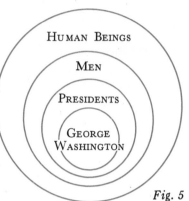

Fig. 5

Since all the conditions for an acceptable definition are not satisfied, this definition is not acceptable.

Exercises

Examine the following statements in terms of the requirements for an acceptable definition:

1. A man is a biped.

2. A deer is an animal.

3. An exponent is a number.

4. Three is a number.

5. A box is a rectangular parallelepiped.

6. A cone is a truncated nappe.

7. It is many sided.

8. It has two equal sides.

9. A triangle is a polygon with three equal sides.

10. A rectangle is a polygon with all sides equal.

11. The median is a line from the vertex to the opposite side.

12. The bisector of an angle is a line that divides the angle into two equal angles.

13. Before accepting or rejecting the following statement, for what words would you request a definition? *Ed may not play in Saturday's game because his scholastic standing is unsatisfactory.*

14. Name the group of which the italicized word is a member.
  a. *Biology* is an interesting subject.
  b. George held the *thermometer* in his left hand.

15. Explain why these definitions are unsatisfactory:
  a. Cows are farm animals.
  b. A chestnut tree is a tree that bears chestnuts.

16. Reverse the following: *A line segment is the portion of a straight line included between any two points upon the line.*

ASSUMPTIONS IN LOGICAL REASONING

Mr. Roth, the principal of Park Side High School, read two different articles in "Future Vocations for Young Americans." One article stated that too many students who were not capable were trying to study mathematics. It suggested that the school personnel should guide students into other courses. The other article indicated that the very survival of our nation depends upon an increase in the number of students studying mathematics.

Both arguments seemed to be logical but the conclusions were quite different. Should Mr. Roth encourage more students to study mathematics?

In examining a conclusion to see if it is true or false, one must examine the premises to see if they are true. The conditions we assume to be true are called *assumptions* or *axioms*. In geometry, as well as in daily reasoning, we must be aware of the assumptions and the definitions used in the premises. Different assumptions or different definitions may lead to contradictory conclusions.

Conclusions should always be based on acceptable definitions and assumptions.

In the study of geometry the assumptions accepted during the study of arithmetic and of algebra will continue to be acceptable.

Study carefully the assumptions listed. You should understand each one and become completely familiar with it. These assumptions will be used throughout this book.

Assumption 1

If equals are added to equals the sums are equal.

Illustration: If $x - 3 = 5$

$$\underline{+3 = +3} \text{ (Add 3 to both members.)}$$

then $x - 3 + 3 = 5 + 3$

$$x = 8$$

Assumption 2

If equals are subtracted from equals the remainders are equal.

Illustration: If $A + B = 3 + B$

$$\underline{-B = -B} \text{ (Subtract } B \text{ from both members.)}$$

then $A + B - B = 3 + B - B$

$$A = 3$$

Assumption 3

If equals are multiplied by equals the products are equal.

Illustration: If $\frac{1}{2}A = 30$

then $2 \cdot \frac{1}{2}A = 2 \cdot 30$ (Multiply both members by 2.)

$$A = 60.$$

Assumption 4

If equals are divided by equals the quotients are equal.

Illustration: If $2x = 8$

then $\dfrac{2x}{2} = \dfrac{8}{2}$ (Divide both members by 2.)

$$x = 4.$$

Assumption 5

A quantity may be substituted for its equal.

Illustration: If $A + B = 150'$ and $B = 60'$, then $A + 60' = 150'$.

Assumption 6

Quantities equal to the same or to equal quantities are equal. (Two line segments are said to be equal if their lengths have the same measure.)

Illustration: If $A = C$ If $AB = 24''$

and $B = C$,   and $CD = 2'$,

then $A = B$.   then $AB = CD$.

Assumption 7

Any quantity equals itself.

Illustration: $AB = AB$.

Assumption 8

Like powers or like roots of equal quantities are equal.

Illustration: If $x = 2$ If $x^2 = 4$

            then $x^2 = 2^2$.   then $x = \pm \sqrt{4}$.

                $x^2 = 4$. $x = \pm 2$.

Assumption 9

The whole is equal to the sum of its parts and is greater than any one of its parts.

Illustration: $12 = 8 + 4$ and 12 is greater than 8 or 4.

Assumption 10

A line segment can be extended in either direction.

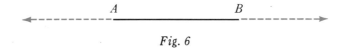

Fig. 6

Assumption 11

A line segment has but one midpoint.

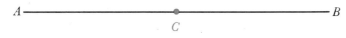

Fig. 7

Assumption 12

A straight line is the shortest line that can be drawn between two points.

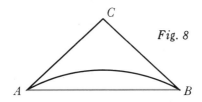

Fig. 8

Assumption 13

Two straight lines cannot intersect in more than one point.

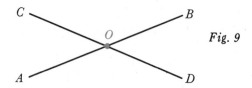

Fig. 9

Assumption 14

Between two points one and only one straight line can be drawn.

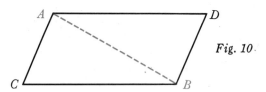

Fig. 10

Exercises

State the assumptions that are the bases for each of the conclusions below.

1. **Given:** $R = S$, $T = S$.
   Conclusion: $R = T$.

2. **Given:** $ab = a^2x$.
   Conclusion: $b = ax$.

3. **Given:** Points A and B.
   Conclusion: Line AB may be constructed.

4. **Given:** e the midpoint of AB,
               d is not e.
   Conclusion: d is not the midpoint of AB.

5. **Given:** $a^2 = 4$.
   Conclusion: $a = \pm 2$.

6. **Given:** $a^3 = 27$.
   Conclusion: $a = 3$.

7. **Given:** $AE = CF$, $EB = FD$.
   Conclusion: $AB = CD$.

8. **Given:** $AB = CD$, $AE = CF$.   A   B   C   D   E   F
   Conclusion: $EB = FD$.   Ex. 7-8

9. Given:

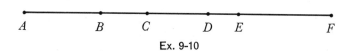

Ex. 9-10

Conclusion: $AE = AB + BC + CD + DE$.

10. Given: Same as above.
Conclusion: AE is greater than AD.

11. Given: $A = B$, $D = B$.
Conclusion: $AD = B^2$.

12. Given: Line l contains points M and N,
Line m contains point M,
Line l is not line m.
Conclusion: Point N is not on line m.

13. Given: $A = B$, $C = D$, and $C = A$.
Conclusion: $B = D$.

14. Given: Line segments AB, AC, and BC.
Conclusion: AB is less than $(AC + BC)$.

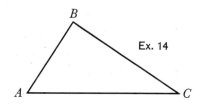

Ex. 14

15. Given: RS is divided into three equal segments at P and O,
KW is divided into three equal segments at L and M,
$RP = KL$.
Conclusion: $RS = KW$.

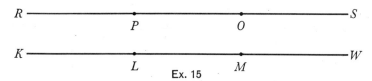

Ex. 15

16. Given: Each of two pairs of skis is listed to sell for $65.
A 20% discount is allowed on each.
Conclusion: Each pair can be purchased for the same amount.

17. **Given:** $BC = DE$, $DE = AB$.
    Conclusion: $BC = AB$.
18. **Given:** $K = 3m + 2$, $K = 2m - 7$.
    Conclusion: $K = -25$.
19. **Given:** $BC = EF$, $EF = BA$.
    Conclusion: $BC = BA$.
20. **Given:** $BD = AB$, $DC = AB$.
    Conclusion: $BD = DC$.

TOOLS OF GEOMETRY

Each building in the Manhattan skyline is a good example of what can be achieved at an architect's drawing board.

Architects who make scale drawings for the carpenter and bridge builder to follow often have need for parallel rulers, T-squares, transparent triangles, and a drawing board. A ruler may be used to measure length. The drawing of an angle may be aided by using a protractor.

All these instruments are used in drawing figures. If you copy or draw a figure using only an unmarked straightedge and a compass, the figure is said to be *constructed*. You must be alert to the difference between *draw* and *construct*.

"Construct" means to represent using only an unmarked straightedge and a compass.

Developmental Exercises

DE—1. Using a compass and straightedge duplicate the given line segment.

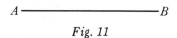

Fig. 11

Solution

- Draw any line, *l*, to be used as a working line. Choose any point, *P*, on this line.

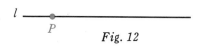

Fig. 12

- Place the steel point of the compass on *A*. Open or close the compass until the pencil point is on *B*.

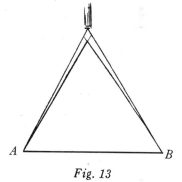

Fig. 13

- With the steel point on *P* and the compass points at the distance equal to *AB*, strike an arc across *l*.
- Label the point of intersection of the arc and line *Q*.
- *PQ* is equal to *AB*.

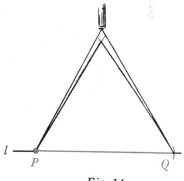

Fig. 14

In using the compass hold it at the top between a thumb and two fingers. Incline the compass slightly forward to rotate the pencil point as you keep a steady pressure on the steel point. The pencil point should be kept sharpened and both points of the compass adjusted to the same length when closed.

DE—2. Bisect a line segment.

Solution

- Draw a line segment such as *AB*.

A ———————————————————— B

Fig. 15

- Set one point of your compass at *A*, and with the points opened more than one-half the length of *AB*, mark arcs above and below *AB*.

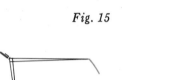

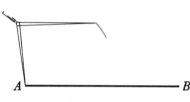

Fig. 16

- Keeping the compass points the same distance apart, place one point at *B*, and mark arcs above and below *AB*. Do the first and second pairs of arcs cross? If not, make one or both pairs longer.

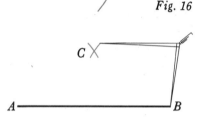

D ✕   *Fig. 17*

- Mark the points of crossing with the letters *C* and *D*.
- Using a straightedge, draw a line between points *C* and *D*. Where this line crosses *AB*, place the letter *P*. The line *CD* bisects line *AB*. Point *P* bisects *AB*. Point *P* is called the *midpoint* of *AB*.

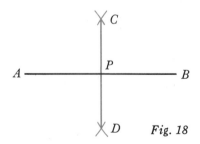

Fig. 18

A midpoint divides a line segment into two equal line segments. A line segment has one, and only one, midpoint.

Exercises

Draw lines of the lengths indicated below, then copy the lines using only an unmarked ruler and a compass.

    1. a. 3 in.   **b.** 4 in.

    2. a. $3\frac{1}{2}$ in.   **b.** 5 in.

Draw line segments in about the same position as those below but longer. Bisect each line.

    3.   **4.**   **5.**

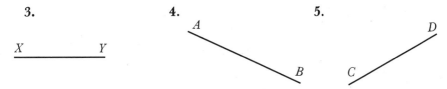

    6. Draw a line segment. Label it *XY*. Use a compass and straight-edge to construct a line segment equal to 2*XY*.

    7. Use a compass to arrange the four line segments in order of length, listing the shortest first.

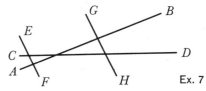

Ex. 7

    8. Draw two unequal line segments. Label them *x* and *y*. Construct a line segment equal to $2x+3y$.

    9. Draw segments *AB* and *CD* with *CD* greater than *AB*. On a line of indefinite length, construct a line segment equal to $(CD-AB)$.

    10. Draw a figure as indicated below and bisect *BC*. Can you think of a short cut for bisecting *BC* in this figure?

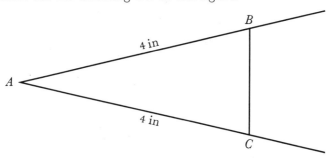

Ex. 10

ANGLES

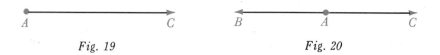

In taking off, the flaps of the Convair 880 jet airliner are lowered. The angle
of the flaps changes the shape of the wing to increase the lift.

In landing an airplane a cadet is instructed to set the flaps on the
wings at various angles on the final approach. What is the meaning of
"15 degrees of flap?" An understanding of the meaning of an angle is
necessary to answer this question.

*A part of a line having one endpoint and extending without limit in one and
only one direction is a* **ray.** See Figure 19. Any point of a line may be
considered as the endpoint of two rays into which the line is divided.
These two rays extend in opposite directions. Thus, in Figure 20 point
A is the endpoint of rays AB and AC.

A C B A C

Fig. 19   *Fig. 20*

When two rays have a common endpoint, an angle is formed. The rays are called the *sides* or *arms* of the angle; the common point is called the *vertex* of the angle.

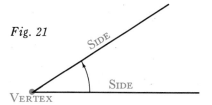

Fig. 21

The angle in Figure 22 may be named as ∠0, ∠1, ∠AOB, or ∠BOA (∠ is the symbol for angle). If three letters are used the middle letter designates the vertex.

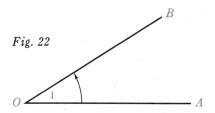

Fig. 22

Developmental Exercises

DE—1. Name the angles in Figure 23.

Fig. 23

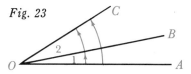

Solution

The lower angle may be named ∠AOB, ∠BOA, or ∠1. The upper angle may be named ∠BOC, ∠COB, or ∠2. The large angle which includes both smaller angles may be written as ∠AOC or ∠COA. ∠O cannot be used since it might refer to any of the three angles formed at O.

DE—2. Using Figure 23 complete the following:

  a. ∠AOB + ∠BOC = ?
  b. ∠AOC − ∠BOC = ?
  c. ∠AOC − ∠AOB = ?

Solution

a. From the axiom—the whole is equal to the sum of its parts—∠AOB + ∠BOC = ∠AOC.

b. If ∠BOC is subtracted from the whole, ∠AOC, ∠AOB remains. Therefore, ∠AOC − ∠AOB = ∠BOC.

c. If ∠AOC is subtracted, ∠BOC remains. Therefore, ∠AOC − ∠AOB = ∠BOC.

Exercises

1. Use three letters to name each angle in the diagram at the right.

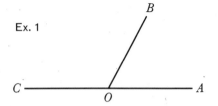

Ex. 1

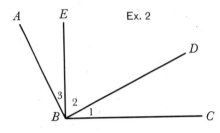

Ex. 2

2. Name each of the angles at the left by using:

    a. three letters,

    b. a capital letter at the vertex, if possible,

    c. a number inside the angle.

3. Draw two angles having the same vertex and a common side.

4. Draw two angles with a common vertex but not a common side.

5. Draw three straight lines, *AB*, *CD*, and *EF*, all intersecting at point *G*. Use three letters to name each angle formed.

6. Draw four straight lines, *RS*, *TU*, *VW*, and *XY*, all intersecting at point *M*. Use three letters to name each angle formed.

In Exercises **7-8** *refer to the diagram at the right. Use three letters for each answer.*

7. a. $\angle 3 + \angle 2 = \angle ?$

    b. $\angle ABC - \angle 1 = \angle ?$

    c. $\angle CBA - \angle 1 = \angle ?$

8. a. $\angle ABD - \angle EBA = \angle ?$

    b. $\angle 1 + \angle 3 = \angle ? - \angle ?$

    c. $\angle 1 + \angle 2 + \angle 3 = \angle ?$

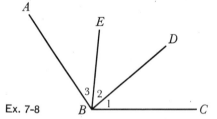

Ex. 7-8

9. Draw a straight line and label it *AB*. Rotate line *AB* about point *A*, $\frac{1}{4}$ of a complete rotation. Label the final position of the line *AC*. Use three different methods to name the angle formed.

10. Draw an angle formed by a line making

    a. $\frac{1}{4}$ of a complete rotation.

    b. $\frac{1}{2}$ of a complete rotation.

    c. $\frac{3}{4}$ of a complete rotation.

    d. a complete rotation.

ANGLE MEASUREMENT

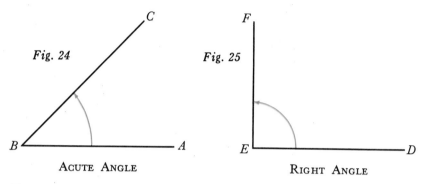

Fig. 24

Fig. 25

ACUTE ANGLE

RIGHT ANGLE

The size of an angle depends on the amount of rotation between the sides and not on the length of the sides. The angle in Figure 25 is greater than the angle in Figure 24 if the amount of rotation between the sides of the first is greater.

> **The size of an angle depends on the amount of rotation between the sides.**

In Figure 25 there is one-fourth of a complete turn (rotation) from *ED* to *EF*. Such an angle is called a *right angle*. In Figure 24 the separation is less than one-fourth of a complete turn. Such an angle is an *acute angle*. If the rays are separated by one-half a rotation, a *straight angle* is formed. The angle between a right angle (one-fourth of a rotation) and a straight angle (one-half a rotation) is an *obtuse angle*. In Figure 28 the amount of separation is more than one-half a turn and less than a complete turn. Such an angle is a *reflex angle*.

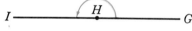

Fig. 26   STRAIGHT ANGLE

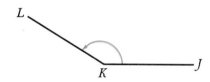

Fig. 27   OBTUSE ANGLE

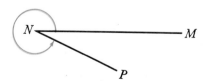

Fig. 28   REFLEX ANGLE

The measure of an angle is usually given in *degrees*. One degree is the measure for $\frac{1}{360}$ of one complete rotation. Thus, a complete rotation is 360 degrees. A right angle is one-fourth of 360 degrees or 90 degrees. Two angles are said to be *equal* if they have the same measure.

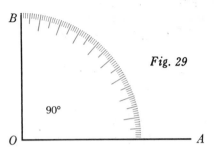

Fig. 29

The degree is divided into 60 equal parts, each called one *minute*. The symbol for minute is ′. The minute is divided into 60 equal parts, each called one *second*. The symbol for second is ″. 37 degrees, 23 minutes, 18 seconds may be written 37°23′18″. Also, it may be written 37°23.3′ since 18″ is equivalent to $\frac{18}{60}$ or .3′.

1 revolution = 360° (degrees)   1° = 60′ (minutes)   1′ = 60″ (seconds)

If two angles have the same vertex and a common side (one ray is a side of each angle) between them, they are called *adjacent angles*. In each figure below, point A is the vertex of $\angle CAB$ and $\angle DAC$, AC is a common side. Thus, $\angle DAC$ and $\angle CAB$ are adjacent angles.

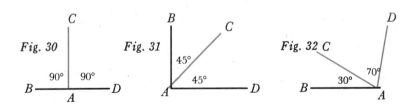

If two angles added together form $\frac{1}{4}$ of a complete revolution (a right angle), they are called *complementary angles*. See Figure 31.

If the sum of two angles is $\frac{1}{2}$ of a complete revolution (a straight angle), the angles are called *supplementary angles*. Complementary and supplementary angles may or may not be adjacent angles.

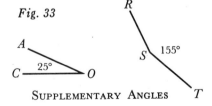

Fig. 33

SUPPLEMENTARY ANGLES

Developmental Exercises

DE—1. Classify the following angles.

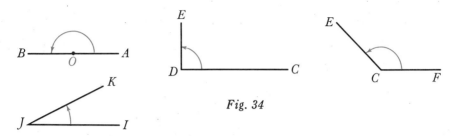

Fig. 34

Solution

∠*AOB* is $\frac{1}{2}$ of a complete rotation and is therefore a straight angle. Another way of defining a straight angle is the following: When the sides of an angle extend in opposite directions so as to be in the same straight line, the angle formed is a straight angle.

∠*CDE* is $\frac{1}{4}$ of a complete rotation and is therefore a right angle.

∠*FCE* is an obtuse angle. Why?

∠*IJK* is an acute angle. Why?

DE—2. Determine the number of degrees in ∠*ABC*.

Solution

Fig. 35

The protractor is an instrument used to measure angles.

Fig. 36

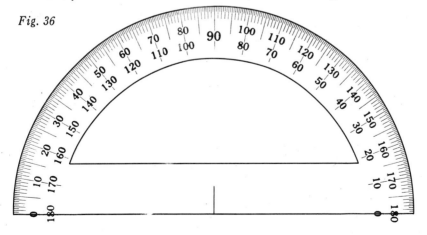

● Place the protractor along a side of the angle so that the center mark of the protractor is on the vertex of the angle. In Figure 37 the center mark is at *B*.

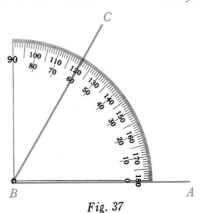

Fig. 37

● The measure of the angle will be found on the scale which has its zero point on the side of the angle. Notice that in this position the inner scale has its zero point on side *AB*. Thus the measure of the angle will be found on the inner scale.

● Read the measure of the angle where side *BC* crosses the inner scale. In Figure 37 ∠*ABC* measures 60°.

  Now place the protractor along side *BC* with the center mark at the vertex. Which scale has its zero mark on side *BC*? On which scale will you read the measure of ∠*ABC*?

DE—3. Using a protractor draw an angle of 40°

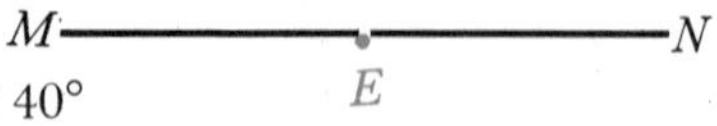

Solution

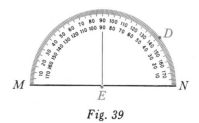

Fig. 38

● Draw a working line *MN* with any point *E*.

● Place the protractor along line *MN* with its center at point *E*.

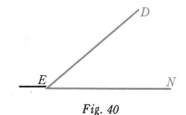

Fig. 39

● Find 40 on the inner scale of the protractor. Mark this place on the paper point *D*.

● Remove the protractor and draw a line through points *E* and *D*.
● The measure of ∠*NED* is 40°.

Fig. 40

Exercises

1. If rays *MN* and *NO* are extended, what is the effect on the size of ∠*MNO?*

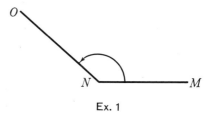

Ex. 1

2. Arrange the angles according to size, beginning with the largest.

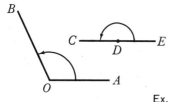

Ex. 2

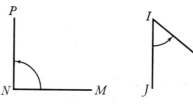

3. Tell whether each angle in Exercise **2** is acute, right, etc.

4. Draw two acute angles that are not equal.

5. Draw two obtuse angles that are not equal.

6. Can you draw two right angles that are not equal? Why or why not?

7. Can you draw two straight angles that are not equal? Why or why not?

8. Can you draw two reflex angles that are not equal? Why or why not?

*Tell whether each of the angles in Exercises **9-10** are acute, right, or obtuse.*

9. a. 118°   **b.** 25°30′   **c.** 13.6°   **d.** 156°27′

10. a. 48°   **b.** 90°00′   **c.** 80°   **d.** 149°60′

Perform the indicated operations.

11. a. 34°15′10″+12°12′9″   **b.** 30°42′40″+10°30′25″
    c. 50°30′25″ − 10°40′30″   **d.** 90° − 46°30′15″

12. a. 20°30′35″+10°25′30″   **b.** 90°30′30″+90°30′30″
    c. 78°27′6″ − 19°9′7″   **d.** 89°30′20″ − 10°40′25″

13. Make a sketch to determine if twice an acute angle is necessarily an obtuse angle.

14. Make a sketch to determine if half an obtuse angle is necessarily an acute angle.

15. In the figure formed by three intersecting straight lines, angle *AGF* is a right angle.

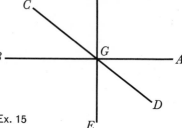

　　a. List two pairs of complementary angles.

　　b. List four pairs of supplementary angles.

　　c. List four acute angles.　　Ex. 15

　　d. List three obtuse angles.

16. List all pairs of complementary angles.

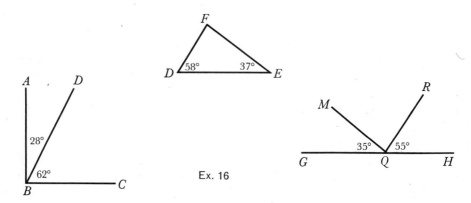

Ex. 16

17. Find the complement of 15°30′16″. Find its supplement.

18. Find the complement of 45°16′8″. Find its supplement.

19. If two angles are equal and complementary, how many degrees are in each angle?

20. If two angles are equal and supplementary, how many degrees are in each angle?

21. What kind of angle is the supplement of an obtuse angle?

22. What kind of an angle is the supplement of a right angle?

23. If an angle is $\frac{2}{3}$ of its supplement, express in an equation the sum of the angle and its supplement.

24. The larger of two supplementary angles exceeds the smaller by 84°. How large is each angle?

25. The complement of an angle is 10° less than three times the angle. How large is each angle?

26. The supplement of an angle is 15° more than twice the angle. Find the number of degrees in each angle.

27. How many degrees are in an angle which is three times as large as its complement?

28. The supplement of an angle is 20 more than three times its complement. Write and solve an equation that shows the size of the angle.

29.

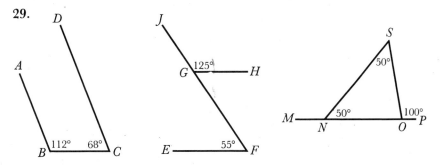

    a. List one angle supplementary to angle *BCD*.
    b. List two angles each supplementary to angle *JGH*.
    c. List one angle supplementary to angle *POS*.

30. Through how many degrees does the hour hand of a clock turn between 3 o'clock and 6 o'clock? The minute hand?

By using a protractor find the size of the following angles:

31.   **32.**   **33.**

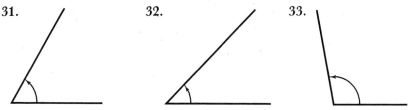

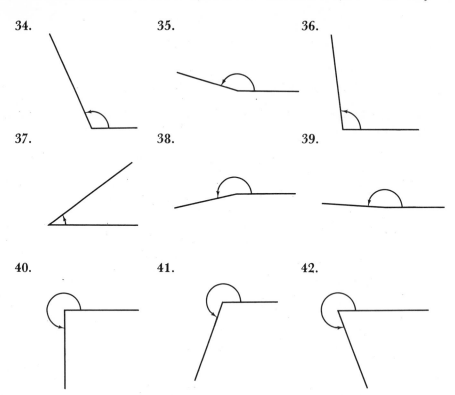

34. **35.** **36.**

37. **38.** **39.**

40. **41.** **42.**

Using a protractor draw an angle having the following measures:

43. 45° **44.** 57° **45.** 90° **46.** 120°

47. 150° **48.** 180° **49.** 162° **50.** 157°

51. 93° **52.** 190° **53.** 225° **54.** 250°

55. 270° **56.** 360° **57.** 350° **58.** 359°

CONSTRUCTING EQUAL ANGLES

Mr. Carlson, a metalsmith, made a design of an emblem with an angle in one corner. He wished to give balance to the design by making another angle the same size in another corner. With a protractor he could measure the angle and draw another one the same size. However, he could geometrically *construct* the new angle. That is, he could duplicate the first angle using only an unmarked straightedge and a compass. Study the developmental exercises below to see how this is done.

Developmental Exercises

DE—1. Using only a compass and straight-edge construct an angle equal to a given angle.

Solution

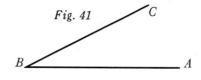

Fig. 41

- Draw ∠*ABC* and working line *EF* with point *W*.

Fig. 42

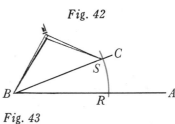

- Set the steel point of the compass at *B* and with any convenient radius draw an arc cutting *BC* at *S* and *BA* at *R*.

Fig. 43

- Without changing the opening of your compass (the same radius) place the steel point at *W* and draw an arc cutting *EF* at *V*.

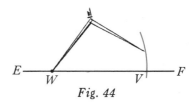

Fig. 44

- Place one end of the compass at *R* and the other at *S* so that the opening is equal to the distance between *R* and *S*.

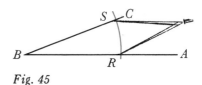

Fig. 45

- Using the distance between *R* and *S* as the radius and *V* as the center (place the steel point at *V*), draw an arc cutting the arc through *V* at *X*.
- With the straightedge draw a line through *W* and *X*. ∠*VWX* = ∠*ABC*.

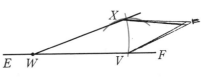

Fig. 46

DE—2. Using only a compass and straightedge construct an angle bisector.

Solution

An angle bisector is a line through the vertex of the angle dividing the angle into two equal angles.

● Draw any angle, such as ∠*CAB*.

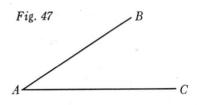

Fig. 47

● With the steel point of the compass at point *A* mark an arc that cuts across both rays *AB* and *AC.* Label the points of intersection *D* and *E* respectively.

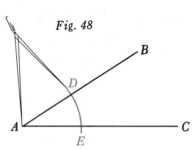

Fig. 48

● With *D* as a center mark off an arc between *AC* and *AB*. Without opening or closing the compass and using *E* as a center, make another arc between lines *AC* and *AB*. Mark the point where the arcs intersect *P.*

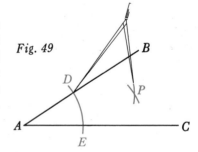

Fig. 49

● Draw a straight line connecting points *A* and *P*. The line *AP* bisects ∠*CAB*.

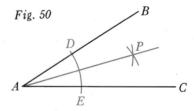

Fig. 50

Exercises

With a protractor draw the following angles and then construct (use only straight-edge and compass) an angle having the same measure.

1. a. $15°$ **b.** $45°$ **c.** $70°$ **d.** $120°$

2. a. $60°$ **b.** $95°$ **c.** $150°$ **d.** $220°$

3. Draw an angle of $45°$. Construct the angle bisector.

4. Bisect each of two adjacent supplementary angles.

5. Bisect each of two adjacent complementary angles.

6. Divide a straight angle into four equal angles.

7. One of two complementary angles is represented by $3x+4$, the other by $2x+6$. How large is each?

8. With a protractor draw $\angle ABC = 135°$. Construct $\angle DEF$ equal to $\angle ABC$. Construct $\angle EGH$ also equal to $\angle ABC$ with the vertex, G, one inch from E on the side EF. The right side of $\angle DEF$ should coincide with the left side of $\angle EGH$. In like manner, construct a $135°$ angle whose vertex is on the side GH. Repeat this operation until 8 angles have been constructed. Does the figure have 8 one-inch sides? If not, repeat the construction.

CONSTRUCTING PERPENDICULAR LINES

Fig. 51

If a straight angle ($180°$) is bi-sected, two adjacent right ($90°$) angles are formed. The sides of the right angles are said to be *perpendicular*.

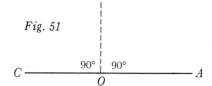

Assumption 15

In a plane through a given point there is one, and only one, perpendicular to a given line.

Assumption 16

The shortest path from a point to a line is the length of the perpendicular from the point to the line.

The developmental exercises below will show you how to construct perpendicular lines. Remember the only tools used in a geometric construction are the straightedge and compass.

Developmental Exercises

DE—1. Construct a perpendicular to a line from a point not on the line.

Solution

● Draw a line, *AB*, and a point, *C*, not on *AB*. You are to construct a perpendicular to *AB* through *C*.

Fig. 52

● Place the steel point of the compass at *C*. With the ends of the compass opened more than the distance from *C* to *AB*, mark an arc cutting *AB* at two points. Label these points of intersection *E* and *F*.

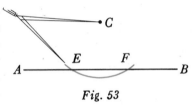

Fig. 53

● Place the steel point at *E* and with a radius greater than one-half the distance between *E* and *F*, mark an arc below *AB*. With this same radius and *E* as center, cut the arc. Label this point of intersection *P*.

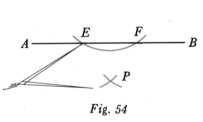

Fig. 54

● Using a straightedge draw a line from *P* to *C*. The line *CP* is perpendicular to *AB*. The symbol for perpendicular is ⊥. Thus, *CP* ⊥ *AB* (read *CP* is perpendicular to *AB*).

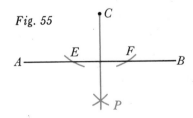

Fig. 55

DE—2. Construct a perpendicular to a line at a point on the line.

Solution

● Draw a line, *AB*, with point *C* on the line. You are to construct a perpendicular to *AB* through *C*.

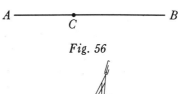

Fig. 56

● Place the steel point of the compass on *C* and with any convenient length as radius, mark arcs intersecting *AB* at *E* and *F*.

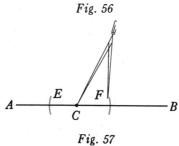

Fig. 57

● With *E* as the center (the steel point placed at *E*) and any length greater than one-half the distance between *E* and *F* as radius, draw an arc above the line *AB*.

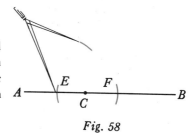

Fig. 58

● With this same radius and *F* as the center, cut the arc at *P*.

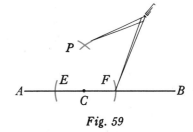

Fig. 59

● With a straightedge draw a line from point *C* to point *P*. *CP* ⊥*AB*.

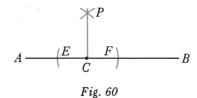

Fig. 60

When a perpendicular is constructed at the midpoint of a line segment, it is called the *perpendicular bisector* of the line segment.

DE—3. Construct the perpendicular bisector of a line.

Solution

● Draw any line segment, AB.

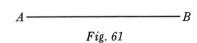

Fig. 61

● With A as the center and any radius greater than one-half the distance from A to B, draw an arc above and below AB. Label these arcs x and y respectively.

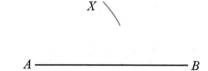

Fig. 62

● With B as the center and the same radius cut arcs x and y. Label these points of intersection M and N.

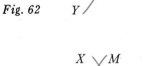

● With a straightedge draw line MN. Line MN is the perpendicular bisector of AB.

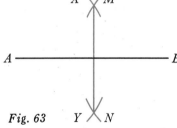

Fig. 63

Exercises

*Draw figures somewhat like those below but with longer line segments and then construct a perpendicular through point **P**.*

1. a.
   b.
   c.

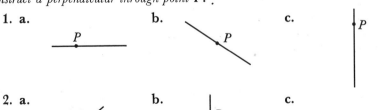

2. a.
   b.
   c.

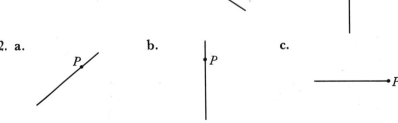

3. a.   •*P*   **b.**   **c.**

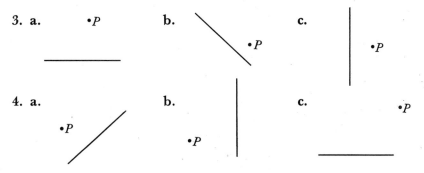

4. a.   **b.**   **c.**

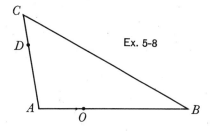

Copy the diagram and construct the required perpendiculars.

5. Construct a perpendicular at *O* to *AB* and from *O* to *CB*.

6. Construct a perpendicular at *D* to *AC;* from *D* to *CB;* and from *D* to *AB*.

7. Construct the perpendicular bisectors of the three sides of triangle *ABC*.

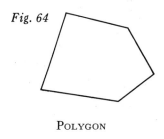

Ex. 5-8

8. Construct a perpendicular from *C* to *AB*. (Hint, extend *AB* if necessary.)

CLASSIFICATION OF TRIANGLES

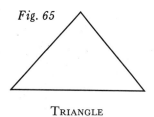

Fig. 64

POLYGON

Fig. 65

TRIANGLE

A broken line closed to bound a portion of a plane is called a **polygon.** *A three-sided polygon is called a* **triangle.** The triangle is the simplest closed figure that you can make. The size and shape of a triangle cannot be changed if the sides remain unchanged. This is not true of other polygons. Thus, the triangle is called the *rigid polygon*.

This bridge extending over the Hudson River in New York illustrates the use of triangular framework for rigidity.

The symbol for triangle is △. A triangle is identified by the letters at its vertices, the intersections of the sides. Thus, the triangle in Figure 66 is △*ABC*. The sides of a triangle are named according to their endpoints, for example, *AB*, *BC*, and *AC*. Sometimes for simplicity the sides are identified by the lower case form of the letter denoting the opposite vertex. See the figure.

Classification According to Angles:

If one angle of a triangle is a right angle, the triangle is called a *right triangle.*

If one angle of a triangle is an obtuse angle, the triangle is called an *obtuse triangle.*

If the angles of a triangle are all acute, the triangle is called an *acute triangle.*

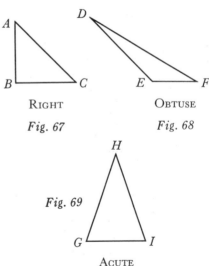

RIGHT

Fig. 67

OBTUSE

Fig. 68

Fig. 69

ACUTE

Classification According to Sides:

If all the sides of a triangle are of the same length, the triangle is called an *equilateral triangle*.

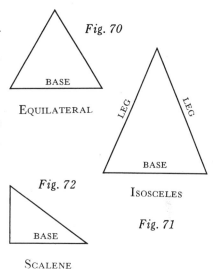

Fig. 70

EQUILATERAL

If only two sides of a triangle are the same length, the triangle is called an *isosceles triangle*.

ISOSCELES

Fig. 71

If no two of the sides of a triangle are the same length, the triangle is called a *scalene triangle*.

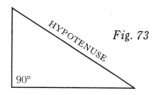

Fig. 72

SCALENE

In any triangle the side upon which it appears to rest is called the *base of the triangle*. The equal sides of an isosceles triangle are often called *legs;* the third side of the isosceles triangle is called its *base* and the angle formed by the equal sides is known as the *vertex angle* of the isosceles triangle. The side opposite the right angle in a right triangle is its *hypotenuse*.

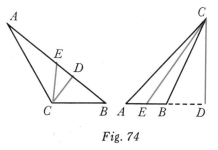

Fig. 73

In any triangle a line from any vertex perpendicular to the opposite side, extended if necessary, is an *altitude* of the triangle. In Figure 74 *CD* is an altitude. A *median* of a triangle is a line from any vertex of a triangle to the midpoint of the opposite side. In Figure 74 *CE* is a median.

Fig. 74

Developmental Exercises

DE—1. Name the function of *BD* in Figure 75.

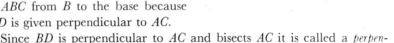

Fig. 75

Solution

Line *BD* is the bisector of *AC* because *AC*=8 units and *DC*=8 units.

Also, line *BD* is the altitude of △*ABC* from *B* to the base because *BD* is given perpendicular to *AC*.

Since *BD* is perpendicular to *AC* and bisects *AC* it is called a *perpendicular bisector* of *AC*.

DE—2. Draw a scalene triangle. Construct a median.

Solution

A median is a line from any vertex to the midpoint of the opposite side.

● Construct the bisector of side *AC*. Label the point of intersection (the midpoint) *D*.

● Draw line *BD*. *BD* is a median of △*ABC*.

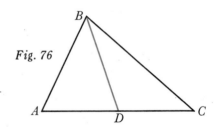

Fig. 76

Exercises

Copy and fill in the missing word.

1. A triangle with no two sides equal is a _____ triangle.

2. A triangle with an obtuse angle is an _____ triangle.

3. A triangle with two sides equal is an _____ triangle.

4. A perpendicular from a vertex to the opposite side is the

_____.

5. Name the function of the lines in the diagram if ∠*ACB* = 90° and *AR* = *RB*.

    a. *CA*   **b.** *CN*

    c. *CR*   **d.** *BA*

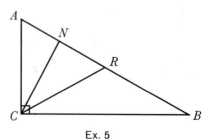

Ex. 5

6. Draw several isosceles triangles. In each construct a bisector of one of the angles opposite a leg of the triangle. Write a generalization.

7. Name the function of *BE* in each of the triangles and give a reason for your answer.

a.

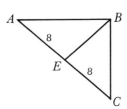

b.

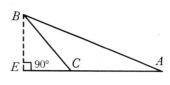

c.

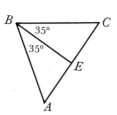

d.

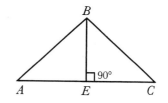

8. Draw a scalene triangle, *XYZ*, making the base *XY* the longest side. Construct the bisector of angle *X*, the median to side *ZY*, and also the altitude of **ZY**.

9. Draw a scalene triangle. Label it *ABC*. Construct the median to side *BC* and the altitude to side *AC*.

10. Draw a triangle like △*ABC* but larger. Construct the altitude to *BC* and the bisector of ∠*C*.

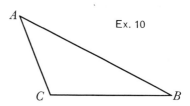

Ex. 10

11. Draw △*ABC*. Select any point, *P*, within the triangle. Construct a perpendicular from *P* to any side.

12. Draw a line segment. Label it *AB*. Construct a line segment one-fourth as long as *AB*.

13. Draw an acute angle. Construct an angle twice as large as the one you drew.

14. Draw a triangle, *ABC*, with $\angle B = 70°$, side $a = 3''$, and side $c = 2\frac{1}{2}''$. Construct the perpendicular bisectors of each of the sides of the triangle. Do they intersect in one point?

15. Draw a triangle, *ABC*, with $\angle B = 110°$, side $a = 3''$, and side $c = 1\frac{1}{2}''$. Construct the perpendicular bisectors of each of the sides of the triangle. Make a generalization about the intersection of these bisectors. Has your generalization been proved?

16. Construct the bisectors of the angles of the triangle constructed in Exercise **14.** Do the angle bisectors intersect in one point?

17. Construct the bisectors of the angles of the triangle constructed in Exercise **15.** Make a generalization about the intersection of the angle bisectors. Has your generalization been proved?

18. Construct the altitude to the base of the triangle drawn in Exercise **14.**

19. Construct the altitude to the base of the triangle drawn in Exercise **15.**

20. Construct an angle which is equal to the difference between two given angles.

21. Bisect the vertex angle of an isosceles triangle. Construct the perpendicular to the base at its midpoint. State a reasonable generalization concerning the bisector and perpendicular constructed. Test your generalization on a scalene triangle.

22. Draw *XY*, the perpendicular bisector of *PQ*. Join *O*, any point on *XY*, to *P* and to *Q*. Measure *OP* and *OQ*. Can you form a generalization about the length of *OP* and *OQ?* Can you be sure that this will always be true?

23. Illustrate the following statement with a geometric figure: If lines are drawn from any point on the bisector of an angle perpendicular to the sides of an angle, they are equal.

24. Illustrate the following statement with a geometric figure: Lines drawn from a point on the bisector of an angle which cut off equal segments from the vertex of the angle are equal.

CONSTRUCTION OF TRIANGLES

Mr. Lunsgard, a metalsmith, needed to recast a broken triangular mold. The unbroken part is indicated by the solid lines in Figure 77. He had the base and two base angles of a triangle and he needed to make another triangle just like the original one. He could reproduce the triangle in several ways. He could select any working line and lay off a segment equal to *BC* and with a protractor he could make angles equal to angle *B* and to angle *C*. The sides of the triangle could be extended to the vertex. Thus, the triangle could be completed.

Fig. 77

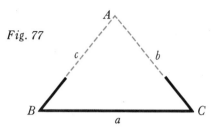

Also, he could construct the new triangle geometrically. That is, he could copy the two angles and side and complete the triangle by using only an unmarked straightedge and a compass.

‖ *Developmental Exercises*

DE—1. Construct a triangle given two angles and the included side.

Fig. 78

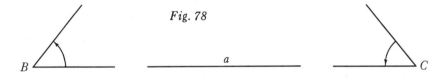

Solution
● On a working line, lay off *B'C'* (read *B* prime, *C* prime) equal to side *a*.
● At *B'* construct an angle equal to ∠*B*. At *C'* construct an angle equal to ∠*C*.
● Extend the non-common sides of ∠*B'* and ∠*C'* until they meet at some point, *A'*. △*A'B'C'* is the desired triangle.

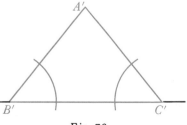

Fig. 79

DE—2. Construct a triangle given three sides.

a   b   c

Fig. 80

Solution

● On a working line lay off *AB*
equal to segment *c*.

Fig. 81

● With *B* as center and the length
of segment *a* as radius, strike an arc.

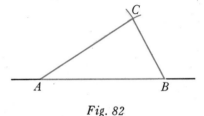

A   B

● With *A* as center and the length
of segment *b* as radius, intersect the
first arc. Label the intersection of the
two arcs *C*. Draw lines *BC* and *AC*.
△*ABC* is the desired triangle.

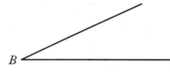

A   B

Fig. 82

DE—3. Construct a triangle having two sides and the included angle given.

a

c

Fig. 83

B

Solution

● On a working line lay off *B'C'*
equal to side *a*.

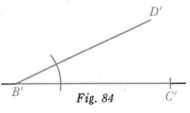

● At *B'* construct an angle, *C'B'D'*,
equal to ∠*B*.

B'   Fig. 84   C'

● On *D'B'* lay off *B'A'* equal to segment *c*. Connect *A'* and *C'*. △*A'B'C'*
is the desired triangle.

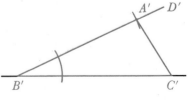

B'   C'

Fig. 85

Exercises

Construct △*ABC if the following data are given:*

1.	$a = 2''$	$b = 2\frac{1}{2}''$	$c = 3''$
2.	$a = 3''$	$b = 1\frac{1}{2}''$	$c = 2\frac{1}{2}''$
3.	$a = 2\frac{1}{2}''$	$b = 2\frac{1}{2}''$	$c = 2''$
4.	$a = 4''$	$b = 3''$	$c = 2''$
5.	$\angle B = 40°$	$\angle C = 60°$	$a = 2''$
6.	$\angle B = 60°$	$\angle C = 60°$	$a = 2\frac{1}{2}''$
7.	$\angle B = 90°$	$\angle C = 45°$	$a = 2\frac{1}{2}''$
8.	$\angle A = 110°$	$\angle B = 20°$	$c = 2''$
9.	$\angle B = 50°$	$c = 2''$	$a = 2\frac{1}{4}''$
10.	$\angle B = 20°$	$c = 3''$	$a = 2\frac{1}{2}''$

11. $a = 2''$, $b = 3''$, $c = 6''$. Discuss this construction. What is your conclusion about the relationship between the lengths of the sides if a construction is possible?

12. $\angle A = 95°$, $\angle B = 89°$, $c = 2\frac{1}{2}''$. Discuss the construction. What is your conclusion about the relationship between the size of the angles if a construction is possible?

13. $\angle A = 45°$, $\angle B = 60°$, $\angle C = 85°$. Discuss this construction. What is your conclusion?

14. $\angle B = 40°$, $b = 2''$, $c = 3''$. Discuss the possibilities of this construction. What is your conclusion?

SOLID GEOMETRY

Plane geometry is the study of figures lying in a flat surface, two-dimensional figures. Spatial or solid geometry is the study of three-dimensional figures, figures that occupy space. The artist may represent these three-dimensional figures on a plane by means of a perspective drawing. He draws the lines so that they appear to meet, if extended, at a distant point. Some right angles are drawn as acute or obtuse angles to aid in making the flat diagram represent a solid. In drawing a spatial figure on a plane it is often helpful to make the lines closer to you more intense than the more distant lines.

Many of the principles of plane geometry may be extended to apply to solid geometry. Two planes intersect to form an angle, such an angle is called a *dihedral angle.*

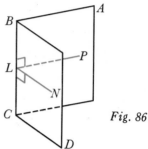

The two planes, *AC* and *DB*, are called the *faces* of the dihedral angle, and the line of intersection is called the *edge* of the angle. The dihedral angle is named by designating its edge or its faces and edge. Thus, the dihedral angle in Figure 86 is named *BC* or *A — BC — D*.

Fig. 86

To aid your imagination you may crease a piece of paper so that the crease represents line *BC* and lies in each plane.

If in each plane of the dihedral angle a line is drawn perpendicular to the edge at the same point, the angle formed is called a *plane angle of the dihedral angle.* In Figure 86 $PL \perp BC$ and $NL \perp BC$, $\angle PLN$ is a plane angle of the dihedral angle $A — BC — D$.

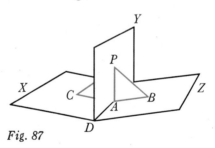

Fig. 87

A dihedral angle may be bisected by a plane to form two equal dihedral angles. In Figure 87 plane *Y* bisects the dihedral angle made by planes *X* and *Z*. The plane angles, $\angle PAB$ and $\angle PAC$, are equal.

A plane can be perpendicular to a line and to another plane. To aid your understanding a pencil held perpendicular to one-half a sheet of creased paper may be used to represent this.

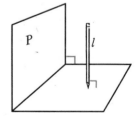

Fig. 88

Exercises

1. Name the dihedral angle in the diagram.

2. Name the plane angle in the diagram.

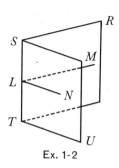

Ex. 1-2

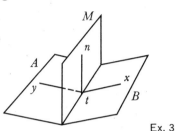

Ex. 3

3. Plane M bisects dihedral angle AB. Name the equal plane angles. Name the equal dihedral angles.

4. Describe the intersection of two planes. Is this always true?

5. Draw a dihedral angle.

6. Draw a plane perpendicular to another plane.

7. How is a plane angle constructed? Make a drawing to illustrate this.

8. How many planes can contain a given line?

9. Show by a sketch how many lines can be drawn through a point in a plane.

10. Intersecting planes form supplementary dihedral angles and complementary dihedral angles if their plane angles are supplementary or complementary, respectively. Copy the diagram at the right and add a third plane containing line ABC so that you can represent complementary and supplementary dihedral angles.

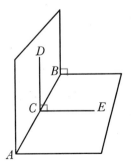

Ex. 10

EXTEND YOUR HORIZON

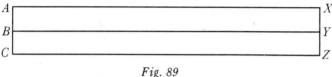

Fig. 89

Mark two rectangular strips of paper as shown. With one, match point C with Z, A with X, and fasten the ends together. A surface such as Figure 90 will result.

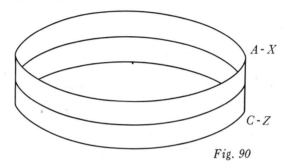

Fig. 90

With the other, twist one end of the strip through $180°$ so that point C matches point X and point A matches point Z. Fasten the ends together.

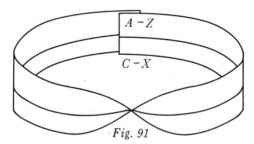

Fig. 91

a. Color one side of each. What do you find?

b. Describe how each will appear when you cut along line BY. Make the cuts, observe and compare with your prediction.

c. Repeat from the beginning, but locate points B and Y so that $BC = 2AB$ and $YZ = 2XY$.

CHAPTER SUMMARY

Mathematical reasoning is based on
1. undefined terms.   (page 14)
2. definitions.   (page 16)
3. assumptions.   (page 19)

An acceptable definition must
1. be expressed in words previously defined or accepted as undefined.
2. name the term being defined.
3. place the term in its smallest class.
4. state the characteristic which makes it different from other members of its class.
5. be true when its form is reversed.
6. include no unnecessary information.   (page 16)

Angles are classified according to size
1. acute   2. right
3. obtuse   4. straight
5. reflex   (page 31)

Triangles are classified according to
1. angles   2. sides
   a. acute   a. equilateral
   b. right   b. isosceles
   c. obtuse   c. scalene
                               (page 46)

Triangles may be constructed if
1. two angles and the included side are known.   (page 51)
2. two sides and the included angle are known.   (page 52)
3. three sides are known.   (page 52)

Other possible constructions are
1. the duplication of an angle.   (page 39)
2. the bisector of an angle.   (page 40)
3. a perpendicular to a line through a point not on the line.
(page 42)
4. a perpendicular to a line through a point on the line.   (page 43)
5. a perpendicular bisector of a line segment.   (page 44)

CHAPTER REVIEW

Vocabulary

Match the word in the left hand column with its correct definition in the right hand column.

1. Perpendicular Lines (⊥)

   a. A three-sided polygon.

   b. A closed broken line in a plane.

2. Polygon

   c. An angle in a plane.

   d. Two angles whose sum is a right angle.

3. Angle

   e. Two angles whose sum is a straight angle.

4. Complementary Angles

   f. An angle formed by the intersection of two planes.

5. Triangle (△)

   g. A line dividing an angle into two equal parts.

6. Altitude of a Triangle

   h. A line in a triangle from a vertex to the midpoint of the opposite side.

7. Angle Bisector

   i. A line in a triangle from a vertex perpendicular to the opposite side.

8. Ray

   j. A portion of a line having one and only one endpoint.

9. Median of a Triangle

   k. A portion of a line having two endpoints.

10. Supplementary Angles

    l. A figure formed by two rays with a common endpoint.

*11. Dihedral Angle

    m. Two lines which meet to form right angles.

Exercises

1. Name the line segments in each of the diagrams.

a.

A——C•——D•——B

b.

M——O•——P•——R•——N

c.

d.

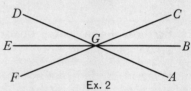

2. Name the angles in the diagram at the right.

Ex. 2

Examine the following statements in terms of the requirements for an acceptable definition.

3. Undefined terms are something you understand.

4. Lines which intersect to form right angles.

5. George Washington was the first president of the United States and he cut down a cherry tree.

6. A point is a dot.

7. A perpendicular line is a line that is perpendicular to another line.

8. A triangle is a three sided polygon.

9. How do you know that between two points one and only one straight line can be drawn?

10. State the assumptions that are the basis for each of the conclusions below:

    a. Given: $A = B, B = C$.
       Prove: $A = C$.
    b. Given: $AC = BD$.
       Prove: $AB = CD$.
    c. Given: $AB = CD$.
       Prove: $AC = BD$.

•——•——•——•————
A B C D

Ex. 10b-10c

11. Two angles are complementary and one is 19 degrees more than three times the other. How large is each?

12. A $3\frac{1}{8}$ inch line is bisected. How long is each part?

13. Two angles are supplementary and one is 40 degrees less than the other. How large is each?

14. Name the vertex of each of the angles in the diagram; use 3 letters to name each angle.

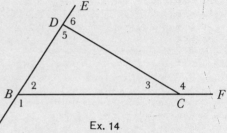

Ex. 14

15. Perform the indicated operations:
   a. $80°10'15'' - 12°19'27''$ **b.** $90°27'40'' + 72°49'51''$

16. Perform the indicated operations:
   a. $13°15'42'' + 5°19'49''$ **b.** $90° - 39°49'15''$

17. How large is an angle which is four times as large as its complement?

18. The complement of an angle is $220°$ less than twice its supplement. How large is the angle?

19. Find the size of the angle which is 8 degrees more than its complement.

20. The sum of two angles is 80 degrees and their difference is 20 degrees. How large is each angle?

21. Two equal angles are represented as follows: one is $\dfrac{x-2}{5}$; the other is $\dfrac{x+60}{6}$; how large are the angles?

22. Find the angle whose supplement is three times as large as its complement.

23. How many degrees are there in $\frac{2}{3}$ of a straight angle? In $\frac{4}{5}$ of a right angle?

24. If the number of degrees in two supplementary angles is represented by $\dfrac{x+25}{2}$ and $\dfrac{x-30}{3}$, how many degrees are in each angle?

Constructions

Study each diagram shown below. Classify it as the method for constructing an altitude, a median, a perpendicular-bisector, or an angle bisector.

1.

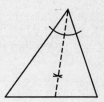

2.

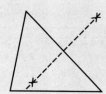

3.

4.

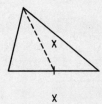

5.

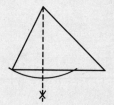

6.

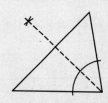

7.

8.

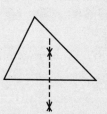

9.

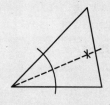

10.

11.

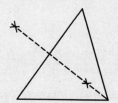

12.

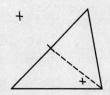

13. Construct an isosceles triangle with a base of $1\frac{1}{2}$ inches and legs each $2\frac{1}{8}$ inches in length.

14. Draw an acute angle. Construct the bisector of the angle. Use your protractor to measure each part of the angle. Does your construction appear to be accurate?

15. Draw an angle of 75 degrees.

16. From the midpoint of the base of an isosceles triangle, construct perpendiculars to the equal sides.

17. Bisect an angle and from any point on its bisector construct perpendiculars to the equal sides.

18. Draw two supplementary adjacent angles. Bisect each angle. How many degrees are in each angle?

19. Draw a line segment, *AB*. Draw another line segment, *CD*, meeting *AB* at *C* so that angle *ACD* is equal to angle *BCD*.

20. Construct a large equilateral triangle. Measure any angle in the triangle. Use this angle to construct an angle of 15°.

21. Draw a line segment, *AB*, two inches in length. Construct *AC* perpendicular to *AB* and 3 inches long. On the same side of *AB* construct *BD* perpendicular to *AB* and 2 inches long. From *E*, the midpoint of *AB*, draw *EC* and *ED*. Measure angle *CED* with your protractor. How large is it?

22. Draw an angle, *ABD*. Construct an angle twice as large as angle *ABD* and label it *CEF*.

23. Construct triangle *ABC* given two angles and the included side.

24. Construct triangle *DEF* given three sides.

CHAPTER TEST

1. Mathematical reasoning is based on undefined terms, definitions, and assumptions. Give an example of each.

2. Examine the following statement in terms of the requirements for an acceptable definition: A kangaroo is a member of the herbivorous marsupial mammals of Australia.

3. State the assumptions that are the bases for each of the conclusions below.

    a. Given: $A = B.$
       Conclusion: $A + C = B + C.$

    b. Given: Line *m* containing points *A* and *B;* line *n* containing point *A;* line *m* is not line *n.*
       Conclusion: Line *n* does not contain point *B.*

4. In the diagram below, $AB = BC = AC.$ *AE* is constructed perpendicular to *BC, DB* is constructed perpendicular to *AC.*

    a. Use three letters to represent the right angles in this diagram.

    b. Name the isosceles triangle.

    c. Name the equilateral triangle.

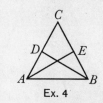
Ex. 4

5. The diagram at the right is made of four straight lines. $DO \perp AB.$ Using three letters name

    a. the complementary angles.

    b. the supplementary angles.

    c. the adjacent angles.

Ex. 5

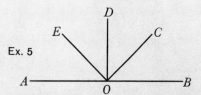

6. One of two equal angles is represented by $\dfrac{4x - 90}{7}$; the other angle is represented by $\dfrac{2x + 30}{5}$. How large are the angles?

7. Using a protractor determine the number of degrees in the angle at the right.

Ex. 7

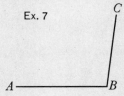

8. Using a protractor draw an angle of $120°.$

9. Construct the angle bisector of the angle in Exercise **8.**

10. Construct an isosceles right triangle.

*11. Show by a drawing the meaning of "plane angle of a dihedral angle."

Chapter 2

VALID CONCLUSIONS

CONCLUSIONS THROUGH MEASUREMENT

A research chemist precisely measures the chemical changes and carefully records the data. On the basis of many experiments he arrives at a generalization. You too may make generalizations through measurements.

Developmental Exercises

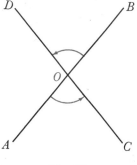

DE—1. Use a protractor to measure $\angle BOD$. Measure $\angle AOC$, also.

Fig. 92

Solution

$\angle BOD = 80°$, $\angle AOC = 80°$, thus $\angle BOD = \angle AOC$.

Such angles as BOD and AOC in this figure are called *vertical angles*. *Vertical angles* have the same vertex and the sides of one are extensions of the sides of the other angle through their common vertex. Note from the diagram that they lie in opposite positions. Angles DOA and COB are vertical angles, too.

If you measured two vertical angles twenty times, and each time you found the angles to be equal, you probably would be willing to agree to the generalization below.

If two straight lines intersect, then the vertical angles formed are equal.

DE—2. Draw two acute triangles and two obtuse triangles. Use a protractor to measure each angle and then find the sum of the degrees in the angles of each triangle. What would you be willing to generalize about the sum of the angles of a triangle?

Solution

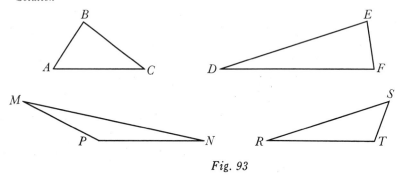

Fig. 93

From measuring you might be willing to generalize that the sum of the angles in each triangle is approximately 180°. Thus, you might be willing to agree that:

The sum of the angles of a triangle is 180°.

You must beware of generalizations based on measurement. A measurement helps you in discovering a generalization but it does not prove it. Notice in Developmental Exercise **3** how measurement of special figures may lead you to a false generalization.

DE—3. In each drawing below, *D* is the midpoint of *BC*, that is *AD* is a median. Measure the length of *AD* and the length of *BC* in each drawing.

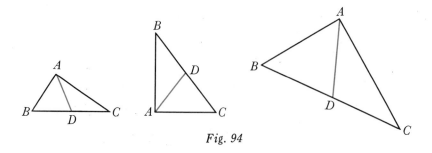

Fig. 94

a. What generalization regarding the median *AD* of any triangle is suggested by your measurements?

b. Test this generalization with other triangles. Does it hold true?

Solution

a. By setting one compass end at D and the other at B, when an arc of a circle is struck through B, it also will extend through point A. Since D is the midpoint of BC, it appears that $BD = AD$. Therefore, this experiment suggests that the median of a triangle is equal to one-half of the base.

b. When the generalization is tested by drawing other triangles such as the following, it can be noted that in not one of the three triangles does the median equal one-half the base. One exception is sufficient to disprove any generalization.

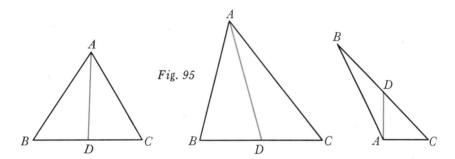

Fig. 95

Exercises

Name the pairs of vertical angles in Exercises **1-4.**

1.

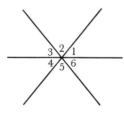

2.

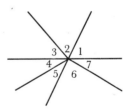

3.

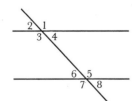

4.

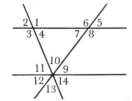

5. Use a ruler to measure the length of each side of each triangle of Developmental Exercise **3.** What generalization would you make in comparing the sum of the lengths of any two sides of a triangle and the third side? Can you be sure of this generalization?

6. Draw three closed four-sided figures. Find the number of degrees in the sum of the angles of each figure. What generalization would you be willing to make about the sum of the angles of a four-sided figure? Can you be sure of this generalization?

7. Construct four isosceles triangles of varying dimensions. Use a protractor to measure the base angles of your triangles. What generalization might you make about the base angles of an isosceles triangle? Can you be sure of this generalization?

8. Construct four equilateral triangles. Measure each angle formed. What generalization is suggested by the measurement? Can you be sure of this generalization?

9. Construct four equiangular triangles. Measure the length of each side. What would you be willing to generalize about the length of the sides of an equiangular triangle? Has your generalization been proved?

10. Draw three right triangles, each having one acute angle equal to 45°. Measure the legs of each triangle. What might you conclude? Has your generalization been proved?

11. Construct three isosceles triangles and then construct the altitudes to the equal sides in each triangle. Measure the length of the altitudes. What generalization is suggested by the measurements? Has your generalization been proved?

12. Below are three right triangles. ∠1 in each triangle measures 30°. ∠2 in each triangle measures 60°. Compare the length of the side opposite ∠1 to the length of the side opposite ∠2. Make a generalization. Has your generalization been proved?

 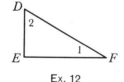 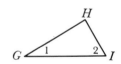

Ex. 12

CONCLUSIONS THROUGH REASONING

John knew two girls from Italy and they seemed to be always happy. He concluded, "Italian girls are always happy." A conclusion based on a limited number of experiences is the result of *inductive reasoning*.

Mary was watching two boys toss pennies. She remarked, "I bet the next toss will be a head or a tail." Her conclusion was the result of inductive reasoning. If she had watched the penny fall 1000 times she could not have been certain the next fall would be a head or a tail. The penny might fall and remain on its edge. The more throws Mary observed the more probable the conclusion would become but it would never be certain.

Conclusions may also be the result of *deductive reasoning*.

All graduates of Central High School are men.

Fran Smith is a graduate of Central High School.

Therefore, Fran Smith is a man.

In deductive reasoning the conclusion is valid if logical steps in reasoning are followed. Notice that two conditions, called *premises*, are given. The first premise is "All graduates of Central High School are men." The second premise is "Fran Smith is a graduate of Central High School."

If either premise is false and the reasoning is logical, the conclusion is false, but if the premises are accepted the conclusion must be accepted. It is important to notice that in deductive reasoning the conclusion must follow logically from the premises. If the conclusion follows logically from the premises, the conclusion is valid even though it may be false. If it does not follow from the premises, the conclusion is invalid even though it may be true. For example, from the following two premises:

All employees are lazy,

Harold Clark is an employee,

follows the conclusion

Harold Clark is lazy.

The conclusion follows logically from the premises. Therefore, it is valid. The premises may be false but this fact has nothing to do with the validity of the reasoning. Of course, if both premises are true, then the conclusion also is true.

Notice how diagrams may help in checking the steps in reasoning. Represent the set of all lazy people by region *A*. According to the premise, all employees are within this region. These employees are represented by the region *B*. According to the second premise, Harold Clark is in region *B*. Region *C*, entirely within *B*, represents Harold Clark. Notice that region *C* is also within *A*. Thus, the valid conclusion is that Harold Clark is lazy.

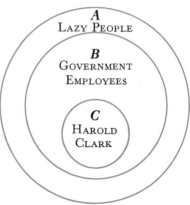

Fig. 96

Developmental Exercises

DE—1. Test the validity of the argument by using diagrams. Is the conclusion true?

> Premises: All Central High School graduates are men;
> Fran Smith did not graduate from Central High School.
> Conclusion: Fran Smith is not a man.

Solution

The region *A* represents all men. In this region is *B* which represents all Central High School graduates. Fran Smith is not in this region and, therefore, may be represented by region *A* or *C*. Fran Smith may or may not be a man. The conclusion is invalid but whether it is true or false is not known.

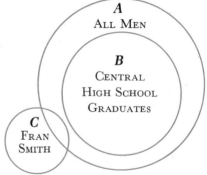

Fig. 97

DE—2. Test the validity of the argument by using diagrams. Is the conclusion true?

>Premises: All Central High School graduates are men.
>
>Fran Smith is not a man.
>
>Conclusion: Fran Smith did not graduate from Central High School.

Solution

The region **A** represents all men. The graduates of Central High School are contained within the class of all men and they are represented by region **B**. Fran Smith is not a man, therefore, Fran Smith is outside the class of all men and cannot be represented in region **A**. Therefore, Fran Smith cannot be in the class of Central High School graduates. The conclusion is valid. However, whether the conclusion is false or true is unknown. The truth of the conclusion depends on the truth of both premises.

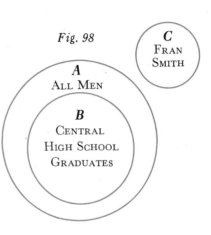

Fig. 98

If the conclusion logically follows from the premises, the conclusion is valid; if it does not, it is invalid. If both premises are true and the conclusion is valid, the conclusion is true; otherwise the conclusion is not necessarily true.

Exercises

Test the validity of the reasoning by using diagrams. Are the conclusions true?

1. Premises: All Mexicans are Americans. John is a Mexican.
   Conclusion: John is an American.

2. Premises: All students who pass mathematics are intelligent. Mary can pass mathematics.
   Conclusion: Mary is intelligent.

3. Premises: Giving to the poor is always good. Beggars are always poor.
   Conclusion: Giving to beggars is always good.

4. Premises: Americans speak English. John speaks Spanish.
   Conclusion: John is not an American.

5. Premises: All good cars are expensive. This car is expensive.
   Conclusion: This car is good.

6. Premises: Movie stars use *S* and *S* soap. Movie stars are lovely.
   Conclusion: If I use *S* and *S* soap, I'll be lovely.

7. Premises: Henry took Health Pills. Henry didn't have a cold.
   Conclusion: John won't have a cold if he takes Health Pills.

8. Premises: All triangles are polygons. All squares are polygons.
   Conclusion: All triangles are squares.

9. Premises: All squares are polygons. All quadrilaterals are polygons.
   Conclusion: All squares are quadrilaterals.

10. Premises: All triangles are circles. All circles are polygons.
    Conclusion: All triangles are polygons.

11. Premises: No triangles are circles. Some triangles are polygons.
    Conclusion: Some polygons are not triangles.

12. Premises: No rectangles are triangles. Some rectangles are squares.
    Conclusion: Some squares are not triangles.

13. Premises: All *X*'s are *Z*'s. All *R*'s are *Z*'s.
    Conclusion: All *X*'s are *R*'s.

14. Premises: All *X*'s are *Z*'s. Some *R*'s are *Z*'s.
    Conclusion: Some *X*'s are *R*'s.

15. Premises: Some *X*'s are *Z*'s. Some *R*'s are *Z*'s.
    Conclusion: Some *R*'s are *X*'s.

16. Premises: Some *X*'s are *Z*'s. All *R*'s are *Z*'s.
    Conclusion: Some *R*'s are *X*'s.

17. Premises: No *X*'s are *Z*'s. All *Z*'s are *R*'s.
    Conclusion: No *X*'s are *R*'s.

18. Premises: No *X*'s are *Z*'s. All *X*'s are *R*'s.
    Conclusion: Some *X*'s are *R*'s.

19. Premises: Some angles are acute. Figure *x* is an angle.
    Conclusion: *x* is acute.

20. Premises: Some rhombuses are square. All squares are parallelograms.
    Conclusion: Some rhombuses are parallelograms.

DEDUCTIVE REASONING

Throughout this book you will use diagrams to show the position of lines and angles. Because angles or line segments appear to be equal is not sufficient reason for discussing relationships as though the angles or line segments have been constructed equal.

Examine the following three diagrams.

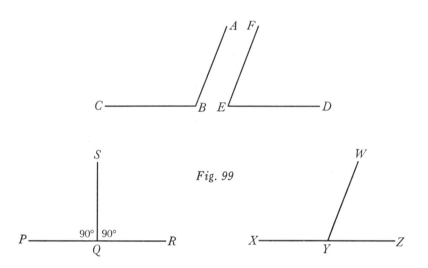

Fig. 99

You may not state that $\angle ABC + \angle DEF = 180°$ although it appears to be a reasonable statement. You can be sure that $\angle SQP + \angle RQS = 180°$ because each of the two angles is a right angle. If line XYZ is a straight line then $\angle WYX + \angle ZYW = 180°$. Such statements must be established deductively, that is, based on logical reasoning. Study the developmental exercises below to learn how to form correct conclusions from the data given.

‖Developmental Exercises

Write a valid conclusion that would result from the premises.

DE—1. Premises: Every United States citizen was born in the United States. Mr. Black is a United States citizen.

Solution

Conclusion: Mr. Black was born in the United States.

DE—2. Premises: A triangle having two equal sides is an isosceles triangle. In $\triangle ABC$, $AB = AC$.

> *Solution*
> Conclusion: $\triangle ABC$ is an isosceles triangle.

DE—3. Premises: If two straight lines intersect, then the vertical angles formed are equal. $\angle A$ and $\angle B$ are vertical angles formed by two intersecting straight lines.

> *Solution*
> Conclusion: $\angle A = \angle B$.

Exercises

Study the following situations and judge the validity of the conclusions listed. Justify each valid conclusion by stating previously accepted assumptions.

1. **Given:** $A = B$.
   Prove: $A - 2 = B - 2$.

2. **Given:** AB is a straight line, $\angle 2 = \angle 3$.
   Prove: $\angle 1 + \angle 3 = 180°$.

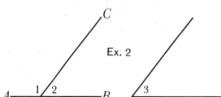

Ex. 2

3. **Given:** $AB = BC$,
   $DE = EF$.
   Prove: $AB + BC = DE + EF$.

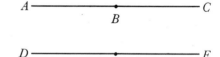

Ex. 3

4. **Given:** $\angle 1 = \angle 3$.
   Prove: $\angle 2 = \angle 3$.

Ex. 4

Ex. 5

5. Given: $AB \perp CD$.
   Prove: $\angle ABC = \angle ABD$.

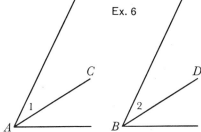

Ex. 6

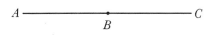

6. Given: $\angle 1 = \angle 2$,
   CA bisects $\angle A$,
   DB bisects $\angle B$.
   Prove: $\angle A = \angle B$.

7. Given: $AB = BC$,
   $DE = EF$,
   $BC = EF$.
   Prove: $AB = DE$.

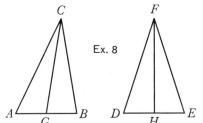

Ex. 8

Ex. 7

8. Given: $AB = DE$,
   CG and FH are
   medians.
   Prove: $AG = DH$.

When one is possible, write a valid conclusion for the following premises. Indicate which conclusions are true.

9. Premises: If a person breaks a mirror that person will have seven years of bad luck. Bill Jones broke a mirror.

10. Premises: If the sum of two angles is $180°$, then the angles are supplementary. $\angle 1 + \angle 2 = 180°$.

11. Premises: If equals are added to equals the sums are equal. $A = B$ and $C = D$.

12. Premises: A quantity may be substituted for its equal in an expression without changing the value of the expression. $AB = W$ and $CD = W$.

CONDITIONAL STATEMENTS

In your everyday experiences you are not as conscious of assumptions and conclusions as you are in geometry. Whenever you say, "If . . ." data follows that is assumed to be true by you. Others may not accept these same assumptions but this will not influence your conclusion. It is important to derive the conclusion from the accepted assumptions.

A study of Plane Geometry emphasizes the *if-then* principle and affords practice in developing the habit of establishing correct conclusions from accepted statements. Perform the experiments in the developmental exercises and observe the *if-then* relationships.

Developmental Exercises

DE—1. Draw an isosceles triangle and join the midpoints of two sides as shown. Measure *XY* and *AB*. Divide the length of *AB* by the length of *XY*. Express your generalization in an *if-then* statement.

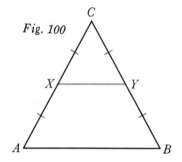

Fig. 100

Solution

The length of *AB* is twice the length of *XY*. *If* a line joins the midpoints of two sides of a triangle *then* it is equal to one-half of the third side. The certainty of the *then* part depends on complete fulfillment of all the conditions stated in the *if* part.

Repeat the directions in Developmental Exercise **1** but use first an equilateral triangle, then a right triangle, and then a scalene triangle. Do you agree with the generalization below?

If a line joins the midpoints of two sides of a triangle, then it is equal in length to one-half of the third side.

Remember that while a generalization has been made, it has not been proved.

DE—2. Construct an equilateral triangle. Construct the bisector of one angle. Extend the bisector to the opposite side of the triangle. Measure the parts of the opposite side and express your observation in an *if-then* statement.

Solution

$CD = DB$.

If a line bisects an angle of an equilateral triangle, then it bisects the side opposite the angle.

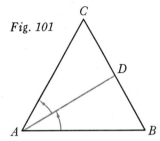

Fig. 101

DE—3. If two supplementary adjacent angles are bisected, then the bisectors are perpendicular.

    a. What relationships are included in the *if* part?

    b. What is the *then* part?

Solution

    a. $\angle DFA + \angle BFD = 180°$,

        $\angle DFA$ is adjacent to $\angle BFD$,

        EF bisects $\angle DFA$,

        CF bisects $\angle BFD$.

    b. The *then* part is $EF \perp FC$.

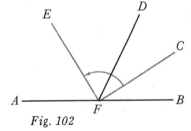

Fig. 102

DE—4. Bisect the base angles of an isosceles triangle. Extend the bisectors until they meet the opposite sides. Measure the bisectors. Summarize in an *if-then* statement.

Solution

$BE = DC = 3.4$ cm.

If the base angles of an isosceles triangle are bisected and the bisectors extend to the opposite sides, then the bisectors are equal.

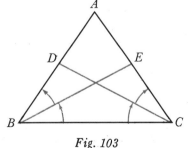

Fig. 103

Exercises

1. If the vertex angle of an isosceles triangle is bisected, then the bisector (if extended) bisects the base and is perpendicular to the base. Illustrate this statement.

2. Study the diagram. Judge whether the conclusion stated is valid. Since $\angle A + \angle B = 180°$ and $\angle C + \angle D = 180°$, then $\angle A = \angle D$.

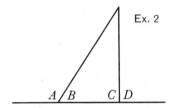

Ex. 2

3. If $a = 4$ and $b = 3$, then $ab = 12$. Justify the conclusion.

4. Construct AB, the perpendicular bisector of XY. Join any point, C, on AB to X and to Y. Measure CX and CY. Summarize in an *if-then* statement.

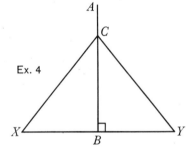

Ex. 4

5. If two angles of $\triangle ABC$ are equal, then the sides opposite those angles are equal. Assume that this statement is true and construct a diagram to illustrate it.

6. Draw an angle. Construct its bisector. At any point on the bisector, construct a perpendicular to the bisector. Extend this perpendicular to meet the sides of the angle. Use your protractor to measure the angles formed by the perpendicular and the sides of the angle. What do you find? Summarize in an *if-then* statement.

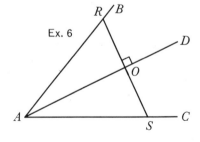

Ex. 6

7. In the diagram $\angle CDA =$ $\angle BDC$ and $AD = DB$. What is the relation between CD and AB? Why?

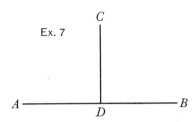

Ex. 7

8. In the isosceles triangle ABC, vertex $\angle C$ is bisected. Assume that the bisector of the vertex angle of an isosceles triangle bisects the opposite side of the triangle.

    a. Is $\angle A$ equal to $\angle B$? If so, why?

    b. Is CD perpendicular to AB? If so, why?

    c. What conclusion, if any, can be stated?

9. Complete by writing the conclusion, if one is possible.

    a. People who drink milk have large ears.

    b. All cowboys drink milk.

    c._____.

10. All lines in this diagram are straight lines. XY bisects $\angle BOD$. What premise must be accepted to establish that:

    a. $\angle BOD = \angle COA$.

    b. $\angle COX = \angle YOD$.

    c. $\angle COX = \angle XOA$.

    d. $\angle COA$ is bisected.

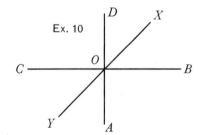

Ex. 10

11. $DC = CE = DE$ by construction. Can you establish that $\angle ADC = \angle BED$? (Do not use your protractor.)

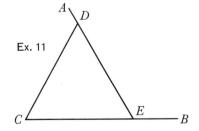

Ex. 11

12. In this diagram $DA \perp AB$. Which of the following statements listed as possible conclusions can you establish?

Ex. 12

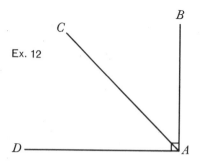

   a. $\angle CAD = \angle BAC$.
   b. $\angle BAD = 90°$.
   c. $\angle CAD + \angle BAC = 90°$.
   d. A right angle is formed by DA and AB.

13. Construct a right triangle. Join the midpoint of the side opposite the right angle to the vertex of the right angle. Measure this line. Measure the parts of the hypotenuse. Express your observation in an *if-then* statement.

Ex. 14

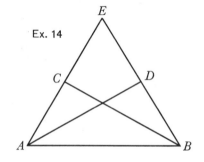

14. In the diagram at the right $\triangle ABE$ is an isosceles triangle. $AD = 1.4$ inches and $BC = 1\frac{2}{5}$ inches. Can you establish that, with no further measuring, $DE = EC$? How do you know?

15. In the diagram CD is the perpendicular bisector of AB. P is any point on CD. Measure AP. Measure BP. Q is any other point on CD. Measure AQ. Measure BQ. Measure CA and CB. Repeat with DA and DB. What conclusion seems reasonable? Summarize this exercise in an *if-then* statement.

Ex. 15

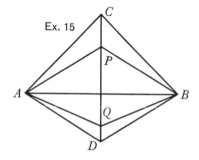

16. Draw a triangle. Construct the bisector of each angle. Express your observation in an *if-then* statement. Test your generalization by repeating with an isosceles triangle, an equilateral triangle, and a right triangle. Does your *if-then* statement refer to a particular kind of triangle or is it true for any triangle?

USING DEDUCTIVE REASONING

Each of the assumptions and definitions listed in Chapter One is a generalization. An application of any one of them leads to a valid conclusion. Observe in the developmental exercises below how the applications of definitions and assumptions are used to develop a proof. The statements are applications of the corresponding reasons (generalizations) and are, therefore, valid conclusions. Notice that each statement, except the first, follows as a result of the preceding statement. The last statement is the relationship that was to be proved.

Developmental Exercises

DE—1. Prove deductively that all right angles are equal.

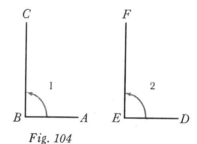

Given: $\angle 1$ and $\angle 2$, any two right angles.

Prove: $\angle 1 = \angle 2$.

Fig. 104

Solution

STATEMENTS	REASONS
1. $\angle 1$ is a right angle, $\angle 2$ is a right angle.	1. Given.
2. $\angle 1 = 90°$, $\angle 2 = 90°$.	2. A right angle contains 90°.
3. $\angle 1 = \angle 2$.	3. Quantities equal to the same quantities are equal. (Assumption 6.)

Notice in the proof that the reasons given are definitions and assumptions. Since $\angle 1$ and $\angle 2$ could be any right angles, it has been proved deductively that all right angles are equal. A statement to be proved is called a *theorem.*

THEOREM 1

All right angles are equal.

DE—2. Prove deductively that all straight angles are equal.

Given: ∠1 and ∠2 are straight angles.

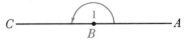

Prove: ∠1 = ∠2.

Fig. 105

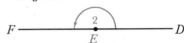

Solution

STATEMENTS	REASONS
1. ∠1 is a straight angle, ∠2 is a straight angle.	1. Given.
2. ∠1 = 180°, ∠2 = 180°.	2. A straight angle contains 180°.
3. ∠1 = ∠2.	3. Quantities equal to the same quantity are equal.

Thus, it has been proved that:

║THEOREM 2

║All straight angles are equal.

DE—3. Prove deductively that all vertical angles are equal.

Given: Lines *AB* and *DC* intersecting at point *O*.

Prove: ∠1 = ∠3.

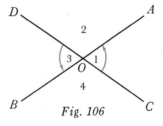

Fig. 106

Solution

STATEMENTS	REASONS
1. ∠1 + ∠2 = 180°, ∠3 + ∠2 = 180°.	1. If two angles are supplementary, their sum is 180°.
2. ∠1 = 180° − ∠2, ∠3 = 180° − ∠2.	2. If equals are subtracted from equals, the differences are equal.
3. ∠1 = ∠3.	3. Quantities equal to the same quantity are equal.

Notice in the proof that from three assumptions it is deduced that
$\angle 1 = \angle 3$. Since $\angle 1$ and $\angle 3$ could be any pair of vertical angles, it has
been proved deductively that vertical angles are equal.

|| THEOREM 3
|| **All vertical angles are equal.**

Exercises

1. Define vertical angles.

2. Name all pairs of vertical angles in the diagrams below.

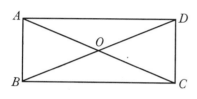

Ex. 2

3. If *AB*, *CD*, and *EF* are straight
lines, name all the angles in the
diagram that are equal.

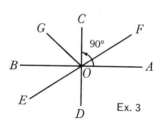

Ex. 3

4. If *AB* and *CD* are straight
lines, but *XY* is not a straight line,
name the angles in the diagram that
are equal.

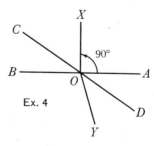

Ex. 4

5. $\angle X + \angle Y = 180°$. $\angle X = 90°$. Prove that $\angle X = \angle Y$.

6. Given: *RS* is a straight line,
$\angle RWU = 90°$.

Prove: $\angle TWR = \angle RWU$.

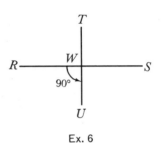

Ex. 6

In Exercises **7-10** *supply the missing data.*

    7. Prove the following theorem:

> **THEOREM 4**
>
> **If two adjacent angles are supplementary, their exterior sides form a straight line.**

    Given: $\angle AOC$ and $\angle COB$
            are adjacent,
            $\angle AOC$ and $\angle COB$
            are supplementary.

    Prove: *AOB* is a straight line.

Ex. 7

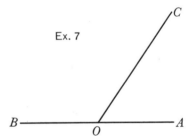

STATEMENTS	REASONS
1. $\angle AOC$ and $\angle COB$ are supplementary. $\angle AOC$ and $\angle COB$ are adjacent.	1. Given.
2. ?	2. The sum of the measures of two supplementary angles is 180°.
3. ?	3. The whole is equal to the sum of its parts.
4. ?	4. Quantities equal to the same or equal quantities are equal.
5. *AOB* is a straight line.	5. Why?

8. Prove the following theorem:

THEOREM 5

If the exterior sides of two adjacent angles lie in a straight line, the angles are supplementary.

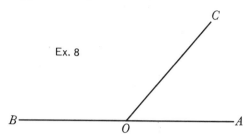

Ex. 8

Given: AOB is a straight line,
  $$\angle AOC + \angle COB = \angle AOB.$$
Prove: $\angle AOC$ and $\angle COB$ are supplementary.

STATEMENTS	REASONS
1. AOB is a straight line.	1. Given.
2. ?	2. If the sides of an angle extend in opposite directions, the angle is a straight angle.
3. ?	3. The measure of a straight angle is 180°.
4. ?	4. The whole is equal to the sum of its parts.
5. ?	5. Quantities equal to the same or equal quantities are equal.
6. $\angle AOC$ and $\angle COB$ are supplementary.	6. Why?

  a. From what words in the stated theorem is the relationship $\angle AOC + \angle COB = \angle AOB$ obtained?

  b. Does the size of $\angle AOC$ or $\angle COB$ in the diagram influence the proof in any way?

  c. Which of the reasons are definitions? Which are assumptions?

  d. In Reason 2 can the definition of a straight angle as one-half of a complete revolution be used instead of the definition given? Why or why not?

9. Prove the following theorem:

|| **THEOREM 6**

|| **If two adjacent angles are complementary, their exterior sides are perpendicular.**

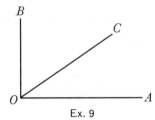

Ex. 9

Given: $\angle AOC$ and $\angle COB$ are adjacent,
$\angle AOC + \angle COB = 90°$.
Prove: $AO \perp OB$.

STATEMENTS	REASONS
1. ?	1. Given.
2. $\angle AOB = \angle AOC + \angle COB$.	2. Why?
3. $\angle AOB = 90°$.	3. Why?
4. $AO \perp OB$.	4. Why?

10. Prove the following theorem:

|| **THEOREM 7**

|| **If the exterior sides of two adjacent angles are perpendicular, the angles are complementary.**

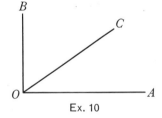

Ex. 10

Given: $AO \perp OB$,
$\angle AOC$ and $\angle COB$ are adjacent.

Prove: $\angle AOC + \angle COB = 90°$.

STATEMENTS	REASONS
1. ?	1. Given.
2. $\angle AOB$ is a right angle	2. Why?
3. $\angle AOB = 90°$.	3. Why?
4. $\angle AOB = \angle AOC + \angle COB$.	4. Why?
5. $\angle AOC + \angle COB = 90°$.	5. Why?
6. $\angle AOC$ and $\angle COB$ are complementary.	6. Why?

MORE ABOUT DEDUCTIVE REASONING

In legal cases lawyers often search through records to find the conclusions drawn by other courts. They realize that logical reasoning by the judge will take into consideration previous assumptions and conclusions. In geometry, the proof of a theorem is based on previously proved theorems, assumptions, definitions, and undefined terms.

‖Developmental Exercises

DE—1. Given: $\angle 1 = \angle 3$,
All lines in the sketch are straight lines.

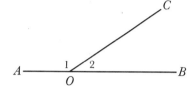

Prove: $\angle 2 = \angle 4$.

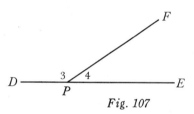

Fig. 107

Solution

STATEMENTS	REASONS
1. $\angle 1$ and $\angle 2$ are supplementary, $\angle 3$ and $\angle 4$ are supplementary.	1. Two angles which form one-half of a complete rotation are called supplementary angles.
2. $\angle 1 + \angle 2 = 180°$, $\angle 3 + \angle 4 = 180°$.	2. The sum of two supplementary angles is 180°.
3. $\angle 1 + \angle 2 = \angle 3 + \angle 4$.	3. A quantity may be substituted for its equal in any expression without changing the value of the expression.
4. $\angle 1 = \angle 3$.	4. Given.
5. $\angle 2 = \angle 4$.	5. If equals are subtracted from equals the differences are equal.

Thus, the following theorem has been proved.

‖THEOREM 8
‖**Supplements of equal angles are equal.**

DE—2. Given: $\angle 3 + \angle 1 = 180°$.

Prove: $\angle 2 = \angle 3$.

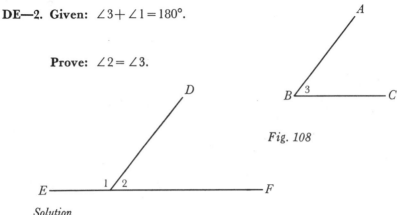

Fig. 108

Solution

STATEMENTS	REASONS
1. $\angle 1$ and $\angle 2$ are supplementary.	1. Two angles which form a straight line, i.e., one-half of a complete rotation, are supplementary.
2. $\angle 1 + \angle 2 = 180°$.	2. The sum of two supplementary angles is 180°.
3. $\angle 1 + \angle 3 = 180°$.	3. Given.
4. $\angle 1 = \angle 1$.	4. A quantity is equal to itself.
5. $\angle 2 = \angle 3$.	5. Supplements of equal angles are equal.

Thus, it has been proved that supplements of the same angle are equal.

This new deduction is called a *corollary*. Notice that the proof of this corollary depended on Theorem 8, *supplements of equal angles are equal.* All of the statements and reasons in the proof led to the use of this theorem. Thus, the conclusion is a direct consequence of the theorem. *A* **corollary** *is a conclusion which is established by the application of a theorem with which the conclusion has a logically close relationship.*

Corollary

Supplements of the same angle are equal.

Statement 4, used in proving the corollary, is a unique relationship which states that a quantity is equal to itself. This relationship implies not only an equality but a sameness. PQ is identical to itself, PQ. You will sometimes see this property written as $PQ \equiv PQ$. The symbol $\equiv$ is read "is identical to." The reason is frequently shortened to "identity."

DE—3. Given: $\angle 1$ and $\angle 2$ are complementary,
$\angle 3$ and $\angle 4$ are complementary,
$\angle 2 = \angle 4$.

Prove: $\angle 1 = \angle 3$.

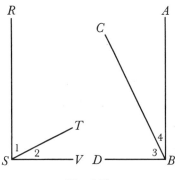

Fig. 109

Solution

STATEMENTS	REASONS
1. $\angle 1$ and $\angle 2$ are complementary, $\angle 3$ and $\angle 4$ are complementary, $\angle 2 = \angle 4$.	1. Given.
2. $\angle 2 + \angle 1 = 90°$, $\angle 4 + \angle 3 = 90°$.	2. The sum of the measures of two complementary angles is 90°.
3. $\angle 2 + \angle 1 = \angle 4 + \angle 3$.	3. A quantity may be substituted for its equal in any expression without changing the value of the expression.
4. $\angle 1 = \angle 3$.	4. If equals are subtracted from equals, their differences are equal.

Since $\angle 1$ and $\angle 3$ are complements of equal angles, we have the conclusion:

‖ THEOREM 9
‖ **If two angles are complements of equal angles, they are equal.**

This theorem may now be used to establish other relationships. Closely related to this theorem is the statement *Complements of the same angle are equal.* Observe how Theorem 9 is used in the proof of this corollary.

DE—4. Prove the following:

║**Corollary**
║**Complements of the same angle are equal.**

Given: $\angle 1 + \angle 2 = 90°$,
$\angle 3 + \angle 2 = 90°$.

Prove: $\angle 1 = \angle 3$.

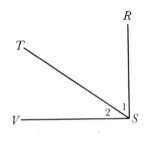

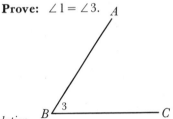

Fig. 110

Solution

STATEMENTS	REASONS
1. $\angle 1 + \angle 2 = 90°$, $\angle 3 + \angle 2 = 90°$.	1. Given.
2. $\angle 2 = \angle 2$.	2. Identity.
3. $\angle 1 = \angle 3$.	3. Complements of equal angles are equal.

The steps in making a proof are generally in this order:

a. A labeled diagram is made (or constructed, if directed).

b. Data supplied is listed in terms of the diagram.

c. The conclusion to be established is also listed in terms of the diagram.

d. An analysis of the logical connection between the conclusion and given data is made before writing the first statement of the proof.

e. The proof is written to summarize, and to arrange in correct sequence, the deductions made.

DE—5. Given: *AC* and *BD* are straight lines which intersect at *O*. $\angle BOC = 42°$.

Prove: The number of degrees in each angle in the figure is ? .

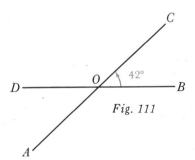

Fig. 111

Solution

STATEMENTS	REASONS
1. *AC* and *BD* are intersecting straight lines.	1. Given.
2. $\angle BOC = 42°$.	2. Given.
3. $\angle DOA = \angle BOC$.	3. Vertical angles of intersecting straight lines are equal.
4. $\angle DOA = 42°$.	4. A quantity may be substituted for its equal in any expression without changing the value of the expression.
5. $\angle BOC$ is the supplement of $\angle COD$.	5. Two angles which form one-half of a complete rotation are supplementary.
6. $\angle DOA$ is the supplement of $\angle AOB$.	6. Same as Reason 5.
7. $\angle BOC + \angle COD = 180°$.	7. The sum of two supplementary angles is 180°.
8. $\angle DOA + AOB = 180°$.	8. Same as Reason 7.
9. $42° + \angle COD = 180°$.	9. Same as Reason 4.
10. $42° + \angle AOB = 180°$.	10. Same as Reason 4.
11. $\angle COD = 138°$.	11. If equals are subtracted from equals, the remainders are equal.
12. $\angle AOB = 138°$.	12. Same as Reason 11.

After you have had more experience in writing formal proofs your teacher may permit you to leave out some of the more obvious steps and use abbreviations for reasons that occur frequently.

DE—6. Find the number of degrees in an angle that is twice its complement.

Solution

Let $x =$ the number of degrees in the angle that is twice its complement.

Then $90 - x =$ number of degrees in its complement.

$2(90 - x) =$ twice the complement of the given angle.

$$x = 2(90 - x).$$
$$x = 180 - 2x.$$
$$x + 2x = 180 - 2x + 2x.$$
$$3x = 180.$$
$$\frac{3x}{3} = \frac{180}{3}.$$

$x = 60$, number of degrees in the angle.

DE—7. The number of degrees in two adjacent complementary angles are $\frac{3a}{2}$ and $15+\frac{5a}{2}$. How large is each?

Solution

$$\frac{3a}{2}+15+\frac{5a}{2}=90.$$

$$\frac{8a}{2}+15=90.$$

$$4a+15=90.$$

$$4a+15-15=90-15.$$

$$4a=75.$$

$$\frac{4a}{4}=\frac{75}{4}.$$

$$a=18\tfrac{3}{4}.$$

Then, $\frac{3a}{2}=\frac{3}{2}\,(18\tfrac{3}{4})=28\tfrac{1}{8}$. The measure of the first angle is $28\tfrac{1}{8}°$ or $28°7'30''$. $15+\frac{5a}{2}=15+\frac{5}{2}(18\tfrac{3}{4})=61\tfrac{7}{8}$. The measure of the second angle is $61\tfrac{7}{8}°$ or $61°52'30''$.

Ex. 1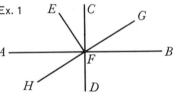

Exercises

1. *AB*, *CD*, and *GH* are straight lines, $CD\perp AB$, and $EF\perp GH$. Name all the pairs of angles that are equal.

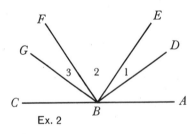

Ex. 2

2. $\angle 1$ and $\angle 2$ are complementary, $\angle 3$ and $\angle 2$ are complementary.

a. What conclusion do you reach regarding $\angle 1$ and $\angle 3$? Justify that conclusion.

b. If $\angle ABF=\angle EBC$, what conclusion do you reach regarding $\angle ABD$ and $\angle GBC$? Justify that conclusion.

3. $\angle A$ and $\angle 1$ are complementary, $AD\perp DC$. Point out the generalizations that would enable you to establish that $\angle A=\angle 2$.

Ex. 3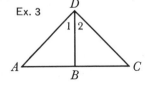

4. Copy and complete the table:

If $x =$	20°	30°	40°			$2a°$	$3a°$	$3y°$	$a° - 10°$
then $(90° - x) =$				50°	75°				

5. Find the angle which is 20° greater than its complement.

6. Two complementary angles are $\dfrac{7x°}{2}$ and $\dfrac{3x°}{2}$. What value has x? How many degrees are in each angle?

7. If two complementary angles have the ratio 2 to 3, how large is each? If the ratio is 4 to 7?

8. Explain how the exterior sides of two adjacent complementary angles are related.

Write a proof for each of the following exercises. Be certain each statement is supported by a reason that is one of the three groups of acceptable reasons.

9. Given: $\angle 2 = \angle 3$.
  Prove: $\angle 1 = \angle 4$.

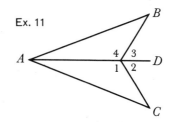

Ex. 9

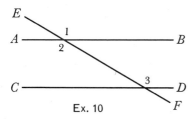

E
A ———— B
C ———— D
F

Ex. 10

10. Given: $\angle 1 = \angle 3$.
  Prove: $\angle 2 = \angle 3$.

Ex. 11

11. Given: $\angle 1 = \angle 4$.
  Prove: $\angle 2 = \angle 3$.

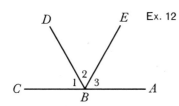

Ex. 12

12. Given: $\angle ABD = \angle EBC$.
  Prove: $\angle 1 = \angle 3$.

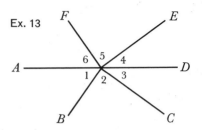

Ex. 13

13. Given: $\angle 3 = \angle 4$,
      $\angle 5 = \angle 2 = 90°$.
   Prove: $\angle 1 = \angle 6$.

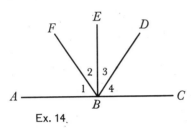

Ex. 14.

14. Given: $EB \perp AC$,
      $\angle 2 = \angle 3$.
   Prove: $\angle 1 = \angle 4$.

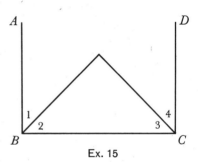

Ex. 15

15. Given: $AB \perp BC$,
      $DC \perp BC$,
      $\angle 2 = \angle 3$.
   Prove: $\angle 1 = \angle 4$.

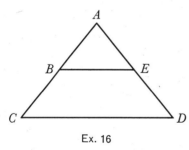

Ex. 16

16. Given: $AB = AE$,
      $AC = AD$.
   Prove: $BC = DE$.

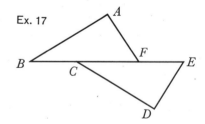

Ex. 17

17. Given: $BC = FE$.
   Prove: $BF = CE$.

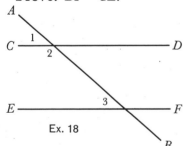

Ex. 18

18. Given: $\angle 1 = \angle 3$.
   Prove: $\angle 2 + \angle 3 = 180°$.

19. Given: $AC = AD$,
$BC = DE$.
Prove: $AB = AE$.

Ex. 19

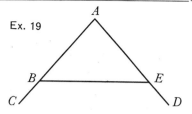

Ex. 20

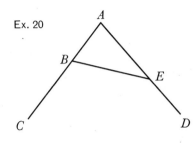

20. Given: $BC = AE$,
$AB = DE$.
Prove: $AC = AD$.

Ex. 21

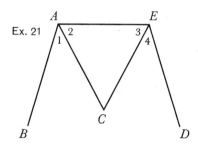

21. Given: $\angle BAE = \angle DEA$,
$\angle 2 = \angle 3$.
Prove: $\angle 1 = \angle 4$.

Ex. 22

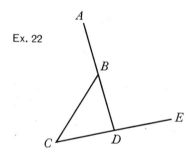

22. Given: $BD = DC$,
$CD = DE$,
$AB = BD$.
Prove: $AD = CE$.

23. Given: $AB = FE$,
$AB = BC$,
$FE = DE$.
Prove: $AC = FD$.

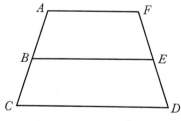

Ex. 23

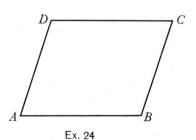

Ex. 24

24. Given: $AB = CD$,
$AD = DC$,
$BC = AB$.
Prove: $AD = BC$.

CONGRUENCE

Each tubeless tire on this assembly line is exactly the same size and shape.

On every assembly line parts are made almost exactly the same size and shape. Each part is a copy of the pattern and can be made to coincide with any other piece made from that pattern. These are called *congruent* parts.

Figures that can be made to coincide are congruent figures.

In Chapter One you found that a triangle may be constructed the same size and shape as another triangle if

(*1*) two sides and the included angle are duplicated,

(*2*) two angles and the duplicated side are duplicated, or,

(*3*) three sides are duplicated.

These triangles are *congruent* triangles. The symbol for "congruent to" is $\cong$.

Assumption 17

If two triangles have two sides and the included angle of one equal respectively to two sides and the included angle of the other, then the triangles are congruent. This relationship may be expressed briefly as **s.a.s = s.a.s.**

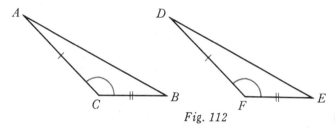

Fig. 112

Assumption 18

If two triangles have two angles and the included side of one equal respectively to two angles and the included side of the other, then they are congruent. This relationship may be expressed briefly as **a.s.a. = a.s.a.**

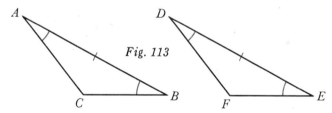

Fig. 113

Assumption 19

If two triangles have three sides of one equal respectively to three sides of the other, then the triangles are congruent. This relationship may be expressed as **s.s.s. = s.s.s.**

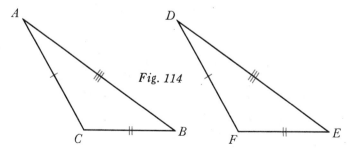

Fig. 114

The equal parts (lines or angles) of congruent triangles, grouped in pairs, are called *corresponding parts*.

Assumption 20

Corresponding parts of congruent triangles are equal.

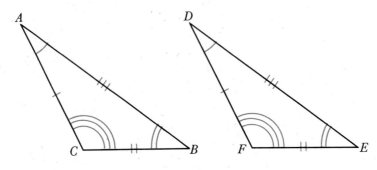

Fig. 115

Developmental Exercises

DE—1. $\triangle MNO \cong \triangle RST$ (read triangle MNO is congruent to triangle RST). Name the corresponding parts.

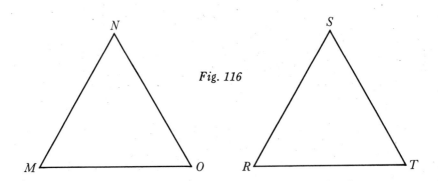

Fig. 116

Solution

Equal sides and angles are marked in the same way. Right angles are marked with a little box. Corresponding sides are opposite angles known to be equal and corresponding; corresponding angles are opposite sides that are known to be equal and corresponding. The corresponding parts are

$MN = RS$; $MO = RT$; $NO = ST$; $\angle N = \angle S$; $\angle M = \angle R$; $\angle O = \angle T$.

DE—2. Given: $\angle 1 = \angle 2$,

$BC = CD$,

$BG = DF$.

    Prove: $\angle G = \angle F$.

Fig. 117

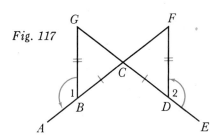

Solution

An analysis of what must be proved will help you discover a proof. Study the analysis below to see how the proof is developed from it.

$\angle G = \angle F$, if they are corresponding angles of congruent triangles. $\triangle GBC$ is congruent to $\triangle CDF$ if two sides and the included angle of one triangle are equal respectively to the corresponding parts of the other triangle.

Since BC and CD are given equal and BG and DF are given equal, **s.a.s = s.a.s.** if $\angle GBC = \angle FDC$. Those angles are supplements of $\angle 1$ and $\angle 2$ respectively. Furthermore, $\angle 1$ is given equal to $\angle 2$.

The proof can now be arranged as follows:

STATEMENTS	REASONS
1. $\angle 1 = \angle 2$, $BC = CD$, $BG = DF$.	1. Given.
2. $\angle 1 + \angle CBG = 180°$, $\angle 2 + \angle FDC = 180°$.	2. Two angles which form one-half of a complete rotation are supplementary.
3. $\angle CBG = \angle FDC$.	3. Supplements of equal angles are equal.
4. $\triangle GBC \cong \triangle CDF$.	4. **s.a.s. = s.a.s.**
5. $\angle G = \angle F$.	5. Corresponding angles of congruent triangles are equal.

Review each step to note the following:

    a. Each step, except the very last one, supports a step which follows it.

    b. Each reason in *if-then* form, or that can be so expressed, meets two tests:

        1. The *if* clause has been previously established,

        2. The *then* clause is a general form of its corresponding statement.

    c. Each reason is

        1. an accepted definition, or

        2. an accepted assumption, or

        3. a theorem previously established.

DE—3. Prove the following theorem:

> **THEOREM 10**
>
> **If two isosceles triangles have a common base, then a line joining their vertex angles bisects the vertex angles.**

Given: $AB = AC$,
$BD = DC$.

Prove: AD bisects $\angle BAC$,
AD bisects $\angle CDB$.

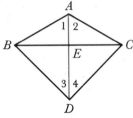

Fig. 118

Solution

$\angle 1 = \angle 2$ if they are corresponding angles of congruent triangles. Also, $\angle 3$ will equal $\angle 4$ if the triangles ABD and ADC are congruent.

Since $AB = AC$, $BD = DC$ from the data given, and $AD = AD$ by identity, the proof can be arranged as follows.

STATEMENTS	REASONS
1. $AB = AC$, $BD = DC$.	1. Given.
2. $AD = AD$.	2. Identity.
3. $\triangle ABD \cong \triangle ACD$.	3. s.s.s. = s.s.s.
4. $\angle 1 = \angle 2$, $\angle 3 = \angle 4$.	4. Corresponding angles of congruent triangles are equal.
5. AD bisects $\angle BAC$, AD bisects $\angle CDB$.	5. An angle which has been divided into two equal angles has been bisected.

The illustration for Developmental Exercise **3** may be drawn as shown:

Given: $AB = AC$, $BD = DC$.

However, the line segment AD, as now drawn, does not divide angle CDB into angles. Since a line extends indefinitely in either direction, the line segment AD, in Figure 119 may be extended through D to meet line BD. You now can prove that $\angle CDB$ is bisected.

Fig. 119

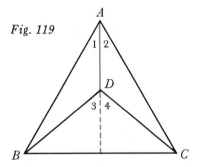

DE—4. Given: AD and BE are straight
lines.
$\angle B = \angle E$,
AD bisects BE.

Prove: $\angle A = \angle D$.

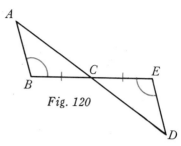

Fig. 120

Solution

$\angle A = \angle D$ can be proved if $\triangle ABC \cong \triangle CDE$ can be proved.
$\triangle ABC \cong \triangle CDE$ can be proved if $\angle B = \angle E,$ **(a)**
$BC = CE,$ **(s)**
$\angle ACB = \angle ECD$ **(a)** can be proved.

STATEMENTS	REASONS
1. $\angle B = \angle E$, AD bisects BE.	1. Given.
2. $BC = CE$.	2. Parts of a bisected line segment are equal.
3. $\angle ACB = \angle ECD$.	3. Vertical angles of intersecting straight lines are equal.
4. $\triangle ABC \cong \triangle CDE$.	4. **a.s.a. = a.s.a.**
5. $\angle A = \angle D$.	5. Corresponding angles of congruent triangles are equal.

DE—5. If corresponding angles of two congruent triangles are bisected, then the bisectors are equal.

Given: $\triangle ABC \cong \triangle EFG$,
BD bisects $\angle ABC$,
FH bisects $\angle EFG$

Prove: $BD = FH$.

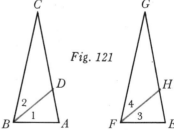

Fig. 121

Solution

If $\triangle ABC \cong \triangle EFG$, then $\angle C = \angle G$, $BC = FG$, and $\angle ABC = \angle EFG$.
If $\angle ABC$ is bisected, then $\angle 1 = \angle 2$.
If $\angle EFG$ is bisected, then $\angle 3 = \angle 4$.
You can now show $\angle 2 = \angle 4$ and $\triangle BCD \cong \triangle FHG$.

STATEMENTS	REASONS
1. $\triangle ABC \cong \triangle EFG$, BD bisects $\angle ABC$, FH bisects $\angle EFG$.	1. Given.
2. $\angle C = \angle G$, $BC = FG$, $\angle ABC = \angle EFG$.	2. Corresponding parts of congruent triangles are equal.
3. $\angle 1 = \angle 2$, $\angle 3 = \angle 4$.	3. Parts of a bisected angle are equal.
4. $\angle 2 = \angle 4$.	4. Halves of equals are equal.
5. $\triangle BDC \cong \triangle FHG$.	5. a.s.a. = a.s.a.
6. $BD = FH$.	6. Same as Reason 2.

Exercises

1. Construct a triangle given three angles. What do you find? Do you think it would be correct to state that if two triangles have three angles respectively equal then they are congruent? Why or why not?

2. Construct a triangle given two sides and an angle opposite one of the sides. What do you find? Do you think it would be correct to state that if two triangles have two sides and an angle opposite one of the sides respectively equal then they are congruent? Why or why not?

List the numbers 3-12 in a column. After each number write **s.s.s. = s.s.s.** *or* **a.s.a. = a.s.a.** *or* **s.a.s. = s.a.s.** *to show why the triangles are congruent.*

3. Given: $\angle 1 = \angle 2$,
$\qquad\qquad$ $\angle 3 = \angle 4$.
$\quad$ **Prove:** $\triangle ABD \cong \triangle BCD$.

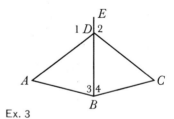

Ex. 3

4. Given: $BD = DF$,
$\qquad\qquad$ $\angle 1 = \angle 2$.
$\quad$ **Prove:** $\triangle ABD \cong \triangle FDE$.

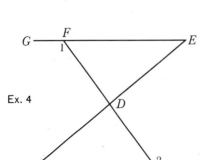

Ex. 4

5. Given: $BC = CD$,
$\qquad\qquad \angle 1 = \angle 4.$
$\quad$ **Prove:** $\triangle BCG \cong \triangle CDF.$

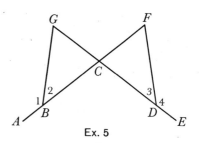
Ex. 5

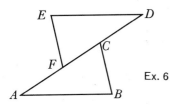
Ex. 6

6. Given: $EF = BC$,
$\qquad\qquad ED = AB$,
$\qquad\qquad \angle E = \angle B.$
$\quad$ **Prove:** $\triangle ABC \cong \triangle EFD.$

7. Given: $\angle 1 = \angle 2$,
$\qquad\qquad \angle 3 = \angle 4.$
$\quad$ **Prove:** $\triangle ABC \cong \triangle ADC.$

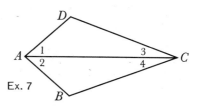
Ex. 7

Ex. 8

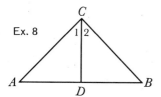

8. Given: $\angle 1 = \angle 2$,
$\qquad\qquad AC = CB.$
$\quad$ **Prove:** $\triangle ACD \cong \triangle CDB.$

9. Given: $BO = OD$,
$\qquad\qquad \angle B = \angle D.$
$\quad$ **Prove:** $\triangle ABO \cong \triangle DCO.$

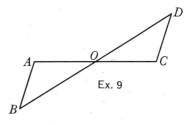
Ex. 9

10. Given: $AB = CD$,
$\qquad\qquad \angle 1 = \angle 6$,
$\qquad\qquad \angle 3 = \angle 4.$
$\quad$ **Prove:** $\triangle ABE \cong \triangle ECD.$

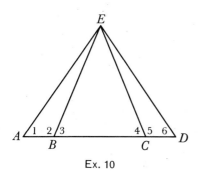
Ex. 10

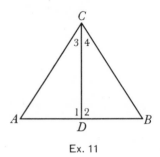

Ex. 11

11. Given: $CD \perp AB$,
　　　　$\angle 3 = \angle 4$.
　Prove: $\triangle ADC \cong \triangle DBC$.

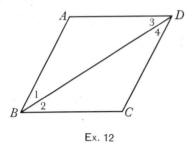

Ex. 12

12. Given: $AB = DC$,
　　　　$\angle 1 = \angle 4$.
　Prove: $\triangle ABD \cong \triangle BCD$.

Write a complete proof for each of the following conclusions.

13. Given: $AB = DE$,
　　　　$BC = FE$,
　　　　$AF = CD$.
　Prove: $\triangle ABC \cong \triangle DFE$.

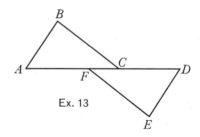

Ex. 13

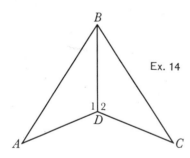

Ex. 14

14. Given: $\angle 1 = \angle 2$,
　　　　$AD = DC$.
　Prove: $\triangle ABD \cong \triangle CBD$.

15. Given: $AB = DF$,
　　　　$BC = DE$,
　　　　$AE = CF$.
　Prove: $\triangle ABC \cong \triangle DEF$.

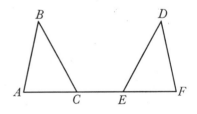

Ex. 15

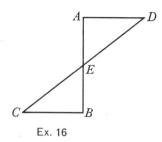

Ex. 16

16. Given: $AD \perp AB$,
$\qquad\qquad CB \perp AB$,
$\qquad\qquad AE = BE$.
$\quad$**Prove:** $\triangle ADE \cong \triangle BCE$.

17. Given: $AC = DF$,
$\qquad\qquad \angle 1 = \angle 2$,
$\qquad\qquad BC = DE$.
$\quad$**Prove:** $\triangle ABC \cong \triangle FED$.

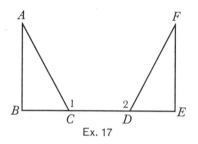

Ex. 17

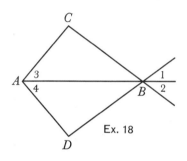

Ex. 18

18. Given: $\angle 1 = \angle 2$,
$\qquad\qquad \angle 3 = \angle 4$.
$\quad$**Prove:** $\triangle ACB \cong \triangle ADB$.

19. Given: $AD = CE$,
$\qquad\qquad \angle 1 = \angle 2$,
$\qquad\qquad BC = FD$.
$\quad$**Prove:** $\triangle ABC \cong \triangle DEF$.

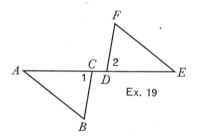

Ex. 19

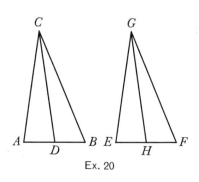

Ex. 20

20. Given: $CD = GH$,
$\qquad\qquad CB = GF$,
$\qquad\qquad AB = EF$,
$\qquad\qquad AD = DB$,
$\qquad\qquad EH = HF$.
$\quad$**Prove:** $\triangle CDB \cong \triangle GHF$.

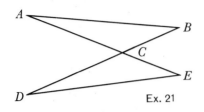

Ex. 21

21. Given: $AC = DC$,
$\quad\quad\quad\quad \angle A = \angle D$.
Prove: $BC = CE$.

22. Given: $AB = FD$,
$\quad\quad\quad\quad AC = FE$,
$\quad\quad\quad\quad FD = FE$,
$\quad\quad\quad\quad EB = CD$.
$\quad\quad$ **Prove:** $\angle ABF = \angle ACF$.

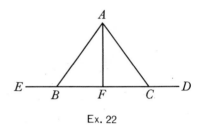

Ex. 22

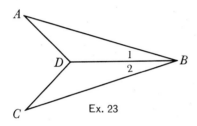

Ex. 23

23. Given: $AB = BC$,
$\quad\quad\quad\quad \angle 1 = \angle 2$.
Prove: $AD = DC$.

24. Given: $AF = EB$,
$\quad\quad\quad\quad DA \perp AB$,
$\quad\quad\quad\quad CB \perp AB$,
$\quad\quad\quad\quad AD = BC$.
$\quad\quad$ **Prove:** $\angle 1 = \angle 2$.

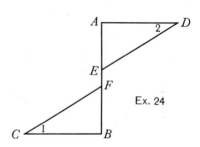

Ex. 24

Ex. 25

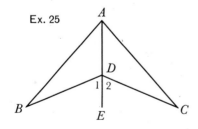

25. Given: $AB = AC$,
$\quad\quad\quad\quad BD = CD$.
Prove: $\angle 1 = \angle 2$.

26. Given: $AB = CD$,
$\quad\quad\quad\quad AE = BF$,
$\quad\quad\quad\quad \angle 1 + \angle 2 = 180°$.
$\quad\quad$ **Prove:** $\angle E = \angle F$.

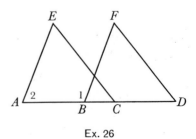

Ex. 26

PROVING CONSTRUCTIONS

No justifications were given for the constructions in Chapter One. You may wish to show that your constructions are correct. The proof of a construction is based on the lines drawn during the construction. These lines are usually evidence that the construction has been done correctly and often offers a clue to the plan for a proof that the method used is acceptable. All construction lines drawn should appear in the final diagram. That is, do not erase any of them. Often these construction lines will not be enough to complete the proof and additional lines must be drawn. These are called *auxiliary*, or *helping*, lines. They are usually dashed to distinguish them from the construction lines. Study the following developmental exercises to see how construction lines and auxiliary lines are used.

Developmental Exercises

DE—1. Bisect an angle. Show that the construction is valid.

Solution

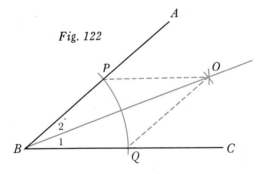

Fig. 122

With *B* as center, equal lengths were marked off on *AB* and *BC*. Thus, *BP = BQ*. With *P* and *Q* as centers and the same radius, point *O* was determined the same distance from *P* and *Q*. Thus, *PO = QO*. These lines are dashed to set them apart from the lines in the basic diagram. *BO = BO* by identity. Since three sides of $\triangle BPO$ are equal respectively to three sides of $\triangle BQO$, the triangles are congruent. Hence, $\angle 1 = \angle 2$ since they are corresponding angles of congruent triangles, and $\angle ABC$ has been divided (bisected) into two equal parts.

DE—2. Bisect a line segment. Show that the line segment has been bisected.

Solution

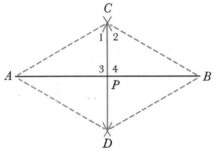

Fig. 123

Triangles *ADC* and *BDC* are congruent by **s.s.s. = s.s.s.** Why? $\angle 1 = \angle 2$ as they are corresponding angles of congruent triangles. $\triangle APC \cong \triangle BPC$ by **s.a.s = s.a.s.** $AP = PB$ as they are corresponding sides of congruent triangles.

You can also observe that $\angle 3 = \angle 4$. Lines *CD* and *AB* are perpendicular since they meet to form equal adjacent angles.

Since the construction and plan of proof are general for bisecting line segments of unknown length, and the bisector is proved perpendicular to the line segment, you may conclude the following:

THEOREM 11
Two points, each equally distant from the ends of a line segment, determine the perpendicular bisector of the line segment.

The two points in the figure are *C* and *D*. This conclusion is often referred to as the *Two-Point Theorem*.

Exercises

1. Draw an acute angle. Construct an angle equal to the given acute angle. Show that the angles are equal.

2. Construct a perpendicular to a line at a given point on the line. Show that the line you constructed is perpendicular to the given line.

3. Construct a perpendicular to a line from a point not on the line. Show that the line you constructed is perpendicular to the given line.

4. Use three different congruence combinations as the basis for a description of three different methods for constructing a triangle congruent to $\triangle ABC$.

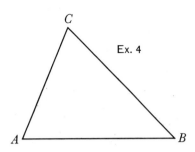

Ex. 4

5. Draw an obtuse triangle. Construct a triangle congruent to it. Bisect the obtuse angle of each triangle. Prove that two of the smaller triangles thus formed are congruent.

6. Draw an acute triangle. Construct a triangle congruent to it. Construct the median of one of the equal sides of each triangle. Prove that the two smaller triangles are congruent.

7. Construct an isosceles triangle and then construct the bisector of the vertex angle. Draw lines from one point of that bisector to the ends of the base. Show that those lines are equal.

8. Draw a triangle. Construct the perpendicular bisector of two of the sides. Show that their point of intersection is equidistant from the three vertices of the triangle.

9. Prove the following theorem:

║THEOREM 12

║Any point on the perpendicular bisector of a line segment is equidistant from the endpoints of the line segment.

10. Make a drawing comparable to the one at the right. Without extending *BC*, construct a line from point *A* that would be perpendicular to *BC* extended.

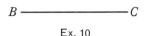

Ex. 10

ANGLES OF AN ISOSCELES TRIANGLE

An isosceles triangle has two equal sides. The unequal side is generally considered the base of the triangle. Then the angles opposite the equal sides are called the *base angles*.

‖ THEOREM 13
‖ **Angles opposite equal sides of a triangle are equal.**

Given: $AC = BC$.

Prove: $\angle A = \angle B$.

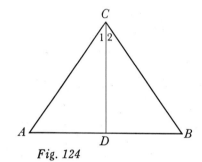

Fig. 124

Construction: Bisect $\angle C$ by line CD.

STATEMENTS	REASONS
1. $AC = BC$.	1. Given.
2. $\angle 1 = \angle 2$.	2. An angle bisector can be constructed.
3. $CD = CD$.	3. Identity.
4. $\triangle ADC \cong \triangle BDC$.	4. s.a.s. = s.a.s.
5. $\angle A = \angle B$.	5. Corresponding angles of congruent triangles are equal.

This theorem may also be stated
The base angles of an isosceles triangle are equal.
Closely related to this theorem is the following corollary.

‖ **Corollary**
‖ **All equilateral triangles are equiangular.**

The proof of this corollary is left to the student.

Developmental Exercises

DE—1. Given: $AB = AC,$
$\angle 5 = \angle 6.$

Prove: $\triangle ADE$ is isosceles.

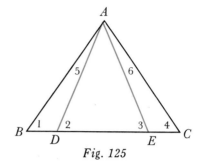

Fig. 125

Solution

Analysis:

You would know:	If you knew:
1. $\triangle ADE$ is isosceles.	1. $AD = AE$.
2. $AD = AE$.	2. $\triangle ABD \cong \triangle AEC$.
3. $\triangle ABD \cong \triangle AEC$.	3. $\angle 5 = \angle 6$, (**a**) $AB = AC$, (**s**) $\angle 1 = \angle 4$. (**a**)
4. $\angle 5 = \angle 6$, $AB = AC$.	4. Given.
5. $\angle 1 = \angle 4$.	5. Angles opposite equal sides of a triangle are equal.

Proof:

Statements	Reasons
1. $AB = AC,$ $\angle 5 = \angle 6.$	1. Given.
2. $\angle 1 = \angle 4$.	2. Angles opposite equal sides of a triangle are equal.
3. $\triangle ABD \cong AEC$.	3. If two triangles have two angles and the included side of one equal respectively to two angles and the included side of the other, they are congruent. **a.s.a. = a.s.a.**
4. $AD = AE$.	4. Corresponding sides of congruent triangles are equal.
5. $\triangle ADE$ is isosceles.	5. A triangle with two sides equal is isosceles.

DE—2. Prove the following theorem:

> **THEOREM 14**
> **If the sides of any quadrilateral are equal, lines joining opposite vertices bisect each other at right angles.**

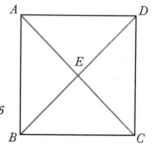

Given: $AB = BC = CD = AD$.

Prove: $AE = EC$,
$BE = ED$,
$BD \perp AC$.

Fig. 126

Solution

Analysis:

Points A and C are each equally distant from B and D, thus, by the Two-Point Theorem, AC is the perpendicular bisector of BD. Likewise, BD is the perpendicular bisector of AC.

Proof:

STATEMENTS	REASONS
1. $AB = BC = CD = AD$.	1. Given.
2. $AE = EC$, $BE = ED$, $BD \perp AC$.	2. Two points, each equally distant from the ends of a line segment, determine the perpendicular bisector of the line segment.

Exercises

Write complete proofs for the following:

1. Given: $AC = BC$.
   Prove: $\angle A = \angle B$.

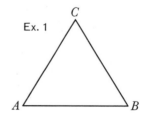

Ex. 1

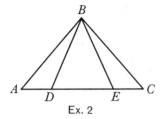
Ex. 2

2. Given: $AB = BC$,
　　　　$AD = EC$.
Prove: $\triangle ABD \cong \triangle BCE$.

3. Given: $AB = BC$,
　　　　$AD = DC$.
Prove: $BD \perp AC$.

Ex. 3
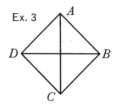

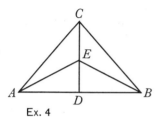
Ex. 4

4. Given: $AC = BC$,
　　　　$AE = BE$.
Prove: $CD \perp AB$.

5. Given: $AB = BC$,
　　　　$AD = DC$.
Prove: $\angle DAB = \angle BCD$.

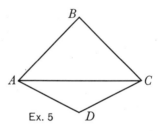
Ex. 5

6. Given: $AB = AC$,
　　　　$DE \perp BC$,
　　　　$FG \perp BC$,
　　　　$BG = EC$.
Prove: $\triangle BDE \cong \triangle CFG$.

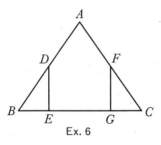
Ex. 6

7. Given: $AB = BC$,
　　　　AD bisects $\angle A$,
　　　　DC bisects $\angle C$.
Prove: $\angle 1 = \angle 2$.

Ex. 7
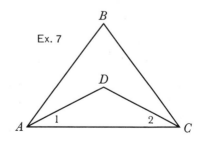

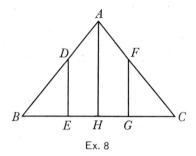

Ex. 8

8. Given: $AD = AF$,
$BE = GC$,
$EH = HG$,
$DE = FG$,
$DE \perp BC$,
$FG \perp BC$.
Prove: $AH \perp BC$.

9. Given: $AB = AC$,
$\angle B = \angle 3$,
$\angle C = \angle 4$.
Prove: $\angle 1 = \angle 2$.

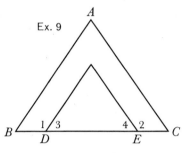

Ex. 9

10. Given: $\angle A = \angle B$,
$AE = BE$.
Prove: $\angle 1 = \angle 2$.

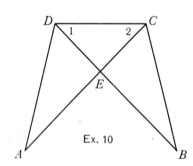

Ex. 10

SOLID GEOMETRY

The foundations of proof in solid geometry, as in plane geometry, are included in the *if-then* pattern of reaching valid conclusions. The foundations are: undefined terms, definitions, assumptions, and theorems.

When one, but not more than one, geometric figure results from a set of conditions, the figure is said to be *determined*.

The intersection of any two geometric figures is the set of all the points common to both.

Assumption 1$_s$
Three points not in a straight line determine a plane.

Assumption 2$_s$

The intersection of two planes is a straight line.

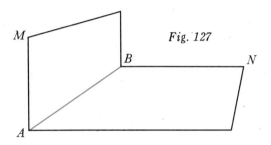

Fig. 127

Assumption 3$_s$

The intersection of a straight line and a plane is a point called the *foot of the line*.

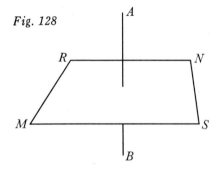

Fig. 128

Assumption 4$_s$

Many planes may have the same line of intersection.

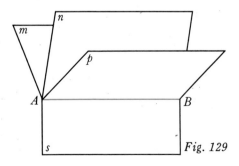

Fig. 129

Assumption 5ₛ

All the perpendiculars to a given line at a given point lie in a plane that is perpendicular to the line at that point.

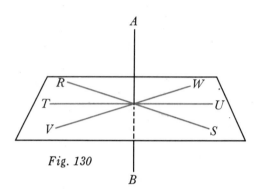

Fig. 130

Developmental Exercises

DE—1. Explain why a line and an external point determine a plane.

Solution

From *Assumption 1ₛ* three points not in a straight line determine a plane. If any two of these points are connected a line is determined. (*Assumption 14*) Thus, the line formed and the third point (the point not on the line) determine a plane.

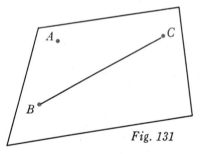

Fig. 131

DE—2. Explain why two intersecting lines determine a plane.

Solution

From *Assumption 1ₛ* three points not in a straight line determine a plane. If these points are connected, two and only two intersecting lines are formed. (Assumption 14) Thus, the two intersecting lines containing the three points determine a plane.

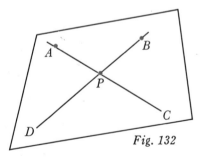

Fig. 132

DE—3. *A line is **perpendicular to a plane*** *if the line is perpendicular to every line in the plane passing through its foot.*

Prove that if a line is perpendicular to each of two intersecting lines at their point of intersection, then it is perpendicular to the plane determined by those lines.

Given: *AB* intersects *BC* and *BD* which determine plane *M*. *AB*⊥*BC*, *AB*⊥*BD*.
Prove: *AB*⊥plane *M*.

Fig. 133

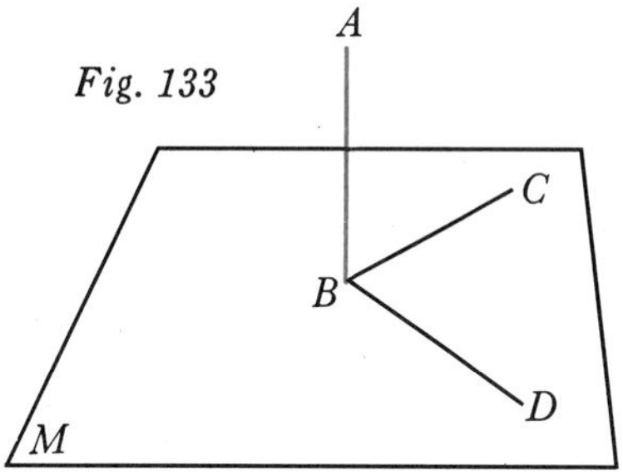

Solution

To prove that a line and plane are perpendicular it is necessary to fulfill the conditions which are included in the definition of a line perpendicular to a plane, i.e., that it is perpendicular to every line in the plane passing through its foot.

One selected line (*BE*) is assumed to be a general line that represents all lines in the plane through the foot of the line. If a plan of proof is valid for the general line, then it could be repeated for each of the other lines which it represents.

Construction: In plane *M*, draw any line *BE*. Draw, in *M*, a line intersecting *BC*, *BE*, and *BD* at *F*, *G*, and *H* respectively. Extend *AB* through *B*, making *AB*=*A'B*. Join *A'* to *F*, *G*, and *H*.

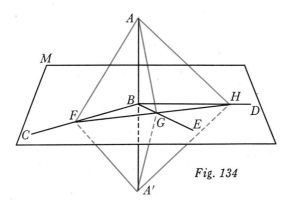

Fig. 134

Statements	Reasons
1. $AB \perp BC$, $AB \perp BD$.	1. Given.
2. $AB = A'B$.	2. Construction.
3. $\angle ABF = 90°$, $\angle A'BF = 90°$.	3. Perpendicular lines form right angles.
4. $\angle ABF = \angle A'BF$.	4. Right angles are equal.
5. $BF = BF$.	5. Identity.
6. $\triangle ABF \cong \triangle A'BF$.	6. If two triangles have two sides and the included angle of one equal respectively to two sides and the included angle of the other, the triangles are congruent. (s.a.s. = s.a.s.)
7. $\triangle ABH \cong \triangle A'BH$.	7. In like manner.
8. $AF = A'F$, $AH = A'H$.	8. Corresponding parts of congruent triangles are equal.
9. $FH = FH$.	9. Identity.
10. $\triangle AFH \cong \triangle A'FH$.	10. If two triangles have three sides of one equal respectively to three sides of the other, the triangles are congruent. (s.s.s. = s.s.s.)
11. $\angle AFG = \angle A'FG$.	11. Same as Reason 8.
12. $FG = FG$.	12. Identity.
13. $\triangle AFG \cong \triangle A'FG$.	13. If two triangles have two sides and the included angle of one equal respectively to two sides and the included angle of the other, the triangles are congruent. (s.a.s. = s.a.s.)
14. $AG = A'G$.	14. Same as Reason 8.
15. $AB \perp BE$.	15. Two-Point Theorem.
16. $AB \perp M$.	16. A line perpendicular to every line (passing through its foot) in a plane is perpendicular to the plane.

Thus, it has been proved that:

THEOREM 1$_8$

If a line is perpendicular to each of two intersecting lines at their point of intersection, then it is perpendicular to the plane determined by those lines.

DE—4. Prove the following theorem:

THEOREM 2₈

If three points, not in a straight line, are each equally distant from the ends of a line segment, then they determine a plane which is the perpendicular bisector of the line segment.

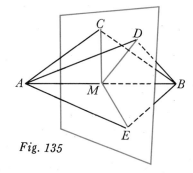

Fig. 135

Given: C, D, and E are not in a straight line.

C, D, and E are each equally distant from points A and B.

Prove: C, D, and E determine a plane which is perpendicular to AB at its midpoint.

Solution

Construction: Join the midpoint of AB to C, D, and E.

STATEMENTS	REASONS
1. C, B, and E are points not in one straight line.	1. Given.
2. $CA = CB$, $DA = DB$, $EA = EB$.	2. Given.
3. CM and AB determine a plane.	3. Two intersecting lines determine a plane.
4. CM bisects AB, $CM \perp AB$.	4. Two-Point Theorem.
5. DM and AB determine a plane.	5. Reason 3.
6. DM bisects AB, $DM \perp AB$.	6. Reason 4.
7. EM and AB determine a plane.	7. Reason 3.
8. EM bisects AB, $EM \perp AB$.	8. Reason 4.
9. DM and CM determine a plane perpendicular to AB.	9. If a line is perpendicular to each of two intersecting lines at their point of intersection, it is perpendicular to the plane determined by those two lines.
10. EM lies in the plane determined by CM and DM.	10. All the perpendiculars to a given line lie in the plane perpendicular to the line at that point.

Exercises

1. By rolling a sheet of paper into the approximate shape of a cylinder you can arrange the position of two points so that a straight line joining them will not lie entirely in the cylindrical surface. Does that show that the definition of a plane is not reversible? Explain.

2. Use a labeled drawing to help explain why
   a. two intersecting lines determine a plane.
   b. two parallel lines determine a plane.
   c. a straight line and an external point determine a plane.

3. Make a sketch of the intersection of two planes. Of three planes.

4. Is the sketch of the intersection of three planes made in Exercise **3** the only one possible? If not, sketch another.

5. Make a sketch to show the greatest number of planes determined by four points. By five points. By six points.

6. Prove that lines drawn to a plane from any point in a line perpendicular to the plane so as to cut off equal distances in the plane from the foot of the perpendicular are equal.

7. Two planes may have a line in common, may they also have a triangle in common?

8. Explain why a stool having three legs is always steady while a chair with four legs may not be steady.

Ex. 9

9. In the diagram, $AD \perp$ plane Q, $DB \perp DC$, $AC = 6''$, $DC = 4''$, and $BC = 8''$. Compute the length of AB. (No proof is required.)

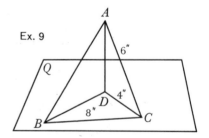

10. Prove that equal line segments drawn from the same point in a line perpendicular to a plane will cut off equal distances in the plane from the foot of the perpendicular.

EXTEND YOUR HORIZON

A type of reasoning frequently met in daily-life activities is called reasoning by *analogy*. It usually is used in comparing two situations which are identical in many, but not in all, respects. For example, Terry is an excellent tennis player. May you conclude that he plays an excellent game of badminton?

While there are many similar qualities required in the two sports, such as sharpness of vision, judgment of distance, and timing of stroke, there are factors in which substantial differences may be evident. False analogies may result from believing that success in one activity guarantees success in another.

Conclusions based on hidden assumptions are often accepted as valid when they are not. A clerk in a drug store may suggest, "Clover White is probably a better bleach than the kind you asked for. It must be good because we sell more of it than any other brand." In a sense, analogy is involved here. If Clover White is well accepted, must it then possess quality? Not at all. It may be priced lower than competing brands, or it may be a highly advertized brand.

Valid analogies can exist. Mathematical proportions use the ideas of an analogy to make comparisons and valid conclusions.

Explain which of the following conclusions are valid. Explain why others are not valid.

(*1*) Yvette Starlette is a beautiful movie star. She uses Vanity Cream. If you use Vanity Cream you will be a beautiful movie star.

(*2*) Heman Muscles is strong and handsome. He uses Wild Beast Hair Tonic. If you use Wild Beast Hair Tonic you will be strong and handsome.

(*3*) Bill is a year older than Ben. Jim is Ben's twin brother. Jim is a year younger than Bill.

(*4*) Last week Normandy defeated Maplewood 12-7 in a football game. The previous week Maine defeated Maplewood by a 12-2 score. Next week Normandy will defeat Maine by two touchdowns.

CHAPTER SUMMARY

If a conclusion logically follows from the premises, the conclusion is valid; if it does not, it is invalid. If both premises are true and the conclusion is valid, the conclusion is true.

If two angles are

1. adjacent and supplementary, their exterior sides lie in a straight line.   (page 84)

2. adjacent with their exterior sides lying in a straight line, the angles are supplementary.   (page 85)

3. adjacent and complementary, their exterior sides are perpendicular.   (page 86)

4. adjacent with their exterior sides perpendicular, the angles are complementary.   (page 86)

Angles are equal if

1. they are vertical angles.   (page 83)
2. they are right angles.   (page 81)
3. they are straight angles.   (page 82)
4. they are complements of the same, or equal, angles. (page 89)
5. they are supplements of the same, or equal, angles. (page 87)
6. they are corresponding parts of congruent triangles. (page 98)
7. they are opposite equal sides of a triangle. (page 110)

Triangles are congruent if

1. **s.s.s. = s.s.s.**   (page 97)
2. **s.a.s. = s.a.s.**   (page 97)
3. **a.s.a. = a.s.a.**   (page 97)

*A plane is determined by

1. three points not in a straight line.   (page 114)
2. a line and an exterior point.   (page 116)
3. two intersecting lines.   (page 116)

*A line is perpendicular to a plane if

1. it is perpendicular to every line in the plane passing through its foot.   (page 117)

2. it is perpendicular to each of two intersecting lines determining a plane at the point of intersection.   (page 117)

CHAPTER REVIEW

Vocabulary

Match the word in the left-hand column with its correct definition in the right-hand column.

1. Vertical Angles

2. Congruent($\cong$)

3. Valid

4. Premise

5. Inductive Reasoning

6. Deductive Reasoning

7. Theorem

8. Plane

9. Identity

10. *If-then* Statement

*11. A line perpendicular to a plane

a. Capable of being justified.

b. Sameness.

c. A statement to be proved.

d. Condition.

e. A line perpendicular to every line in a plane passing through its foot.

f. Can be made to coincide.

g. Reasoning based on undefined terms, definitions, and assumptions.

h. Reasoning based on a limited number of experiences.

i. A statement having two parts, an assumption and a generalization.

j. Two angles having the same vertex and the sides of one extending through the vertex of the sides of the other.

k. A surface such that a line joining any two of its points lies entirely in the surface.

l. Reasoning based on comparison.

m. Two angles having the same vertex and one common side.

Exercises

Analyze and prove the following exercises as directed by your teacher.

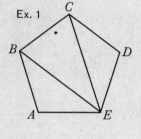

Ex. 1

1. Given: *ABCDE* has equal
   sides and equal
   angles.
   Prove: $\angle EBC = \angle ECB$.

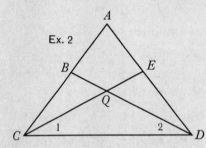

Ex. 2

2. Given: $CA = AD$,
   $\angle 1 = \angle 2$.
   Prove: $BQ = QE$.

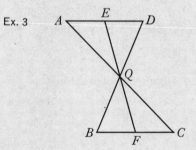

Ex. 3

3. Given: *Q* the midpoint of
   AC,
   Q the midpoint of
   EF.
   Prove: $BC = AD$.

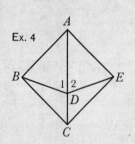

Ex. 4

4. Given: *AC* bisects $\angle BCE$,
   $BC = CE$.
   Prove: $\angle 1 = \angle 2$.

5. Given: $BC = DC$,
   $AC = CE$.
   Prove: *QC* bisects $\angle BCD$.

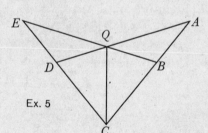

Ex. 5

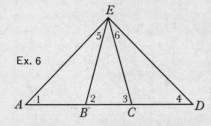

Ex. 6

6. Given: $AC = BD$,
$AE = ED$,
$\angle 2 = \angle 3$.
Prove: $\angle 5 = \angle 6$.

7. Given: *ABCD* has right angles
and equal sides.
R the midpoint of *EF*,
$BE = BF$.
Prove: $\angle 1 = \angle 2$.

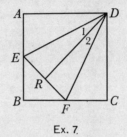

Ex. 7

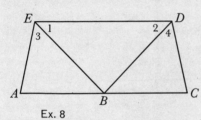

Ex. 8

8. Given: *B* the midpoint of *AC*,
$AE = DC$,
$\angle 1 = \angle 2$.
Prove: $\angle 3 = \angle 4$.

9. Given: $\angle CAB = \angle ABC$,
$\angle 2 = \angle 1$,
$\angle 3 = \angle 4$,
$AD = BD$.
Prove: $\angle 6 = \angle 7$.

Ex. 9

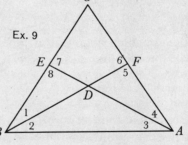

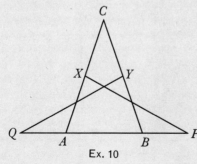

Ex. 10

10. Given: Isosceles $\triangle ABC$,
$\angle PAC = \angle CBQ$,
$AX = XC$,
$BY = YC$,
$YQ = BC$,
$XP = AC$.
Prove: $QY = PX$.

11. Given: $AC \perp BC$,
$\angle BAC = \angle CBA$,
$CX = CY$,
$AX = BY$.
Prove: $\angle 1 = \angle 2$.

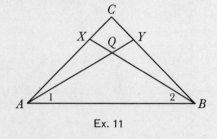

Ex. 11

Ex. 12

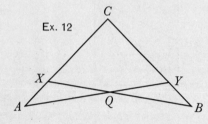

12. Given: $AQ = BQ$,
$XQ = QY$,
$AC = BC$.
Prove: $CX = CY$.

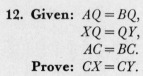

13. Given: $DB = AC$,
$\angle 1 = \angle 2$.
Prove: $DA = BC$.

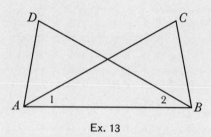

Ex. 13

14. Draw a quadrilateral so that a line joining two opposite vertices bisects those opposite angles. Prove that such a line is the perpendicular bisector of the line joining the other two opposite angles of the quadrilateral.

15. Construct the isosceles triangle ABC. Join C to the midpoint, D, of AB. E represents any point on CD. Join E to points A and B. Use the figure to see the position of the lines. Which of the following statements are given (controlled) conditions and which are possible conclusions?

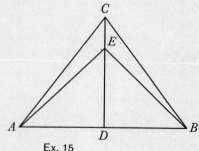

    a. CD is perpendicular to AB.
    b. $AC = CB$.
    c. $AE = EB$.
    d. $AD = DB$.
    e. $\angle ACB$ is bisected.
    f. $\angle AEC = \angle BEC$.

Ex. 15

16. $\angle AOG$ and $\angle GOB$ are supplementary angles. Each has been bisected. Can you establish, without measurement, that CO is perpendicular to EO?

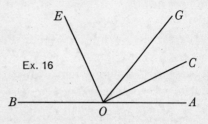

Ex. 16

17. Draw an acute angle, DBA. Using your protractor, locate line DC so that $\angle CDB$ equals $\angle DBA$. Make CD equal to AB (use your compass). Join points C and B. Join points A and D. Measure $\angle DBA$ and $\angle DBC$. Are they equal? Measure AD and BC. Are they equal? Were they constructed equal?

18. Draw a line, AB. Bisect AB, placing the letter E at the midpoint of AB. At A and B construct perpendiculars to AB. Draw a line through E which meets one perpendicular at C and the other at D. Can you establish, without measurement, that $\angle ECA$ equals $\angle EDB$?

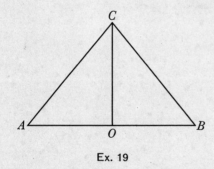

Ex. 19

19. O is the midpoint of AB. $\angle OAC$ equals $\angle CBO$. CO bisects $\angle ACB$. Can you establish, without measurement, that CO is the perpendicular bisector of AB? What conditions must be fulfilled before you may say that CO is perpendicular to AB?

20. Given: $BC = AD$,
$\quad\quad\quad\quad\angle 1 = \angle 3$.
Discover a valid conclusion and summarize this exercise in an *if-then* statement.

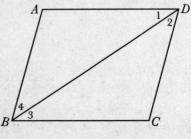

Ex. 20

CHAPTER TEST

If any conclusion listed cannot be deduced, classify it as not valid. Otherwise, write a complete proof.

1. Prove: If an angle is bisected, and a line is drawn perpendicular to the bisector at any point except the vertex of the angle, then the perpendicular line when drawn to the sides of the angle will help to form two congruent triangles.

2. Prove: If equal distances from the vertex are marked on the sides of an angle and their ends joined to any point on the bisector to the angle except the vertex of the angle, then two congruent triangles will be formed.

3. Given: $AD = BC$,
  $AB = DC$.

Prove: $AD = DC$.

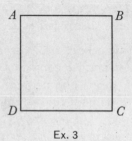

Ex. 3

4. Given: X is the midpoint of AC,
  Y is the midpoint of BC.

Prove: ABC is isosceles.

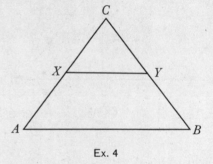

Ex. 4

In Exercises 5 and 6 write a valid conclusion if one is possible.

5. Given: After December 21, the hours of daylight gradually increase. Tomorrow is January 23.

6. Given: Crest automobiles have squeaky brakes. My father drives an automobile whose brakes squeak.

7. Given: $FE = BC$,
          $AB = DE$,
          $\angle 1 = \angle 2$.

Prove: $\angle F = \angle C$.

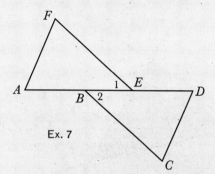

Ex. 7

8. Given: $\angle 6 = \angle 3$,
          $\angle 1 = \angle 2$.

Prove: $\angle 5 = \angle 4$.

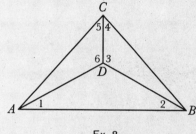

Ex. 8

9. Construct an equilateral triangle. Construct the bisector of one angle. Extend the bisector to the opposite side of the triangle. Measure the parts of this side and express your observation in an *if-then* statement.

10. Construct a right triangle. Join with a straight line the midpoint of the hypotenuse to the vertex of the right angle. Measure this line. Measure the parts of the hypotenuse. Express your observation in an *if-then* statement.

Chapter 3

PARALLEL AND PERPENDICULAR LINES

CONSTRUCTION OF PARALLEL LINES

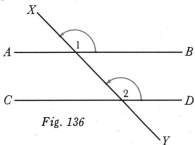

In Figure 136, two lines are drawn so that they make equal angles with a third line. $\angle 1 = \angle 2$. $\angle 1$ and $\angle 2$ are called *corresponding angles*. They are on the same side of XY and also on the same side of AB and CD.

Fig. 136

Parallel lines are defined as straight lines in the same plane that form equal corresponding angles with a third line. In the figure, AB is parallel to CD. Parallel lines are in the same plane and do not intersect. It is possible to have two nonparallel straight lines not in a plane which do not intersect. They are called *skew lines*.

The symbol $\parallel$ means "parallel" or "is parallel to." Thus, $AB \parallel CD$ is read "AB is parallel to CD."

Assumption 21

In a plane, through a point not on a given line, one and only one line can be drawn parallel to the given line.

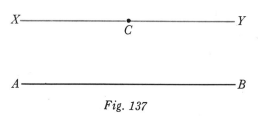

Fig. 137

Developmental Exercises

DE—1. Given: In a plane: $AB \perp MN$,
$\qquad\qquad\qquad CD \perp MN$.

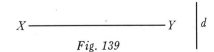

Prove: $AB \parallel CD$.

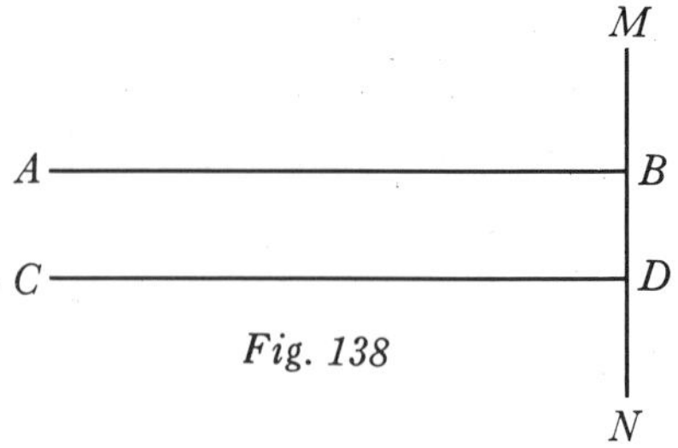

Fig. 138

Solution

STATEMENTS	REASONS
1. $AB \perp MN$, $CD \perp MN$.	1. Given.
2. $\angle MBA = 90°$, $\angle MDC = 90°$.	2. Perpendicular lines form $90°$ angles.
3. $\angle MBA = \angle MDC$.	3. Quantities equal to the same quantity are equal to each other.
4. $\angle MBA$ and $\angle MDC$ are corresponding angles.	4. Definition of corresponding angles.
5. $AB \parallel CD$.	5. Definition of parallel lines.

Thus, the following theorem has been proved:

THEOREM 15

In a plane, two lines perpendicular to the same line are parallel.

DE—2. Construct a line parallel to a given line at a given distance.

> **Given:** Distance d,
> Line XY.
> **Required:** A line $\parallel XY$, d distance from XY.

Fig. 139

Solution

- At any point, P, on XY construct $PQ \perp XY$.
- On PQ, mark off distance d from P. Label this point R.
- At R construct $TS \perp PQ$. $TS \parallel XY$ and d distance from it. How do you know that $TS \parallel XY$?

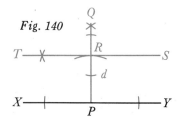

Fig. 140

Many students conclude, after making this construction, that not one line but two lines can be constructed *d* distance from *XY* and parallel to *XY*. Do you agree?

Observe that the construction fulfills all conditions contained in the definition of parallel lines. Remember that the distance from a point to a line is measured along the perpendicular from the point to the line. The distance between two parallels is measured along a line perpendicular to either of them.

DE—3. Given: △*ABC* with ∠*B* bisected.

Prove: Through *A* a line can be constructed which is parallel to the bisector of ∠*B*.

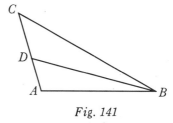

Fig. 141

Solution

Since it is given that ∠*B* is bisected, no construction is required for line segment *BD*. But through *A* a line must be constructed parallel to *BD*.

Often a free-hand sketch of the completed figure is an aid to discovering a relationship between lines or angles which must be controlled. Note in the sketch, *XY* is parallel to *BD* if ∠2 = ∠1.

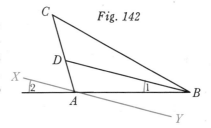

Fig. 142

Since ∠2 may be constructed equal to ∠1, *XY* may be constructed parallel to *DB*. The steps are:

● Extend *AB* beyond *A*.
● Construct ∠2 = ∠1.

● Extend *XA* to *Y*. *XY* is parallel to *DB* because the corresponding angles (∠2 and ∠1) made by the line segment *AB* are equal.

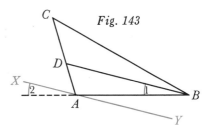

Fig. 143

DE—4. Construct a line parallel to a given line through a given point not on the line.

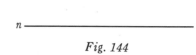

Given: A line, *n*, and a point, *P*, not on *n*.

Required: A line through *P* parallel to *n*.

Fig. 144

Solution

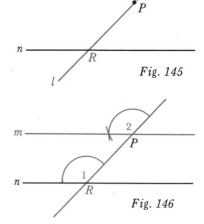

● Draw a line, *l*, through *P* intersecting *n* at *R*.

● Duplicate ∠1 at *P* to obtain line *m*, making the same angle with *l* as line *n*.

Fig. 145

● Since ∠1 = ∠2, corresponding angles are equal, and *m* ‖ *n*.

Fig. 146

Exercises

1. Through each vertex of a triangle construct a line parallel to the opposite side.

2. Write a complete proof for the construction in Developmental Exercise **3**.

3. The box like the figure below is called a *rectangular parallelepiped*. The lateral faces (sides) and bases (top and bottom) are rectangles. The lateral faces are perpendicular to the bases.

a. Are *AB* and *BC* parallel lines?

b. Are *AB* and *EF* skew lines?

c. Are *AB* and *EF* parallel lines?

d. Name several pairs of skew lines.

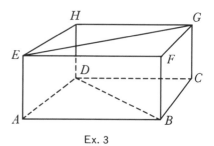

Ex. 3

4. If two lines are parallel, can they have a point in common?

5. If two lines are in the same plane and are not parallel, what must be true about these lines?

6. What three conditions are satisfied by parallel lines?

7. How many lines can be drawn perpendicular to two parallel lines? Make a sketch to support your answer.

8. How many perpendicular lines can be drawn to two skew lines? Make a sketch to support your answer.

9. If two lines are not skew, must they intersect? Make a sketch to support your answer.

10. If two lines are parallel, must they lie in the same plane?

TRANSVERSALS

A transversal is a straight line that intersects two or more lines that lie in the same plane. In Figure 147, line *XY* is a transversal of *AB* and *CD*.

Observe that *XY* forms four angles with each line it intersects. Pairs of some angles in the figure have special names.

Angles such as ∠3 and ∠5 are called *alternate-interior angles.* Observe that the name indicates their position. They lie between *AB* and *CD* and are on opposite sides of

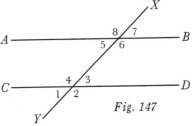

Fig. 147

the transversal. Angles 7 and 1 are *alternate-exterior angles.* You may recall from a previous lesson that corresponding angles are on the same side of a transversal and also on the same side of the lines which the transversal intersects.

Also recall that:

(*1*) If two lines are cut by a transversal and the corresponding angles are equal, the lines are parallel.

(*2*) If two parallel lines are cut by a transversal the corresponding angles are equal.

Developmental Exercises

DE—1. In the figure at the right name

   a. two pairs of alternate-interior angles,

   b. two pairs of alternate-exterior angles, and

   c. four pairs of corresponding angles.

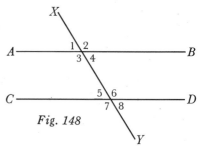

Fig. 148

Solution

   a. ∠3 and ∠6 are alternate-interior angles. ∠4 and ∠5 are also alternate-interior angles.

   b. ∠1 and ∠8 are alternate-exterior angles. ∠2 and ∠7 are also alternate-exterior angles.

   c. The pairs of corresponding angles are ∠1 and ∠5, ∠2 and ∠6, ∠3 and ∠7, ∠4 and ∠8.

DE—2. Given: ∠1 = ∠2.

     Prove: $AB \parallel CD$.

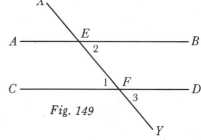

Fig. 149

Solution

STATEMENTS	REASONS
1. ∠1 = ∠2.	1. Given.
2. ∠1 = ∠3.	2. Vertical angles are equal.
3. ∠2 = ∠3.	3. Quantities equal to the same quantity are equal.
4. ∠2 and ∠3 are corresponding angles.	4. Definition of corresponding angles.
5. $AB \parallel CD$.	5. If two lines are cut by a transversal so that the corresponding angles are equal, the lines are parallel.

   Thus, the following theorem has been proved.

THEOREM 16

If two straight lines are cut by a transversal so that the alternate-interior angles are equal, the lines are parallel.

Exercises

1. In Figure 149
   a. Name two pairs of alternate-interior angles.
   b. Name two pairs of alternate-exterior angles.
   c. Name four pairs of corresponding angles.

2. Consider *GF* as a transversal of *CE* and *AH* in the diagram at the right.

a. Name two pairs of alternate-exterior angles.
   b. Name two pairs of alternate-interior angles.
   c. Name four pairs of corresponding angles.

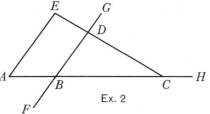

Ex. 2

3. In the diagram at the right what kind of angles are
   a. ∠*C* and ∠*EBA*?
   b. ∠*C* and ∠*FBC*?
   c. ∠*E* and ∠*FBC*?

4. Observe the transversal *GD*
and classify these angles:
   a. ∠*BDC* and ∠*DBE*.
   b. ∠*GBF* and ∠*BDC*.
   c. ∠*DBE* and ∠*BDC*.

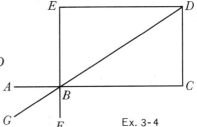

Ex. 3-4

5. If *DC* ∥ *EB* and *BC* ∥ *ED*, (use the diagram in Exercise 3) prove △*EDB* ≅ △*DBC*.

6. Study the letter *Z*. What pair of angles formed by two parallel lines cut by a transversal might it represent? The letter *F*?

7. **Given:** ∠1 = 130°,
                ∠2 = 50°.
   Prove: *AB* ∥ *CD*.

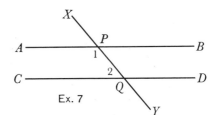

Ex. 7

8. Given: *AD* and *BC* bisect each other.
Prove: *AB* ∥ *CD*.

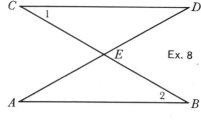

Ex. 8

9. Given: ∠2 = ∠4.
Prove: Two lines parallel.

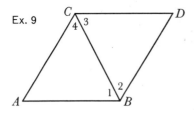

Ex. 9

10. Given: ∠*CXY* = ∠*BYX*,
PX bisects ∠*CXY*,
QY bisects ∠*BYX*.
Prove: *PX* ∥ *QY*.

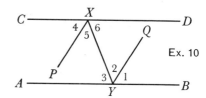

Ex. 10

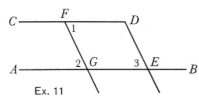

Ex. 11

11. Given: *DE* ∥ *FG*,
∠1 = ∠3.
Prove: *AB* ∥ *CD*.

12. Given: *CE* ∥ *AF*,
∠*C* = ∠*A*.
Prove: *AB* ∥ *CD*.

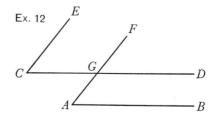

Ex. 12

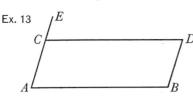

Ex. 13

13. Given: ∠*A* = ∠*D*,
AB ∥ *CD*.
Prove: *AC* ∥ *BD*.

14. Illustrate and prove: If corresponding angles formed by two parallel lines and a transversal are bisected, the bisectors are parallel.

15. Illustrate and prove: If two straight lines intersect so that each bisects the other, two other lines joining the ends of the first pair are parallel.

16. Prove that opposite sides of a quadrilateral are parallel if they are equal.

SUPPLEMENTARY ANGLES AND PARALLEL LINES

Figures 150-151 show two lines, *AB* and *CD*, cut by a transversal, *EF*. If $\angle 4 = 75°$ and $\angle 5 = 75°$, then *AB* ∥ *CD*. Why? Or if $\angle 3 = 40°$ and $\angle 6 = 40°$, then *AB* ∥ *CD*. Why? If $\angle 4 = 40°$ and $\angle 6 = 140°$, $\angle 4$ is supplementary to $\angle 6$. Why? How many degrees are in $\angle 5$? Is *AB* ∥ *CD* in this case? Why?

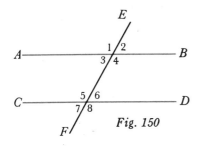

Fig. 150

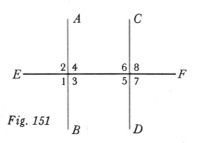

Fig. 151

▌Developmental Exercises

DE—1. Given: $\angle 2 = a° + 60°$,
$\qquad\quad \angle 3 = 120° - a°$,
$\qquad\quad a = 20°$.

Prove: *AB* ∥ *CD*.

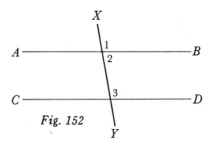

Fig. 152

Solution
$\quad$ *AB* ∥ *CD* if $\angle 1 = \angle 3$.

STATEMENTS	REASONS
1. $\angle 1 + \angle 2 = 180°$.	1. *XY* is a straight angle.
2. $\angle 1 + a° + 60° = 180°$.	2. Why?
3. $\angle 1 + 20° + 60° = 180°$.	3. Why?
4. $\angle 1 = 100°$.	4. Why?
5. $\angle 3 = 120° - a°$.	5. Why?
6. $\angle 3 = 120° - 20°$, $\angle 3 = 100°$.	6. Why?
7. *AB* ∥ *CD*.	7. Lines which form equal corresponding angles with a transversal are parallel.

DE—2. Given: $\angle 2 + \angle E = 180°.$

Prove: $AB \parallel CD.$

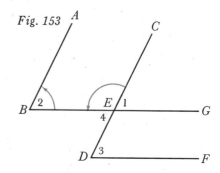

Fig. 153

Solution

$AB \parallel CD$ if $\angle 2 = \angle 4.$

STATEMENTS	REASONS
1. $\angle 2 + \angle E = 180°.$	1. Why?
2. $\angle 4 + \angle E = 180°.$	2. Why?
$\angle 2 = \angle 4.$	
3. $AB \parallel CD.$	3. If two lines are cut by a transversal so that the alternate-interior angles are equal, the lines are parallel.

Thus, the following theorem has been proved.

THEOREM 17

If two straight lines are cut by a transversal so that two interior angles on the same side of the transversal are supplementary, the lines are parallel.

Exercises

1. Prove that $AB \parallel CD$ if $\angle 3$ is supplementary to $\angle 1.$

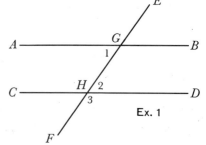

Ex. 1

2. Complete the proof of Theorem 17.

3. Given: $\angle 1 = \angle 2.$

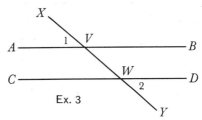

Ex. 3

Prove: $AB \parallel CD.$
(State this problem in the form of an *if-then* proposition.)

4. Given: $\angle 1 + \angle 2 = 180°.$

Prove: $AB \parallel CD.$

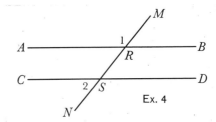

Ex. 4

5. Given: $AB = CD,$
$\quad\quad\quad \angle 1 = \angle 2.$

Prove: $AB \parallel DC.$

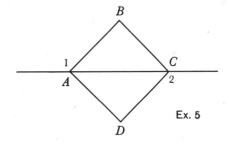

Ex. 5

6. Given: $EA \perp AD,$
$\quad\quad\quad FB \perp AD,$
$\quad\quad\quad AB = CD,$
$\quad\quad\quad EA = FB.$

Prove: $EC \parallel FD.$

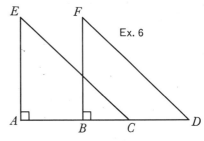

Ex. 6

7. Given: $AE = CE,$
$\quad\quad\quad DE = BE.$

Select, if possible, a conclusion involving parallel lines, and prove that conclusion.

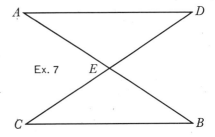

Ex. 7

8. Given: $AE = BE,$
$\qquad\quad CE = DE.$

Select, if possible, a conclusion involving parallel lines, and prove that conclusion.

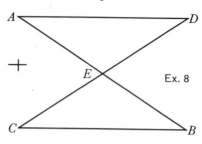

Ex. 8

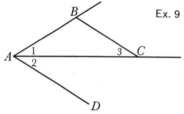

Ex. 9

9. Given: $\angle 1 = \angle 2,$
$\qquad\quad \angle 1 = \angle 3.$
Prove: $BC \parallel AD.$

10. Given: $AB = BC,$
$\qquad\quad\;\; \angle 1 + \angle 3 = 180°.$
Prove: $DE \parallel AG.$

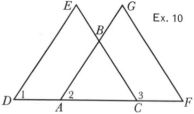

Ex. 10

11. Prove: If two lines are cut by a transversal so that two alternate-interior angles are equal, the bisectors of those two angles are parallel.

12. Dave's hobby is photography. At times he needs a dim light. In his dark room, which was unlighted, he could see no convenient way to extend wiring for electric current. From some flat curtain rods, a discarded but usable hinge, tape and rubber bands, Dave devised a flashlight holder as shown below. Now he has a light whose height is adjustable yet the flashlight will remain perpendicular to the floor at any height. What parallel relationships did Dave control in his arrangement of materials?

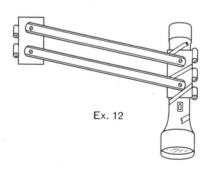

Ex. 12

CONVERSES

Consider the two statements:

(*1*) If two straight lines are cut by a transversal so that any two corresponding angles are equal, the lines are parallel.

(*2*) If two parallel lines are cut by a transversal, the corresponding angles are equal.

Notice that in statement *1* the angles are equal. In *2* they must be proved equal. However, in *2* the lines are parallel; while in *1* they must be proved parallel.

The hypothesis (given datum) in statement *1* has become the conclusion in statement *2*. The conclusion in statement *1* has become the hypothesis in statement *2*. Each statement is the converse of the other.

||**The converse of a proposition can be formed by interchanging any number of hypotheses with an equal number of conclusions.**

For example: *If the vertex angle of an isosceles triangle is bisected, the bisector is perpendicular to the opposite side and divides it into two equal parts.*

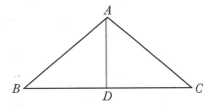

Fig. 154

Given: (If)
  (**a**) $AB = AC$.
  (**b**) AD bisects $\angle BAC$.

Conclusion: (Then)
  (**c**) $BD = DC$.
  (**d**) $AD \perp BC$.

Converse 1
Given:
  (**a**) $AB = AC$.
  (**c**) $BD = DC$.

Conclusion:
  (**b**) AD bisects $\angle BAC$.
  (**d**) $AD \perp BC$.

(Hypothesis **b** has been exchanged for conclusion **c**.)

If a line joins the midpoint of the base of an isosceles triangle to the opposite vertex, the line is perpendicular to the base and bisects the vertex angle.

Converse 2

Given:	Conclusion:
(a) $AB = AC$.	(b) AD bisects $\angle BAC$.
(d) $AD \perp BC$.	(c) $BD = DC$.

(Hypothesis **b** has been exchanged for conclusion **d**.)

If a line is the perpendicular to the base of an isosceles triangle, it bisects the base and the vertex angle.

Converse 3

Given:	Conclusion:
(c) $BD = DC$.	(a) $AB = AC$.
(b) AD bisects $\angle BAC$.	(d) $AD \perp BC$.

(Hypothesis **a** has been exchanged for conclusion **c**.)

If a line bisects an angle of a triangle and the opposite side, it is perpendicular to that side and the triangle is isosceles.

Converse 4

Given:	Conclusion:
(d) $AD \perp BC$.	(a) $AB = AC$.
(b) AD bisects $\angle BAC$.	(c) $BD = DC$.

(Hypothesis **a** has been exchanged for conclusion **d**.)

If a line bisects an angle of a triangle and is perpendicular to the opposite side, the triangle is isosceles and its base is bisected.

A statement containing two hypotheses and two conclusions has five converses. The last illustration is incomplete; the remaining converse is left for you to discover.

The converse of a definition is valid but not all converses of valid propositions are valid. By analyzing the validity of multiconverse relationships you may discover relationships previously unknown to you.

If both a theorem and its converse are valid they are frequently combined into one statement. For example, (*1*) if two straight lines are cut by a transversal forming equal alternate-interior angles, the lines are parallel, and (*2*) if two parallel lines are cut by a transversal, the alternate-interior angles formed are equal, (this is proved later in this chapter) may be combined into (*3*) two lines cut by a transversal are parallel if, and only if, alternate-interior angles are equal. The addition of "only if" implies the converse. In proving statement (*3*) two proofs are actually necessary, the proof of the original statement (*1*) and its converse (*2*).

Exercises

1. Form one converse for each of the following propositions. Discuss the validity of each converse.

a. If two lines are parallel, they do not intersect.

b. If a triangle is isosceles, it contains two equal angles.

c. If a person is born in the United States, he is a United States citizen.

d. A submarine is a boat that is capable of operating under water.

e. All rich men have big cars.

f. Vertical angles are equal.

List the "Given" and "Prove" for all the converses of the propositions indicated below.

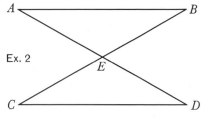

Ex. 2

2. Given: $AE = DE$,
$\quad\quad\quad\quad CE = BE$.
Prove: $AB = CD$.

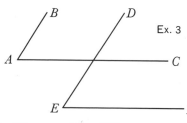

Ex. 3

3. Given: $AB \parallel ED$,
$\quad\quad\quad\quad AC \parallel EF$.
Prove: $\angle A = \angle E$.

4. Given: $AB = BC$,
$\quad\quad\quad\quad AF = GC$,
$\quad\quad\quad\quad DF \perp AC$,
$\quad\quad\quad\quad EG \perp AC$.
Prove: $AD = DB$,
$\quad\quad\quad\quad BE = EC$.

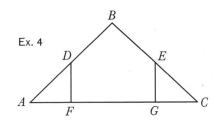

Ex. 4

5. State all the converses of the following proposition: If a line segment joins the midpoints of two sides of a triangle, it is parallel to the third side and equal to one-half the length of the third side.

6. State all the converses of the following proposition: If the bisector of an exterior angle of a triangle is parallel to a side, then the triangle is isosceles.

MORE ABOUT PARALLEL LINES

‖ **THEOREM 18**

A line perpendicular to one of two parallel lines is perpendicular to the other.

Given: $AB \parallel CD$,
$\quad\quad\quad XY \perp CD$.

Prove: $XY \perp AB$.

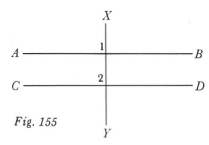

Fig. 155

Analysis:

You would know $XY \perp AB$ if you knew $\angle 1 = 90°$. Since $\angle 1 = \angle 2$ and $\angle 2 = 90°$, the proof can be written.

STATEMENTS	REASONS
1. $AB \parallel CD$, $\quad XY \perp CD$.	1. Given.
2. $\angle 2 = 90°$.	2. If two lines are perpendicular, they form 90° angles.
3. $\angle 1 = \angle 2$.	3. If two parallel lines are cut by a transversal the corresponding angles are equal.
4. $\angle 1 = 90°$.	4. Quantities equal to the same quantity are equal.
5. $XY \perp AB$.	5. If two lines intersect so as to form 90° angles, the lines are perpendicular.

Developmental Exercises

DE—1. Given: $AB \parallel CD$,
  EF and *GI* are two transversals,
  $GI \perp CD$.

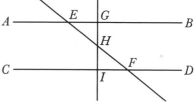

  Prove: $\triangle EHG$ and $\triangle HIF$ are
  right triangles.

Fig. 156

Solution

You would know $\triangle EHG$ and $\triangle HIF$ are right triangles if each contains a right angle. Since $GI \perp CD$, $\angle DIG = 90°$. *AB* and *CD* are parallel, $GI \perp AB$, and $\angle AGI = 90°$, a second right angle.

You may have realized that it was unnecessary to prove $GI \perp AB$ as *AB* and *CD* were given parallel and $\angle GID = \angle AGI = 90°$. There may be another modification of the plan outlined here to establish the conclusion as valid. Try to discover a plan independently. Now write out a formal proof.

Exercises

1. Given: $AB \parallel CD$,
  $OE \perp CD$,
  $GF \perp AB$.

Prove: $OE \parallel FG$.

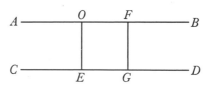

Ex. 1

2. Given: $AB \parallel CD$,
  $CD \perp AD$,
  $AB = CD$.

Prove: $AE = ED$.

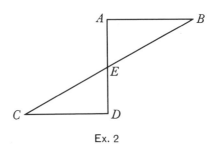

Ex. 2

3. Given: $AB \parallel DC,$
$AB \perp BC,$
$\angle 1 = \angle 2.$

Ex. 3

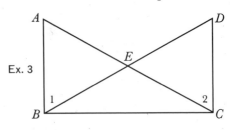

Prove: $BE = CE.$

4. Given: $AB \parallel CD,$
$BA \perp CA,$
$AE = FC,$
$BA = CD.$

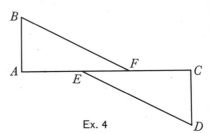

Prove: $BF \parallel ED.$

Ex. 4

DE—2. Prove the following theorem:

║**THEOREM 19**

║**A transversal intersecting two parallel lines forms equal alternate-**
║**interior angles.**

Solution

Given: $AB \parallel CD.$

Prove: $\angle 1 = \angle 2.$

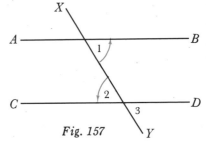

Fig. 157

Analysis:
You would know $\angle 1 = \angle 2$ if you knew $\angle 1 = \angle 3$ and $\angle 2 = \angle 3.$

Proof:

STATEMENTS	REASONS
1. $AB \parallel CD.$	1. Given.
2. $\angle 1 = \angle 3.$	2. If two parallel lines are cut by a transversal, the corresponding angles are equal.
3. $\angle 2 = \angle 3.$	3. Vertical angles are equal.
4. $\angle 1 = \angle 2.$	4. Why?

DE—3. Given: $CD \parallel AB$,
$\triangle ABC$ is isosceles.

Prove: $\angle ECB = \angle 4 + \angle 2$.

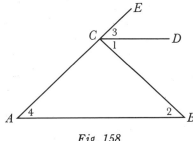

Fig. 158

Solution

Analysis:

You would know:	If you knew:
1. $\angle ECB = \angle 4 + \angle 2$.	1. $\angle 4 + \angle 2 = \angle 3 + \angle 1$.
2. $\angle 4 + \angle 2 = \angle 3 + \angle 1$.	2. $\angle 4 = \angle 3$ and $\angle 2 = \angle 1$.
3. $\angle 4 = \angle 3$.	3. They are corresponding angles formed by a transversal cutting parallel lines.
4. $\angle 2 = \angle 1$.	4. They are alternate-interior angles formed by a transversal cutting parallel lines.
5. $CD \parallel AB$.	5. It is given.

The formal proof is left to you.

Exercises

1. Write a complete proof for Developmental Exercise **3**.

2. Use Theorem 19 to prove the following: If a transversal intersects two parallel lines, the exterior angles on the same side of the transversal are supplementary.

3. Given: $AB \parallel CD$.
State a sequence of reasons to show that:
    a. $\angle 1 = \angle 7$,
    b. $\angle 8 + \angle 3 = 180°$.

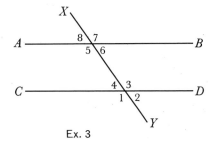

Ex. 3

4. Given: $AB \parallel CD$,
     $XY \parallel ZW$.

Prove: $\angle 9 = \angle 3$,
     $\angle 9 + \angle 6 = 180°$.

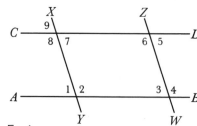

Ex. 4

5. Given: $x \parallel s$,
     $y \parallel t$.

Prove: $\angle 1 = \angle 2$.

Ex. 5

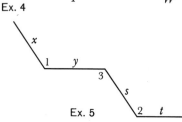

Ex. 6

6. Given: $BG \perp AD$,
     $FC \perp AD$.

Prove: $\angle 1 = \angle 2$.

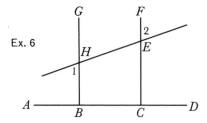

7. Given: $ED \parallel AB$,
     $\angle A = \angle D$.

Ex. 7

Prove: $\angle 1 = \angle 2$.

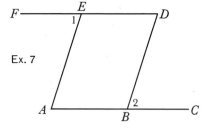

8. Given: $\triangle ABC$ isosceles,
     $XAY \parallel BC$.

Ex. 8

Prove: $\angle 1 = \angle 2$.

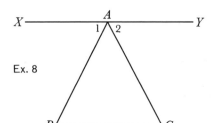

DE—4. Prove the following theorem:

> **THEOREM 20**
>
> **If two parallel lines are cut by a transversal, the interior angles on the same side of the transversal are supplementary.**

Solution

Given: $AB \parallel CD$,
Transversal EF.
Prove: $\angle 2 + \angle 3 = 180°$.

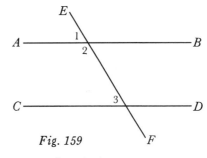

Fig. 159

Analysis:

You would know:	If you knew:
1. $\angle 2 + \angle 3 = 180°$.	1. $\angle 1 + \angle 2 = 180°$, $\angle 1 = \angle 3$.
2. $\angle 1 + \angle 2 = 180°$.	2. They are supplementary angles.
3. $\angle 1$ and $\angle 2$ are supplementary.	3. EF is a transversal.
4. EF is a transversal.	4. It is given.
5. $\angle 1 = \angle 3$.	5. $AB \parallel CD$.
6. $AB \parallel CD$.	6. It is given.

Proof:

Statements	Reasons
1. $AB \parallel CD$.	1. Given.
2. $\angle 1 = \angle 3$.	2. If two parallel lines are cut by a transversal, the corresponding angles formed are equal.
3. $\angle 1$ and $\angle 2$ are supplementary.	3. Two angles which form a straight line, i.e., one-half of a complete rotation, are supplementary.
4. $\angle 1 + \angle 2 = 180°$.	4. The sum of two supplementary angles is 180°.
5. $\angle 2 + \angle 3 = 180°$.	5. A quantity may be substituted for its equal in any expression without changing the value of the expression.

Exercises

1. Given: $\angle 1 = \angle 2$.
   Prove: $\angle 3 = \angle 4$.

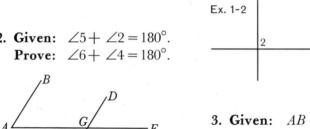

Ex. 1–2

2. Given: $\angle 5 + \angle 2 = 180°$.
   Prove: $\angle 6 + \angle 4 = 180°$.

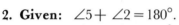

Ex. 3

3. Given: $AB \parallel CD$,
                $AE \parallel CF$.
   Prove: $\angle A = \angle C$.

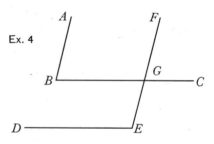

Ex. 4

4. Given: $AB \parallel FE$,
                $BC \parallel DE$.
   Prove: $\angle B + \angle E = 180°$.

5. Prove the following statement: If two parallel lines are cut by a transversal, the bisectors of a pair of alternate-interior angles are parallel.

6. Given: $AB = BC$,
                $BC \parallel AD$.

   Prove: $\angle 1 = \angle 2$.

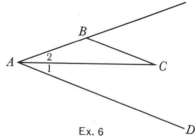

Ex. 6

7. Prove the following: If two sides of a quadrilateral are equal and parallel, the other two sides are equal and parallel.

8. From a given point not on a given line, construct a line making a given angle with the given line.

DE—5. Prove the following theorem:

|| **THEOREM 21**
|| **Two lines each parallel to a third line are parallel to each other.**

Solution

Given: $a \parallel c$,
$\quad\quad\quad b \parallel c$.

Prove: $a \parallel b$.

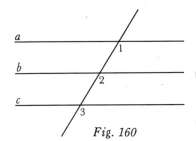

Fig. 160

Analysis:

You would know:	If you knew:
1. $a \parallel b$.	1. $\angle 1 = \angle 2$.
2. $\angle 1 = \angle 2$.	2. $\angle 1 = \angle 3$,
	$\quad \angle 2 = \angle 3$.
3. $\angle 1 = \angle 3$.	3. $a \parallel c$.
4. $a \parallel c$.	4. It is given.
5. $\angle 2 = \angle 3$.	5. $b \parallel c$.
6. $b \parallel c$.	6. It is given.

Proof:

Statements	Reasons
1. $a \parallel c$.	1. Given.
2. $\angle 1 = \angle 3$.	2. If parallel lines are cut by a transversal, the corresponding angles formed are equal.
3. $b \parallel c$.	3. Given.
4. $\angle 2 = \angle 3$.	4. Reason 2.
5. $\angle 1 = \angle 2$.	5. Quantities equal to the same or equal quantities are equal.
6. $a \parallel b$.	6. If two lines are cut by a transversal so that the corresponding angles are equal, the lines are parallel.

Exercises

1. Given: $AG = GF$,
         $GD \parallel AC$,
         $GB \parallel EC$,
         $FH \parallel EC$.

Prove: $\triangle AGB \cong \triangle GHF$.

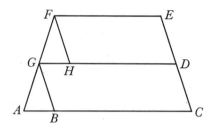

Ex. 1

2. Given: $ED \parallel AB$,
           $\angle EDC = 130°$,
           $\angle CBA = 120°$.
Prove: $\angle DCB = 110°$.

What is the effect of drawing a line through point C parallel to AB?

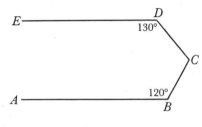

Ex. 2

3. Given: $AB \parallel CD$.

Prove: $\angle DEA = \angle CDE + \angle EAB$.

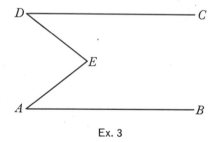

Ex. 3

4. Through the midpoint of a line joining two parallel lines another transversal is drawn. Prove the two transversals cut off equal lengths on the parallel lines.

5. Given: $AE \parallel CD$,
         $\angle B = 145°$,
         $\angle C = 110°$.

Prove: $\angle A = ?$

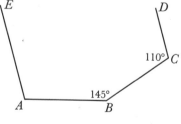

Ex. 5

6. Draw a transversal across two parallel lines. Through the midpoint of the segment of the transversal between the parallel lines draw a second transversal. Prove its segments are equal.

7. Given: $AB \parallel CD$,
$$r \parallel s,$$
$$s \parallel t,$$
$$\angle 10 = 115°.$$
List the number of degrees in each odd numbered angle. Write a reason which supports your answer.

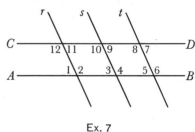

Ex. 7

8. Given: $AB \parallel CD$,
Transversal EF,
$$\angle 1 = \angle 122°.$$
Determine the number of degrees in the numbered angles.

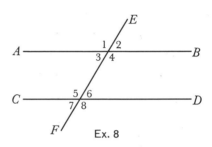

Ex. 8

9. Given: $MN \parallel RS$,
$$NO \parallel WV,$$
$$\angle N = 87°.$$

Find the number of degrees in $\angle VTU$ and $\angle UTW$.

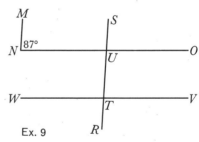

Ex. 9

10. Given: $AB = BC$,
$$XY \parallel AC,$$
$$\angle X = 60°.$$

Find the number of degrees in $\angle A$, $\angle C$, and $\angle Y$.

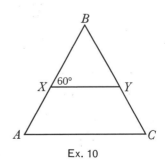

Ex. 10

THE SUM OF THE INTERIOR ANGLES OF A TRIANGLE

In your study of mathematics during previous years you might have measured the angles of a triangle with a protractor. After working with triangles of different shapes and sizes you assumed that the sum of the angles of any one triangle was 180°. Your conclusion seemed valid although you could not prove it.

With the use of conclusions previously established in this text and definitions of parallel lines and straight angles, the conclusion regarding the sum of the angles is deduced. It is a general proof because it refers to a triangle none of whose angles are known.

Developmental Exercises

DE—1. Prove the following theorem:

THEOREM 22

The sum of the interior angles of a triangle is 180°.

Solution

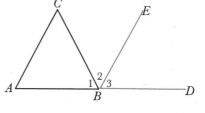

Fig. 161

Given: $\triangle ABC$.

Prove: $\angle A + \angle ABC + \angle C = 180°$.

Construction: Extend side AB. Construct $BE \parallel AC$.
Proof:

STATEMENTS	REASONS
1. $\angle A = \angle 3$.	1. If parallel lines are cut by a transversal, the corresponding angles formed are equal.
2. $\angle C = \angle 2$.	2. If parallel lines are cut by a transversal, the alternate-interior angles formed are equal.
3. $\angle 1 + \angle 2 + \angle 3 = 180°$.	3. Why?
4. $\angle A + \angle ABC + \angle C = 180°$.	4. Why?

Another proof of this theorem may be given.

DE—2. Given: $\triangle ABC$.

   Prove: $\angle A + \angle B + \angle ACB = 180°$.

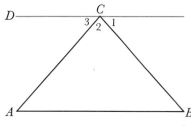

Fig. 162

Solution

Construction: $CD \parallel AB$.

Analysis:

You would know that $\angle A + \angle B + \angle ACB = 180°$ if $\angle 1 + \angle 2 + \angle 3 = 180°$, and $\angle B$ and $\angle A$ are equal to $\angle 1$ and $\angle 3$ respectively.

Proof:

STATEMENTS	REASONS
1. $\angle 1 + \angle 2 + \angle 3 = 180°$.	1. Why?
2. $\angle A = \angle 3$, $\angle B = \angle 1$.	2. Why?
3. $\angle A + \angle B + \angle ACB = 180°$.	3. Why?

Exercises

1. Given: $\triangle ABC$ is isosceles,
$\angle ACB = 50° \ 25'$.

   Prove: $\angle DBC = ?$

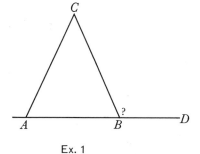

Ex. 1

2. Draw a general quadrilateral. What is the sum of its angles? Prove your conclusion.

3. A base angle of an isosceles triangle contains $38°$. Compute the size of each other angle of the triangle.

4. Given: $\angle A$ and $\angle B$ of $\triangle ABC$.

   Construct: $\angle C$ of the triangle.

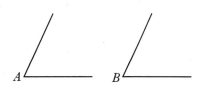

Ex. 4

5. Given: $CB \perp AB$,
$\quad\quad\quad XY \perp AC.$
Prove: $\angle C = \angle XYA.$

Ex. 5

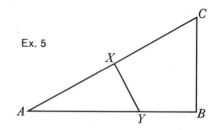

Ex. 6

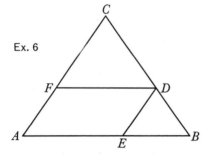

6. Given: $DE \parallel AC$,
$\quad\quad\quad DF \parallel AB.$
Prove: $\angle A + \angle B + \angle C = 180°.$

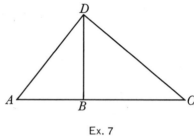

7. Given: $\triangle ADC$ a right triangle,
$\quad\quad\quad DB \perp AC.$
Prove: $\angle A = \angle CDB.$

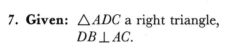

Ex. 7

8. In quadrilateral $ABCD$, $\angle B$ and $\angle D$ are right angles. Prove the two remaining angles are supplementary.

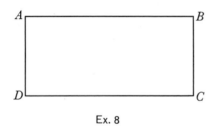

Ex. 8

9. Draw a pentagon. What is the sum of its angles? Repeat with a hexagon.

Ex. 10

10. Two angles of a triangle are $65°$ and $40°$ respectively. How many degrees are in the angle formed by their bisectors?

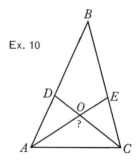

COROLLARIES

A corollary is a theorem that follows so obviously from another theorem that little or no proof is needed to show its validity. Several corollaries are based on the previous theorem, the sum of the interior angles of a triangle is 180°. Study them, making sure you see how they are all consequences of Theorem 22.

Corollary 1
If two angles of one triangle are equal to two angles of another triangle, the third angles are equal.

Corollary 2
A triangle can have but one right angle or one obtuse angle.

Corollary 3
If two right triangles have an acute angle of one equal to an acute angle of the other, the other acute angles are equal.

Corollary 4
The acute angles of a right triangle are complementary.

Corollary 5
If one side of a triangle is extended, the exterior angle thus formed is equal to the sum of the two remote interior angles.

These Egyptian pyramids at Gizeh served as royal tombs. These are considered one of the Seven Wonders of the Ancient World.

Developmental Exercises

DE—1. Given: $\angle BAC = \angle BDE.$

Prove: $\angle BCA = \angle BED.$

Fig. 163

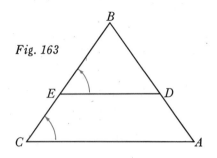

Solution

STATEMENTS	REASONS
1. $\angle BAC = \angle BDE.$	1. Given.
2. $\angle ABC = \angle DBE.$	2. Identity.
3. $\angle BCA = \angle BED.$	3. Corollary 1: If two angles of one triangle are equal to two angles of another triangle, the third angles are equal.

DE—2. Given: $AB \perp BC,$
$DE \perp EF,$
$\angle C = \angle F.$

Prove: $\angle A = \angle D.$

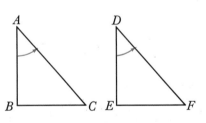

Fig. 164

Solution

STATEMENTS	REASONS
1. $AB \perp BC.$	1. Given.
2. $\angle B$ is a right angle.	2. Why?
3. $\triangle ABC$ is a right triangle.	3. Why?
4. $DE \perp EF.$	4. Given.
5. $\angle E$ is a right angle.	5. Reason 2.
6. $\triangle DEF$ is a right triangle.	6. Reason 3.
7. $\angle C = \angle F.$	7. Given.
8. $\angle A = \angle D.$	8. Corollary 3: If two right triangles have an acute angle of one equal to an acute angle of the other, the other acute angles are equal.

DE—3. Given: $AB \perp BC$.

Prove: $\angle A + \angle C = 90°$.

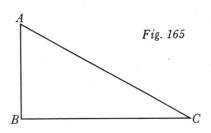

Fig. 165

Solution

STATEMENTS	REASONS
1. $AB \perp BC$.	1. Given.
2. $\angle CBA$ is a right angle.	2. Why?
3. $\triangle ABC$ is a right triangle.	3. Why?
4. $\angle A$ and $\angle C$ are complementary angles.	4. Corollary 4: The acute angles of a right triangle are complementary.
5. $\angle A + \angle C = 90°$.	5. Why?

Exercises

1. Give a proof for Corollary 1.

2. Give a proof for Corollary 2.

3. Give a proof for Corollary 3.

4. Give a proof for Corollary 4.

5. Give a proof for Corollary 5.

6. Give specific examples for each corollary.

7. Given: $\angle A = \angle C$.
Prove: $\angle B = \angle D$.

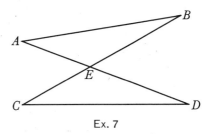

Ex. 7

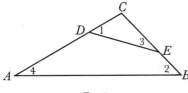

Ex. 8

8. Given: $\angle 1 = \angle 2$.
Prove: $\angle 3 = \angle 4$.

9. Given: $BE = EC$,
                    $\angle A = \angle D$,
                    $\angle ABC = \angle BCD$.
Prove: $\angle 1 = \angle 2$.

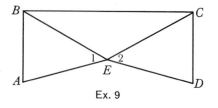

Ex. 9

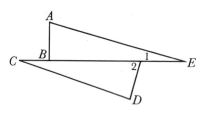

Ex. 10

10. Given: $AC = BC$,
                  $DC = CE$.
Prove: $\angle B = \angle D$.

11. Given: $AB \parallel DC$,
                 $AB \perp AC$.
Prove: $\angle B = \angle D$.

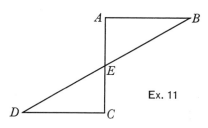

Ex. 11

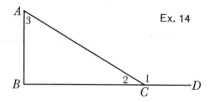

Ex. 12

12. Given: $\angle 1 + \angle 2 = 90°$,
                 $AB \perp CE$.
Prove: $\angle 2 = \angle A$.

Ex. 13

13. Given: $ED \perp AB$,
              $DF \perp AC$.
Prove: $\angle FDE + \angle A = 180°$.

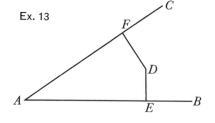

Ex. 14

14. Given: $AB \perp BD$,
                 $\angle 1 = 150°$.
Prove: $\angle 3 = ?$

15. In $\triangle ABC$, AB is extended to D. How many degrees are there in $\angle CBD$ if $\angle A = 35°$ and $\angle C = 75°$? If $\angle A = \dfrac{a°}{4}$ and $\angle C = 2a°$?

16. Illustrate and prove: A triangle is isosceles if the bisector of an angle of the triangle is perpendicular to the opposite side.

17. Given: $\angle 1 = \angle 2$.
   Prove: $\angle B = \angle YXC$.

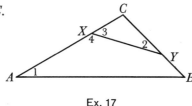

Ex. 17

18. Prove that a line intersecting two equal sides of a triangle and parallel to the third side forms a second isosceles triangle.

19. Extend the base of a general triangle in both directions. Prove the sum of the exterior angles thus formed is greater than the third angle by 180°.

20. Given: $EA \perp AC$,
           $DC \perp AC$,
           $\angle 1 = \angle 2$.
   Prove: $\angle E = \angle D$.

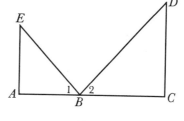

Ex. 20

MORE ABOUT CONGRUENCE

In Chapter Two it was assumed that two triangles are congruent if:

(*1*) Three sides of one are equal respectively to three sides of the other. **s.s.s.**

(*2*) Two sides and the included angle of one are equal respectively to two sides and the included angle of the other. **s.a.s.**

(*3*) Two angles and the included side of one are equal respectively to two angles and the included side of the other. **a.s.a.**

However, there are additional ways of proving two triangles congruent. Study these methods in the following developmental exercises.

Developmental Exercises

DE—1. Construct congruent triangles duplicating two angles and the side opposite one of them.

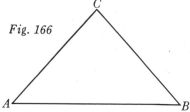

Fig. 166

Given: △*ABC*.

Construct △*A'B'C'*≅△*ABC* by duplicating ∠*A*, ∠*C*, and side *AB*.

Solution

● On the working line an angle can be constructed equal to angle *A*.

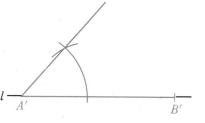

● Side *A'B'* is cut off equal to *AB*. Where is the vertex of ∠*C*?

Fig. 167

● Since the sum of the angles of a triangle is 180°, add, with compasses, the two angles given, such as ∠*A* and ∠*C*, and subtract their sum from a straight angle.

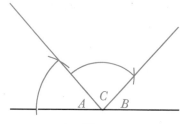

Fig. 168

The remainder is the third angle of the triangle. Now that ∠*B* has become known, the analysis need not be continued because we now have two angles, *A* and *B*, and the included side, *AB*. Now congruent triangles can be constructed.

Thus, it can be concluded that:

THEOREM 23

If two triangles have two angles and an opposite side of one equal respectively to two angles and an opposite side of the other, then the triangles are congruent. a.a.s. = a.a.s.

DE—2. Given: $\angle B = \angle E$,
$\qquad AF = CD$,
$\qquad \angle A = \angle D$.

Prove: $EF = BC$.

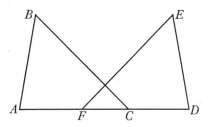

Fig. 169

Solution

Analysis:

You would know:	If you knew:
1. $EF = BC$.	1. They were corresponding sides of congruent triangles *EFD* and *ABC*.
2. $\triangle EFD \cong \triangle ABC$.	2. $\angle B = \angle E$. **a.** $\angle A = \angle D$. **a.** $AC = DF$. **s.**
3. $AC = DF$.	3. $AF = CD$. $CF = CF$.

Proof:

Statements	Reasons
1. $\angle B = \angle E$, $\angle A = \angle D$, $AF = CD$.	1. Given.
2. $CF = CF$.	2. Identity.
3. $CA = DF$.	3. If equals are added to equals the sums are equal.
4. $\triangle EFD \cong \triangle ABC$.	4. **a.a.s. = a.a.s.**
5. $EF = BC$.	5. Corresponding sides of congruent triangles are equal.

Exercises

Write a complete proof for the following conclusions:

1. Given: $\angle 1 = \angle 2$,
$\qquad \angle A = \angle C$.

Prove: $\triangle ADB \cong \triangle DCB$.

Ex. 1

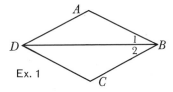

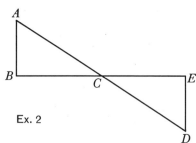

Ex. 2

2. Given: $AB \perp BE$,
  $DE \perp BE$,
  $AC = CD$.
Prove: $\triangle ABC \cong \triangle DEC$.

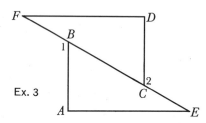

Ex. 3

3. Given: $\angle 1 = \angle 2$,
  $\angle E = \angle F$,
  $AB = CD$.
Prove: $\triangle AEB \cong \triangle DFC$.

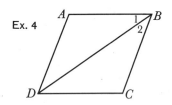

Ex. 4

4. Given: $AB = BC$,
  DB bisects $\angle B$,
  $\angle A = \angle C$.
Prove: $\triangle ABD \cong \triangle BCD$.

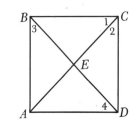

Ex. 5

5. Given: $AB \perp BC$,
  $AD \perp DC$,
  $\angle 1 = \angle 2$,
  $\angle 3 = \angle 4$.
Prove: $\triangle BEC \cong \triangle DEC$.

6. Given: $\angle 1 = \angle 2$,
  $AB \perp CD$.
Prove: $BC = BD$.

Ex. 6

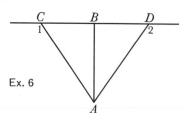

Ex. 7

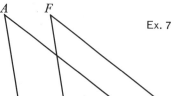

7. Given: $\angle 1 = \angle 2$,
  $\angle A = \angle F$,
  $AB = FD$.
Prove: $BD = CE$.

8. Given: $\angle 3 + \angle 4 = 180°$,
$\qquad \angle 1 = \angle 2$,
$\qquad EF = BA$.

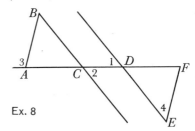

Select and prove the valid conclusion: **a.** $AC = DE$,
$\qquad$ **b.** $AC = DF$.

Ex. 8

9. Prove the following proposition: If two right triangles have an acute angle and an opposite leg respectively equal, the triangles are congruent.

10. If two triangles have an angle and two sides of one equal respectively to an angle and two sides of another, are they congruent?

DE—3. Prove the following theorem:

| **THEOREM 24**
| **Two right triangles are congruent if the hypotenuse and acute angle of one is equal to the hypotenuse and acute angle of the other.**

Solution

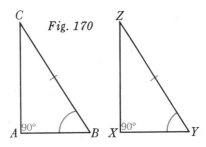

Fig. 170

Given: $\angle BAC = 90°$,
$\qquad \angle YXZ = 90°$,
$\qquad BC = ZY$,
$\qquad \angle B = \angle Y$.
Prove: $\triangle BAC \cong \triangle XYZ$.

Proof:

STATEMENTS	REASONS
1. $\angle B = \angle Y$, $\angle BAC = 90°$, $\angle YXZ = 90°$, $BC = ZY$.	1. Given.
2. $\angle CAB = \angle ZXY$.	2. Why?
3. $\triangle BAC \cong \triangle XYZ$.	3. If two triangles have two angles and a side of one equal respectively to two angles and a side of the other, the triangles are congruent.

DE—4. Prove the following theorem:

‖**THEOREM** 25
‖**In a triangle, sides opposite equal angles are equal.**

Solution

Given: $\angle A = \angle B$.

Prove: $AC = CB$.

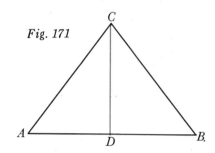

Fig. 171

Analysis:
None of the ways to prove two line segments equal seems to apply here. To prove that AC and CB are corresponding sides of congruent triangles you must have two triangles with AC in one of them and CB in the other. In order to have two triangles, construct DC the bisector of $\angle C$. See Figure 171.

You would know:	If you knew:
1. $AC = CB$.	1. $\triangle ACD \cong \triangle CBD$.
2. $\triangle ACD \cong \triangle CBD$.	2. $\angle A = \angle B$, **a.**
	$\angle 1 = \angle 2$, **a.**
	$CD = CD$. **s.**

Construction: The bisector of $\angle C$. Label this line CD.

Proof:

Statements	Reasons
1. $\angle A = \angle B$.	1. Given.
2. $\angle 1 = \angle 2$.	2. An angle bisector can be constructed.
3. $CD = CD$.	3. Identity.
4. $\triangle ACD \cong \triangle DCB$.	4. If two triangles have two angles and a side of one equal respectively to two angles and a side of the other, they are congruent.
5. $AC = CB$.	5. Corresponding sides of congruent triangles are equal.

Exercises

In Exercises **1-13** *supply the missing parts.*

1-6. Prove the following theorem:

|| THEOREM 26

Two right triangles are congruent if the hypotenuse and leg of one are equal to the hypotenuse and leg of the other.

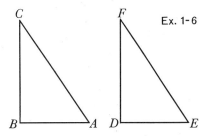

Given: $\angle B = 90°$,
$\qquad\quad \angle D = 90°$,
$\qquad\quad AC = FE$,
$\qquad\quad BC = DF$.

Prove: ?

Ex. 1-6

For convenience consider the right triangles in the position shown below. Side *FE* is in the same position as *AC*.

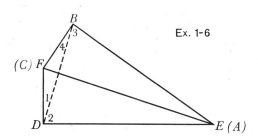

Ex. 1-6

STATEMENTS	REASONS
1. ?	1. Given.
2. ?	2. Angles opposite equal sides of a triangle are equal.
3. $\angle 1 + \angle 2 = \angle 3 + \angle 4.$	3. All right angles are equal.
4. ?	4. If equals are subtracted from equals the remainders are equal.
5. ?	5. Sides opposite equal angles of a triangle are equal.
6. $\triangle ABC \cong \triangle DEF.$	6. ?

7-13. Prove the following theorem:

> **THEOREM 27**
>
> **If a line joins the vertex of an isosceles triangle to the midpoint of the base, then it is perpendicular to the base.**

Given: $\triangle ABC$ isosceles, D bisects AB.

Prove: $CD \perp AB$.

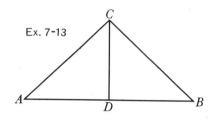

Ex. 7-13

STATEMENTS	REASONS
1. $\triangle ABC$ isosceles, D bisects AB.	1. Given.
2. $AC = CB$.	2. ?
3. ?	3. Angles opposite equal sides of a triangle are equal.
4. ?	4. Parts of a bisected line are equal.
5. $\triangle ADC \cong \triangle CDB$.	5. ?
6. $\angle CDA = \angle BDC$.	6. Corresponding angles of congruent triangles are equal.
7. $\angle CDA + \angle BDC = 180°$.	7. ?
8. $2\angle CDA = 180°$.	8. Substitution assumption.
9. $\angle CDA = 90°$.	9. ?
10. $CD \perp AB$.	10. ?

14. Discover another proof for Theorem 25 using the diagram below.

Given: $\angle CBA = \angle ACB$.

Prove: $AB = AC$.

Construction: $\angle 1 = \angle 2$, $\angle 3 = \angle 4$.

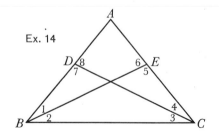

Ex. 14

Ex. 15

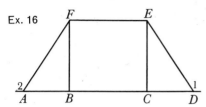

15. Given: $\angle 1 = \angle 2$.
    Prove: $AB = CB$.

Ex. 16

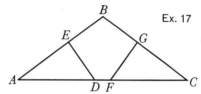

16. Given: $\angle 1 = \angle 2$,
        $FB \perp AD$,
        $EC \perp AD$,
        $FA = ED$.
   Prove: $\triangle ABF \cong \triangle DCE$.

17. Given: $AB = BC$,
        $DE \perp AB$,
        $FG \perp BC$,
        $AF = DC$.
   Prove: $DE = FG$.

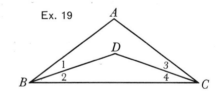

Ex. 17

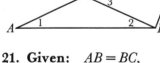

18. Given: $AB = BC$,
        $\angle DAB = \angle BCD$.
   Prove: $AD = DC$.

Ex. 18

19. Given: $AC = AB$,
        $\angle 1 = \angle 2$,
        $\angle 3 = \angle 4$.
   Prove: $BD = DC$.

Ex. 19

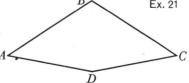

Ex. 20

20. Given: $\angle 3 = \angle 4$,
        $\angle 2 = \angle 3$,
        $\angle 1 = \angle 4$.
   Prove: $AE = BE$.

21. Given: $AB = BC$,
        $\angle A = \angle C$.
   Prove: $AD = DC$.

Ex. 21

22. Given an angle of a triangle, an adjacent side, and the sum of the other two sides, construct the triangle.

The Capitol Building, with its large white dome is one of the most impressive sights in Washington, D. C. The parallel Corinthian columns and pilasters add to its stately beauty.

SOLID GEOMETRY

Parallel planes do not intersect even when extended. *A line is parallel to a plane if, extended indefinitely, it does not intersect the plane.*

Analogies between theorems, definitions, and assumptions of lines in a plane and lines in space are frequent. *In a plane, parallel lines are equally distant. In space, parallel planes are equally distant. Two lines in a plane, perpendicular to a third line in the same plane, are parallel.* The analogous conclusion in space is *Two planes perpendicular to the same line are parallel.* Is the converse valid? If a line is perpendicular to one of two parallel planes, is it perpendicular to the other plane?

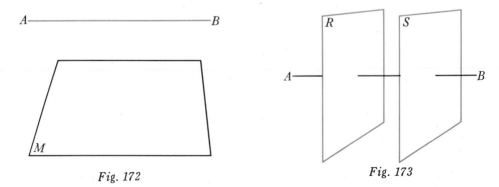

Fig. 172

Fig. 173

Exercises

Prepare and study a sketch which illustrates the conditions stated in each of the following:

1. Through a given external point only one plane can be parallel to a given plane.

2. Intersections of two parallel planes with a third plane are parallel lines.

3. A line parallel to each of two intersecting planes is parallel to their line of intersection.

4. If a line is parallel to a plane, it is parallel to the intersection of that plane with any plane containing the given line.

5. If two lines are parallel, a plane which contains one of the lines, and only one, is parallel to the other line.

6. If a line and a plane are parallel, another line parallel to the first, through a point in the plane, lies entirely in the plane.

7. When a line and a plane are parallel, all points on the line are equidistant from the plane.

8. One plane, and only one plane, can be drawn through a given point and parallel to each of two skew lines.

9. Two lines perpendicular to the same line at the same point determine a plane which is also perpendicular to the line at the point.

10. All the lines which can be drawn perpendicular to a line at the same point lie in the plane which is perpendicular to the line.

11. Two planes that are perpendicular to the same line are parallel.

12. A line that is perpendicular to one of two parallel planes is perpendicular to the other.

13. Parallel line segments included between parallel planes are equal.

14. Through either of two skew lines, one, and only one, plane can be drawn parallel to the other.

EXTEND YOUR HORIZON

When you accept definitions and assumptions, you must also accept all the conclusions which can be deduced from the definitions and assumptions through logical reasoning. These conclusions would be valid.

Euclid, about 300 B.C., assumed that in a plane one and only one line can be drawn parallel to a given line through a point not on the given line. One of the inevitable consequences after accepting the above (the fifth postulate of Euclid) is the conclusion that the sum of the angles of a triangle is 180°. The geometry you are now studying is essentially this Euclidean geometry. Many of the theorems which you have proved depend on the acceptance of Euclid's fifth postulate.

By changing Euclid's fifth postulate, but retaining the others, it is possible through logical reasoning, to derive a new geometry based on this new set of postulates. Such a geometric system may not contain any contradictions in itself, even though it may contradict certain theorems of Euclidean geometry. Since such a geometry is based on logical reasoning, it is as valid as Euclidean geometry.

About 1840, Lobachevski developed a system of geometry different from Euclid's geometry. Lobachevski used all but the fifth of Euclid's postulates. He assumed, in effect, that many lines can be drawn parallel to a given line and through a given point not on the given line. An inevitable consequence of that assumption is the conclusion that the sum of the angles of a triangle is less than 180°. This geometry is called *hyperbolic geometry*.

A geometric system based on equally consistent assumptions was developed by Riemann about 1850. He assumed that there is no line which can be drawn parallel to a given line through a point not on the given line. An inevitable conclusion, which is a consequence of Riemann's assumptions, is that the sum of the angles of a triangle is more than 180°. This Riemannian geometry is also called *elliptical geometry*. It led to a branch of mathematics called *topology*.

On the following page is a brief comparison of the typical characteristics of the Euclidean and non-Euclidean geometries. Notice the number of differences that result from changing only one postulate.

EUCLIDEAN	LOBACHEVSKIAN	RIEMANNIAN
1. There is one and only one line through a given point parallel to a given line.	There are two lines through a given point parallel to a given line.	There is no line through a given point parallel to a given line.
2. The sum of the angles of a triangle is 180°.	The sum of the angles of a triangle is less than 180°.	The sum of the angles of a triangle is more than 180°.
3. Two parallel lines are everywhere equally distant.	Two parallel lines are not equidistant. They approach each other in one direction and diverge in the opposite direction.	There are no parallel lines. Each line intersects every other line.
4. Two parallel lines have many common perpendiculars.	Two parallel or intersecting lines have no common perpendiculars.	Any two lines have a unique common perpendicular.
5. Rectangles (in the sense of parallelograms with a right angle) exist.	Rectangles do not exist.	Rectangles do not exist.

To further study non-Euclidean geometries, refer to the geometries of Bolyai, Saccheri, Lambert, and Gauss. Their conclusions are as valid as Euclid's and are established through logical reasoning based on a group of consistent assumptions and definitions.

Thus, you see that from different assumptions as starting points, contradictory, but equally valid, conclusions can be deduced. The truth of the assumption or conclusion has no bearing on the validity of the reasoning.

When next you find yourself not in agreement with a conclusion, examine the assumptions and definitions on which the conclusion is based in order to understand why the conclusion is unacceptable.

CHAPTER SUMMARY

Two lines are parallel if

1. they are in the same plane and are perpendicular to the same line. (page 132)

2. they are cut by a transversal and form equal corresponding angles. (page 135)

3. they are cut by a transversal so that the alternate-interior angles are equal.   (page 136)

4. they are cut by a transversal so that two interior angles on the same side of the transversal are supplementary.   (page 140)

5. they are parallel to the same line.   (page 153)

If two parallel lines are cut by a transversal

1. the corresponding angles formed are equal.   (page 135)

2. the alternate-interior angles formed are equal.   (page 148)

3. the interior angles on the same side of the transversal are supplementary.   (page 151)

In a triangle

1. the sum of the interior angles is 180°.   (page 156)

2. an exterior angle formed by the extension of a side is equal to the sum of the two remote interior angles.   (page 159)

3. only one right angle or one obtuse angle is possible.   (page 159)

4. having a right angle, the acute angles are complementary. (page 159)

5. sides opposite equal angles are equal.   (page 168)

Two triangles are congruent if

1. two angles and an opposite side of one are equal respectively to two angles and an opposite side of the other. **a.a.s.**   (page 164)

2. they are right triangles and the hypotenuse and acute angle of one are equal to the hypotenuse and acute angle of the other. (page 167)

3. they are right triangles and the hypotenuse and leg of one are equal to the hypotenuse and leg of the other.   (page 169)

The converse of a statement

1. is formed by interchanging any number of hypotheses with an equal number of conclusions.   (page 143)

2. cannot be accepted without proof.   (page 144)

CHAPTER REVIEW

Vocabulary

Match the word in the left hand column with its correct definition in the right hand column.

1. Parallel lines (∥)

2. Skew lines

3. Transversal

4. Converse

5. Hypothesis

6. Hypotenuse

7. Isosceles

8. Corresponding angles

9. Alternate-interior angles

10. Corollary

a. Pairs of angles that lie on opposite sides of the transversal, between the two lines, but not adjacent.

b. Lines in the same plane that form equal corresponding angles with a transversal.

c. Lines not in the same plane that do not intersect and are not parallel.

d. In a right triangle the side opposite the right angle.

e. A conclusion which is established by application of a theorem with which it has a logically close relationship.

f. A line that intersects two or more lines in a plane.

g. A statement formed from another statement by interchanging an equal number of data and conclusions.

h. Having two equal sides.

i. Pairs of angles that lie on the same side of the transversal and on matching sides of the lines cut by the transversal.

j. Given data.

k. Pairs of angles on the same side of a transversal.

Exercises

Answer each of the questions and state the principle upon which your answer depends.

1. If $\angle 1 = \angle 2$, is $AB \parallel CD$?

2. If $\angle 1 = \angle 3$, is $AB \parallel CD$?

3. If $\angle 1 = \angle 5$, is $AB \parallel CD$?

4. If $\angle 3 = \angle 4$, is $AB \parallel CD$?

5. If $\angle 3 = \angle 7$, is $AB \parallel CD$?

6. If $\angle 3 = \angle 5$, is $AB \parallel CD$?

7. If $\angle 3 + \angle 4 = 180°$, is $AB \parallel CD$?

8. If $\angle 2 = \angle 8$, is $AB \parallel CD$?

9. If $\angle 2 + \angle 8 = 180°$, is $AB \parallel CD$?

10. If $\angle 4 = \angle 6$, is $AB \parallel CD$?

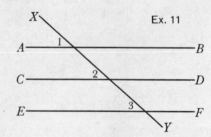

Ex. 1-10

11. Given: $\angle 1 = \angle 2$,
$\angle 2 = \angle 3$.
Prove: $AB \parallel EF$.

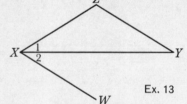

Ex. 11

12. Through each vertex of a triangle construct a line parallel to the side opposite that vertex.

13. Given: $ZY = ZX$,
$\angle 1 = \angle 2$.

Prove: $XW \parallel ZY$.

Ex. 13

14. Given: $\angle 6 = 119°$,
$\angle 1 = 61°$.

Prove: $AB \parallel CD$.

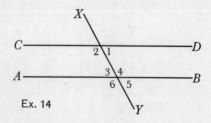

Ex. 14

15. Prove two lines cut by a transversal parallel if the exterior angles on the same side of the transversal are supplementary.

16. Given: PO bisects $\angle CPQ$,
$\quad\quad\quad$ QO bisects $\angle PQA$,
$\quad\quad\quad$ $\angle 1 + \angle 2 = 90°$.

$\quad\quad$ **Prove:** $AB \parallel CD$.

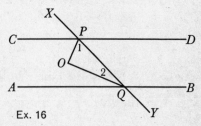

Ex. 16

17. A transversal intersects two parallel lines making one angle six degrees more than three times its supplement. How large is each angle?

18. Illustrate and prove: If two right angles have two sides parallel, then the remaining sides of the angles are parallel.

19. Prove that two isosceles triangles which have a common vertex angle have parallel bases.

20. Given two angles with the sides of one perpendicular to the sides of the other, prove that a line bisecting the first angle is either perpendicular or parallel to the bisector of the second angle.

21. If A is parallel to B, how many degrees has $\angle y$?

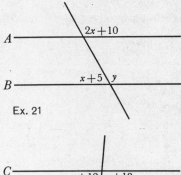

Ex. 21

22. If C is parallel to D, how many degrees has $\angle y$?

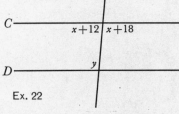

Ex. 22

23. An isosceles triangle has a vertex angle of $35°$. How large is each base angle?

24. An exterior angle of a triangle is 140°. The remote interior angles have the ratio 3:5. How large is each angle of the triangle?

25. Write the converse of the following: The bisectors of the opposite angles of a rectangle are parallel.

26. Given a triangle with one acute angle double another, construct through the vertex of the larger a line which forms two isosceles triangles.

27. Prove that two angles whose sides are respectively parallel are equal.

28. Bisect the base angles of an isosceles triangle. Prove the angle formed by the bisectors is equal to an exterior angle at the base.

29. Illustrate and prove: An exterior angle formed by extending the base of an isosceles triangle is 90° greater than one-half the vertex angle.

30. Draw an acute angle. From a point outside the angle, draw lines perpendicular to the sides of the angle. What relationship between the size of the given angle and the angle between the perpendiculars is valid? Prove your conclusion.

31. State the converse of the following: A line which bisects an exterior angle at the vertex of an isosceles triangle is parallel to the base of the triangle. Is the converse valid?

32. Draw an angle. Construct an angle with its vertex inside the given angle and its sides parallel to the sides of the given angle.

33. From the ends of the base of an isosceles triangle, draw lines perpendicular to the opposite sides. Join the ends of the perpendiculars. Show that this line is parallel to the base of the triangle.

34. Write the converse of the following: A line through the vertex of an isosceles triangle and parallel to the base bisects an exterior angle at the vertex.

35. Show that if two triangles have their angles respectively equal, their sides may be respectively parallel.

36. State and prove the converse of the following: If two oblique lines, drawn from a point to a third line, meet it at equal distances from the foot of the perpendicular to the line, then the oblique lines are equal.

CHAPTER TEST

1. Define parallel lines.

2. State two postulates related to parallel lines.

3. List four sets of conditions which may be used to establish that two lines are parallel.

4. If the angles of a triangle have the ratio of 4 to 3 to 2, how many degrees has each angle?

5. Illustrate and prove: When two parallel lines are cut by a transversal, exterior angles on the same side of the transversal are supplementary.

6. Extend the sides of a triangle in succession, thus forming three exterior angles. Find their sum.

7. Given: $AB \parallel XY$,
    XC and CA trisect
    $\angle BCW$.

Prove: $\triangle ABC$ is equilateral.

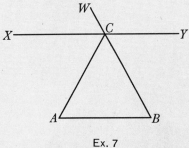

Ex. 7

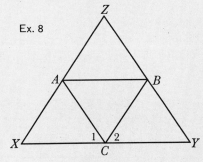

Ex. 8

8. Given: $\angle 1 = \angle 2$,
    $AB \parallel XY$.

Prove: $\triangle ABC$ is isosceles.

9. Prove that segments of parallels which are intercepted by parallels are equal.

10. Prove that the bisectors of the interior angles on the same side of the transversal of two parallel lines are perpendicular to each other.

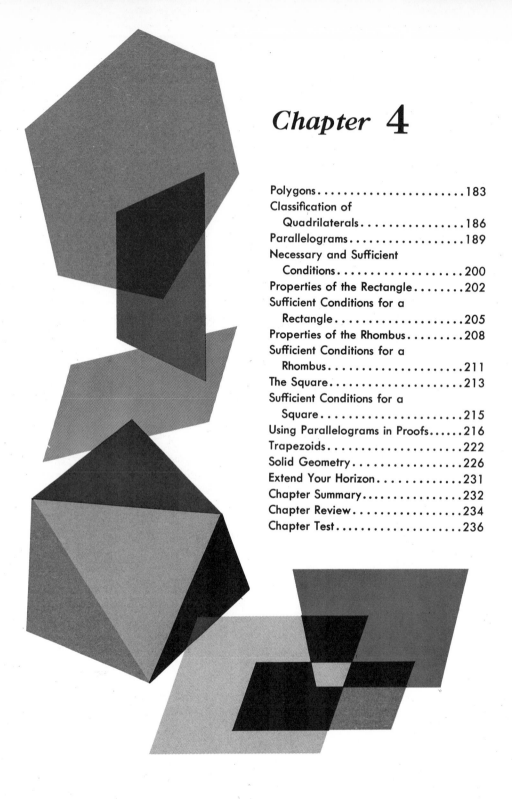

Chapter 4

QUADRILATERALS

POLYGONS

A **polygon** *is a closed broken line which bounds a portion of a plane.* Just as there are classifications for triangles, there are classifications for polygons in general. The classification is determined from the properties of the sides and angles of the polygon under investigation.

The following classification of polygons is based on the nature of the angles of the polygon under investigation:

(*1*) If at least one interior angle of a polygon is greater than a straight angle, the polygon is *concave*.

(*2*) If each of the interior angles of a polygon is less than a straight angle, the polygon is *convex*. Only the convex polygons will be considered in this text.

Fig. 174

CONCAVE POLYGON

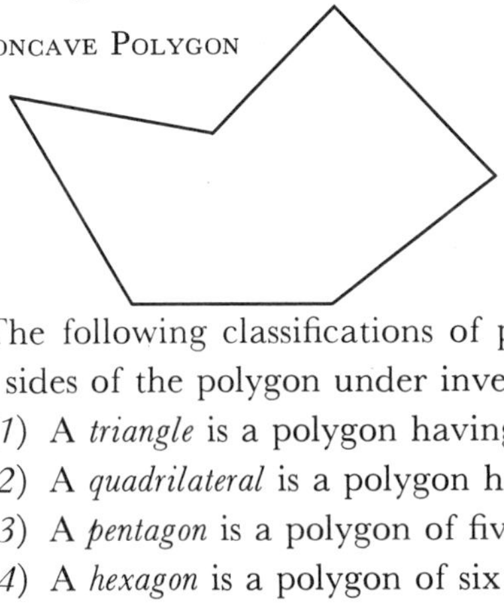

Fig. 175   CONVEX POLYGON

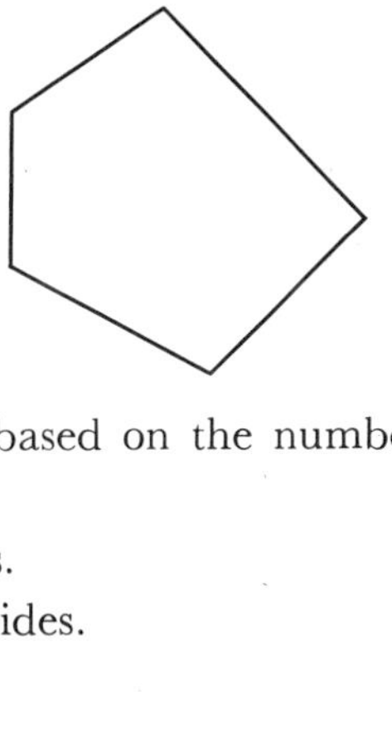

The following classifications of polygons is based on the number of the sides of the polygon under investigation:

(*1*) A *triangle* is a polygon having three sides.

(*2*) A *quadrilateral* is a polygon having four sides.

(*3*) A *pentagon* is a polygon of five sides.

(*4*) A *hexagon* is a polygon of six sides.

(*5*) A *heptagon* is a polygon of seven sides.

(*6*) An *octagon* is a polygon of eight sides.

(*7*) A *nonagon* is a polygon of nine sides.

(*8*) A *decagon* is a polygon of ten sides.

(*9*) An *n-gon* is a polygon of n sides.

If all the angles of a polygon are equal, the polygon is *equiangular*. If all the sides of a polygon are equal, the polygon is *equilateral*. A polygon which is both equiangular and equilateral is called a *regular polygon*.

*A **diagonal** of a polygon is a line connecting any two nonconsecutive vertices.* In Figure 176, *AC*, *AD*, *BD*, and *BE* are diagonals. *AE* is not a diagonal. Why not?

*An **interior angle** of a polygon is an angle formed by two consecutive sides of the polygon.*

*An **exterior angle** of a polygon is an angle formed by one side of the polygon and another side extended.* In Figure 176, ∠1 and ∠2 are exterior angles. ∠*BAE* ∠*AED* and ∠*EDC* are examples of interior angles.

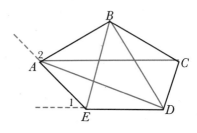

Fig. 176

Developmental Exercises

DE—1. Find the sum of the interior angles of a hexagon.

Solution

Draw a hexagon, a polygon of six sides. From any point within the hexagon, draw lines to each of the vertices. Notice in Figure 177, six triangles are formed. From Theorem 22, the sum of the interior angles of a triangle is 180°. What is the sum of all the angles of all the triangles in the hexagon?

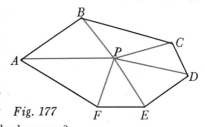

Fig. 177

The sum of all the angles is 6×180° or 1080°. The sum of the angles of the hexagon = the sum of all the angles of the triangles (1080°) − the sum of the angles at *P*. Why?

The sum of the angles at *P* is a complete revolution or 360°. Therefore, the sum of the angles of the hexagon is 1080° − 360° or 720°.

Repeat this process with a pentagon. How is the number of triangles related to the number of sides? How many triangles would be formed in an octagon? A dodecagon? An *n*-gon?

Assumption 22

If lines are drawn from a point within a polygon to each vertex, they form with the sides of the polygon as many triangles as there are sides.

DE—2. Find the sum of the interior angles of an *n*-gon.

Solution

Given: Convex polygon
ABCDE of *n* sides.
Construction: From any point, *P*, within the polygon, draw lines to each of the vertices—*PA*, *PB*, *PC*, *PD*, etc. This can be done because through two non-coincident points one, and only one, straight line can be drawn. *n* triangles are formed.

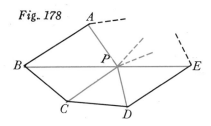

Fig. 178

The sum of the interior angles of all the triangles is $n(180°)$. The sum of the interior angles of the *n*-gon is the sum of all the angles of the triangles — the sum of the angles at *P*.

The sum of the angles at *P* is a complete revolution or $360°$ $(2 \cdot 180°)$. Therefore, the sum of the interior angles of the *n*-gon is $n(180°) - 2(180°)$ or $(n-2)180°$.

> **THEOREM 28**
> **The sum of the interior angles of a convex polygon of n sides is $(n-2)180°$.**

Exercises

1. Write a formal proof for Theorem 28.

2. Using Theorem 28, find the sum of the interior angles of a quadrilateral. Hint: $n = 4$.

3. Find the sum of the interior angles of a nonagon.

4. Using Theorem 28, find the sum of the interior angles of a polygon having 16 sides. Check your answer using the method in Developmental Exercise **1**.

5. What is the size of each angle of a regular quadrilateral? Use your answer from Exercise **2**.

6. What is the size of each angle of a regular nonagon? Use your answer from Exercise **3**.

7. How many sides has a polygon if the sum of the angles is 540°?

8. How many sides has a polygon if the sum of the angles is 1620°?

9. How many sides has a polygon in which each angle is 60°?

10. How many sides has a polygon in which each angle is 144°?

11. Find the sum of the exterior angles of a triangle.

12. Find the sum of the exterior angles of a regular *n*-gon.

CLASSIFICATION OF QUADRILATERALS

The most general quadrilateral is irregular in shape. The sum of its interior angles is always 360°. A quadrilateral is classified according to the restrictions placed on its sides and angles.

A **trapezoid** *is a quadrilateral having two, and only two, sides parallel.*

A **parallelogram** *is a quadrilateral that has both pairs of opposite sides parallel.* Either pair of opposite sides may be considered as its bases. It is customary to refer to the side upon which a parallelogram or trapezoid appears to rest as the *lower base* and the opposite side as the *upper base*. The symbol for parallelogram is ▱.

A **rhombus** *is a parallelogram with two adjacent sides equal.*

A **rectangle** *is a parallelogram with one right angle.*

A **square** *is a rectangle with two adjacent sides equal.* See page 187.

The properties of a parallelogram hold for either a rhombus or a rectangle. Do they also apply to a square? Any assumptions and proved conclusions concerning the general parallelogram are equally valid for a rhombus, rectangle, and square.

Angles having such positions as ∠*A* and ∠*B* or ∠*B* and ∠*C* are called *consecutive* or *successive angles.* ∠*A* and ∠*C* are called *opposite angles.*

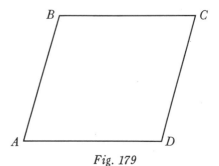

Fig. 179

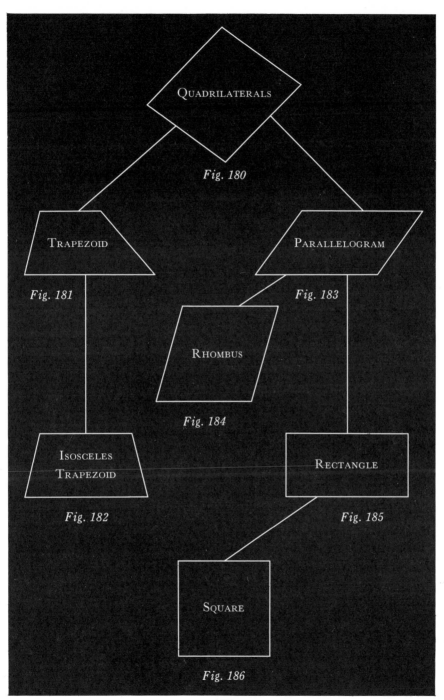

QUADRILATERALS

Fig. 180

TRAPEZOID

PARALLELOGRAM

Fig. 181

Fig. 183

RHOMBUS

Fig. 184

ISOSCELES TRAPEZOID

RECTANGLE

Fig. 182

Fig. 185

SQUARE

Fig. 186

Exercises

1. Illustrate and name two equilateral quadrilaterals.

2. Sketch and name the equiangular quadrilaterals which are not equilateral.

3. Is a square necessarily a rhombus? Is a rhombus a square? Explain how a rhombus and a square differ. What properties do they share?

4. Is a square necessarily a rectangle? Is a rectangle a square? Explain how a rectangle and a square differ. What properties do they share?

5. What properties, if any, may a rhombus and a rectangle have in common? Explain how they differ.

6. Illustrate and name quadrilaterals which are equilateral and also equiangular.

7. Sketch and name the quadrilaterals which are equilateral but are not equiangular.

8. The figure at the right is often called a kite. Write a definition of a kite.

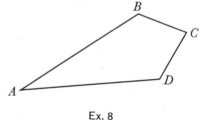

Ex. 8

*In Exercises **9-10**, classify each quadrilateral by naming its nearest class. Give a reason for each classification.*

9.   **10.**

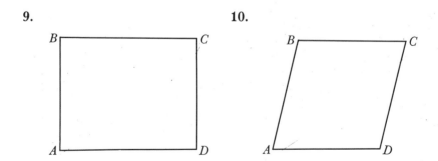

PARALLELOGRAMS

Classify the shape of the windows and doors in your classroom. What is the shape of your book? What is the shape of the chalkboard? All of these are special parallelograms. *A **parallelogram** is a quadrilateral with both pairs of opposite sides parallel.* Notice the front of your school building, how many parallelograms can you identify? Make a list of other examples of parallelograms.

Parallelograms have other special properties which are necessary for a quadrilateral to be a parallelogram. The following lessons discuss these special properties.

Developmental Exercises

DE—1. Prove the following theorem:

THEOREM 29
The opposite sides of a parallelogram are equal.

Solution

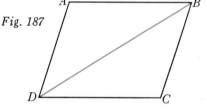
Fig. 187

Given: $AB \parallel DC$,
$AD \parallel BC$.

Prove: $AB = DC$,
$AD = BC$.

Analysis:
To prove lines equal, you may show:
a. they are opposite equal angles of a triangle, or
b. they are corresponding sides of congruent triangles.

By joining points D and B, triangles DBC and ABD can be proved congruent. You can then deduce that $AB = DC$ and $AD = BC$. Write a complete proof.

Corollary 1
The opposite angles of a parallelogram are equal.

Corollary 2
Parallel lines are equidistant at all points.

Corollary 3
The consecutive angles of a parallelogram are supplementary.

DE—2. Given: *ABCD* is a parallelogram,
      DE ∥ *BF*.

Fig. 188

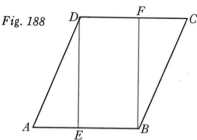

Prove: *DE = BF*.

Solution

STATEMENTS	REASONS
1. *ABCD* is a ▱.	1. Given.
2. *AB* ∥ *CD*, or *BE* ∥ *DF*.	2. Opposite sides of a parallelogram are parallel.
3. *DE* ∥ *BF*.	3. Given.
4. *DEBF* is a ▱.	4. A quadrilateral with its opposite sides parallel is a parallelogram.
5. *DE = BF*.	5. Opposite sides of a parallelogram are equal.

Can you find other ways to prove *DE = BF*?

Exercises

1. Write a formal proof for Theorem 29.

2. Give a general proof for Corollary 1.

3. Give a general proof for Corollary 2.

4. Give a general proof for Corollary 3.

5. If one angle of a parallelogram contains $72°$, how many degrees are there in each of the other angles?

6. Two opposite angles of a parallelogram contain $(3x-7)°$ and $(25-x)°$. How many degrees are there in each angle?

Ex. 7

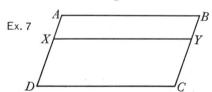

7. Given: *ABCD* is a ▱,
      XY ∥ *AB*.
  Prove: *DX = CY*,
      AX = BY.

8. Prove that perpendiculars to one side of a parallelogram from the opposite vertices are equal.

9. Prove that a line through the midpoint of a diagonal of a parallelogram and ending in a pair of opposite sides, is bisected by the diagonal.

10. In a parallelogram, perpendiculars are constructed to a diagonal from the opposite vertices. Prove the perpendiculars equal.

11. The perimeter of a parallelogram is six times the length of one side and the other side is seven inches longer than this side. What is the perimeter of the parallelogram?

12. The perimeter of a parallelogram is 80 inches and one side is four times as long as the adjacent side. What are the dimensions of the parallelogram?

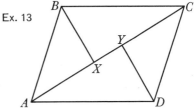

Ex. 13

13. In the diagram at the right, $ABCD$ is a parallelogram, $BX \perp AC$, and $DY \perp AC$.

  Prove: $BX = DY$.

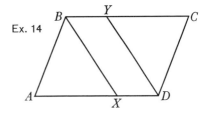

Ex. 14

14. Given: $ABCD$ is a $\square$,
    BX bisects $\angle B$,
    DY bisects $\angle D$.

  Prove: $BX = DY$.

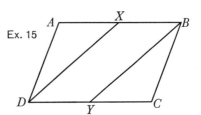

Ex. 15

15. Given: $ABCD$ is a $\square$,
    X the midpoint of AB,
    Y the midpoint of CD.

  Prove: $DX = BY$.

16. Prove that a diagonal that bisects one angle of a parallelogram also bisects the other angle.

DE—3. Prove the following theorem:

‖**THEOREM 30**
‖**The diagonals of a parallelogram bisect each other.**

Solution

Given: *ABCD* is a ☐.

Prove: *AO = OC,*
BO = DO.

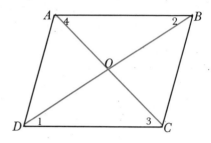

Fig. 189

Analysis:
AO = OC and *BO = DO* if △*ABO* ≅ △*DOC.*
△*ABO* ≅ △*DOC* if *AB = DC,* ∠1 = ∠2, and ∠3 = ∠4.

Proof:

STATEMENTS	REASONS
1. *ABCD* is a ☐.	1. Given.
2. *AB ‖ DC.*	2. The opposite sides of a parallelogram are parallel.
3. ∠1 = ∠2, ∠3 = ∠4.	3. If parallel lines are cut by a transversal, the alternate-interior angles are equal.
4. *AB = DC.*	4. The opposite sides of a parallelogram are equal.
5. △*DOC* ≅ △*AOB.*	5. **a.s.a. = a.s.a.** (Statements 3 and 4)
6. *DO = OB,* *AO = OC.*	6. Corresponding parts of congruent triangles are equal.

Exercises

1. Prove that the four triangles formed by the diagonals of a rhombus are congruent.

2. Prove that the diagonals of a rhombus are perpendicular.

3. Prove that the diagonals of a rhombus bisect its angles.

4. Draw a parallelogram and its diagonals. Join the midpoints of two opposite sides. Outline a plan to prove that such a line bisects each diagonal.

5. Show that any line through the point of intersection of the diagonals of a parallelogram, ending in the opposite sides, is bisected.

6. Join, in succession, the midpoints of the four segments of the diagonals of a parallelogram. Prove another parallelogram is thus formed.

7. Construct a parallelogram by making the diagonals bisect each other. Leave all construction lines on your paper.

8. Construct a parallelogram, $ABCD$, with $\angle B$, AB, and AC given. First take $\angle B$, an acute angle, and AB greater than AC. Then take $\angle B$, an obtuse angle, and AB less than AC. Explain why three solutions to this problem are possible.

DE—4. Prove the following theorem:

> **THEOREM 31**
>
> **If the opposite sides of a quadrilateral are equal, the quadrilateral is a parallelogram.**

Solution

    Given: Quadrilateral $ABCD$,
               $AB = CD$,
               $AD = BC$.

    Prove: $AB \parallel CD$,
             $AD \parallel BC$.

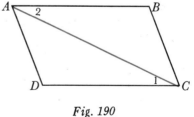

Fig. 190

Analysis:

Two lines are parallel if the alternate-interior angles or the corresponding angles, formed by a transversal, are equal. Thus, it is necessary to construct a transversal. Construct diagonal AC. $DC \parallel AB$ if $\angle 1 = \angle 2$. $\angle 1 = \angle 2$ if $\triangle ADC \cong \triangle ABC$. $\triangle ADC \cong \triangle ABC$ if the sides of one are equal respectively to the sides of the other, **s.s.s. = s.s.s.** Does $AD = BC$? Why? Does $AB = CD$? Why? Does $AC = AC$? Why? In like manner, AD and BC may be proved parallel.

The formal proof is left to the student.

DE—5. Prove the following theorem:

┃**THEOREM 32**

┃**If two sides of a quadrilateral are both equal and parallel, the quadrilateral is a parallelogram.**

Solution

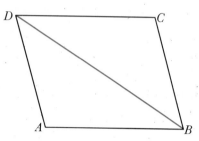

Fig. 191

Given: Quadrilateral *ABCD*,
   AB = *CD*,
   AB ‖ *CD*.

Prove: *ABCD* is a □.

Analysis:

YOU WOULD KNOW:	IF YOU KNEW:
1. *ABCD* is a □.	1. *AB* = *DC* and *AD* = *BC*.
2. *AB* = *CD*.	2. Given.
3. *AD* = *BC*.	3. △*ABD* ≅ △*BDC*.
4. △*ABD* ≅ △*BDC*.	4. *BD* = *BD* (Identity).
	AB = *DC* (Given).
	∠*ABD* = ∠*CDB*.
5. ∠*ABD* = ∠*CDB*.	5. *AB* ‖ *DC*.
6. *AB* ‖ *DC*.	6. Given.

Proof:

STATEMENTS	REASONS
1. *AB* ‖ *CD*.	1. Given.
2. ∠*ABD* = ∠*BDC*.	2. If parallel lines are cut by a transversal, the alternate-interior angles formed are equal.
3. *AB* = *CD*.	3. Given.
4. *DB* = *DB*.	4. Identity.
5. △*DAB* ≅ △*DBC*.	5. **s.a.s.** = **s.a.s.**
6. *AD* = *BC*.	6. Corresponding parts of congruent triangles are equal.
7. *ABCD* is a □.	7. If the opposite sides of a quadrilateral are equal, the quadrilateral is a parallelogram.

Exercises

1. Write the proof for Theorem 31.

2. **Given:** $MNOP$ is a $\square$,
   $NX = PY$.

   Ex. 2

   Prove: $MXOY$ is a $\square$.

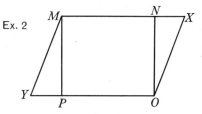

3. Prove that the quadrilateral formed by joining the midpoints of the adjacent sides of a parallelogram is a parallelogram.

4. **Given:** $ABCD$ is a $\square$,
   $DE = BF$.

   Ex. 4

   Prove: $AECF$ is a $\square$.

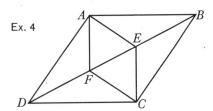

5. Prove that if the opposite sides of a hexagon (six-sided polygon) are parallel and two opposite sides are equal, the other opposite sides are equal.

6. Prove that if two sides of a quadrilateral are parallel, and a pair of opposite angles are equal, the figure is a parallelogram.

7. **Given:** $ABCD$ is a $\square$.
   X and Y are mid-
   points.

   Prove: $AXCY$ is a $\square$.

   Ex. 7

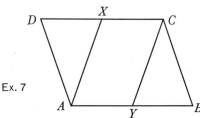

Ex. 8

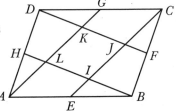

8. **Given:** $ABCD$ is a $\square$,
   $E, F, G,$ and H are
   midpoints.

   Prove: $IJKL$ is a $\square$.

DE—6. Prove the following theorem:

> **THEOREM 33**
>
> **If the diagonals of a quadrilateral bisect each other, the quadrilateral is a parallelogram.**

Solution

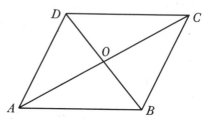

Fig. 192

Given: Quadrilateral *ABCD*,
  Diagonals *AC* and *BD*,
  $DO = OB$,
  $AO = OC$.

Prove: *ABCD* is a □.

Analysis:

ABCD is a parallelogram if:

    a. two sides are equal and parallel,

    b. the opposite sides are equal, or

    c. the opposite sides are parallel.

$DC = AB$ if $\triangle DOC \cong \triangle AOB$.

$DC \parallel AB$ if $\angle BAO = \angle DCO$.

$\angle BAO = \angle DCO$ if $\triangle DOC \cong \triangle AOB$.

$\triangle DOC \cong \triangle AOB$ if $OC = AO$ (s). Given.

$\angle AOB = \angle DOC$ (a).

$OD = BO$(s). Given.

$\angle AOB = \angle DOC$ if they are vertical angles.

Proof:

STATEMENTS	REASONS
1. $DO = OB$, $AO = OC$.	1. Given.
2. $\angle AOB = \angle DOC$.	2. Why?
3. $\triangle AOB \cong \triangle DOC$.	3. If two triangles have two sides and the included angle of one equal respectively to two sides and the included angle of the other, the triangles are congruent.
4. $DC = AB$, $\angle DOC = \angle AOB$.	4. Corresponding parts of congruent triangles are equal.
5. $DC \parallel AB$.	5. Why?
6. *ABCD* is a □.	6. Why?

Exercises

1. Complete the proof for Theorem 33.

2. Given: $ABCD$ is a $\square$,
        $BE = DF$.

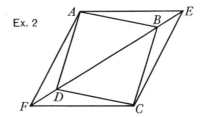

Ex. 2

Prove: $AFCE$ is a $\square$.

3. The median of a triangle is extended its own length through the side to which it is drawn. The end of this extended segment is then joined to the ends of the side. Prove that the figure thus formed is a parallelogram.

4. Prove that if the midpoints of the four halves of the diagonals of a parallelogram are joined in order, another parallelogram will be formed.

5. Construct a parallelogram given one side and the two diagonals.

6. If a quadrilateral has one pair of opposite sides parallel and one diagonal bisected by the other diagonal, the quadrilateral is a parallelogram. Is the above statement valid? If so, prove it. If not, point out reasons for such a decision.

7. Given: $ABCD$ is a $\square$,
        $DP = BQ$.

Prove: $APCQ$ is a $\square$.

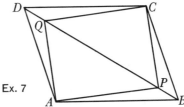

Ex. 7

8. Given: $AC = BD$,
        $DY = XC$,
        $DY \parallel XC$.

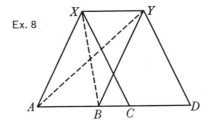

Ex. 8

Prove: $ABYX$ is a $\square$.

DE—7. Prove the following theorem:

> **THEOREM 34**
>
> **If the opposite angles of a quadrilateral are equal, the quadrilateral is a parallelogram.**

Solution

Given: $\angle A = \angle C$,
   $\angle B = \angle D$.

Prove: *ABCD* is a ▱.

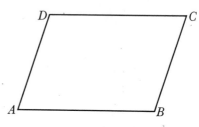

Fig. 193

Analysis:

ABCD is a parallelogram if $AD \parallel BC$ and $AB \parallel CD$.

$AD \parallel BC$ and $AB \parallel CD$ if the interior angles on the same side of the transversal are supplementary.

$\angle D + \angle C = 180°$ if $\angle A + \angle B + \angle C + \angle D = 360°$, $\angle A = \angle C$, and $\angle B = \angle D$.

$\angle A = \angle C$ and $\angle B = \angle D$ is Given.

Why does $\angle A + \angle B + \angle C + \angle D = 360°$?

In like manner it may be shown that $AB \parallel CD$.

Proof:

STATEMENTS	REASONS
1. $\angle A = \angle C$, $\angle B = \angle D$.	1. Given.
2. $\angle A + \angle B + \angle C + \angle D =$ 2(180°) or 360°.	2. The sum of the interior angles of a convex polygon of n sides is $(n-2)180°$.
3. $\angle A + \angle B + \angle A + \angle B = 360°$.	3. A quantity may be substituted for its equal.
4. $\angle A + \angle B = 180°$.	4. If equals are divided by equals, the quotients are equal.
5. $AD \parallel BC$.	5. Why?
6. $AB \parallel CD$.	6. Proof similar to steps 1-5. It is left to you.
7. *ABCD* is a ▱.	7. A quadrilateral that has both pairs of opposite sides parallel is a parallelogram.

DE—8. Prove the following theorem:

> **THEOREM 35**
>
> **If the consecutive angles of a quadrilateral are supplementary, the quadrilateral is a parallelogram.**

Solution

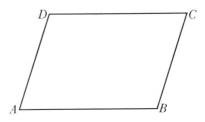

Given: $\angle A + \angle B = 180°$,
$\angle B + \angle C = 180°$,
$\angle C + \angle D = 180°$,
$\angle D + \angle A = 180°$.

Prove: $ABCD$ is a $\square$.

Fig. 194

Analysis:

$ABCD$ is a parallelogram if $\angle A = \angle C$ and $\angle B = \angle D$.
$\angle A = \angle C$ if $\angle A = 180° - \angle B$ and $\angle C = 180° - \angle B$.
$\angle B = \angle D$ if $\angle B = 180° - \angle C$ and $\angle D = 180° - \angle C$.

Complete the proof.

Exercises

1. Given: Quadrilateral $ABCD$,
$\angle EDA = 77°$,
$\angle FCB = 103°$,
$\angle ABC = 103°$.
Prove: $ABCD$ is a $\square$.

Ex. 1

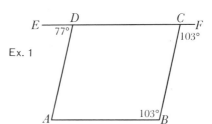

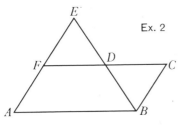

Ex. 2

2. Given: F and D are midpoints of AE and BE respectively.
$DC = DF$.
Prove: $ABCF$ is a $\square$.

3. Given: $AD \parallel BC$,
$\angle B + \angle C = 180°$.
Prove: $ABCD$ is a $\square$.

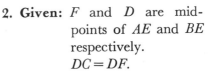

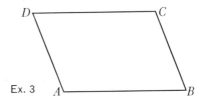

Ex. 3

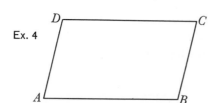

Ex. 4

4. Given: $\angle C = 77°48' = \angle A$,
$\angle B = 5x° + 13°42'$,
$\angle D = 6x° - 4°$.
Prove: $ABCD$ is a $\square$.

5. Prove that a rhombus is formed when lines are drawn to join the midpoint of the base of an isosceles triangle to the midpoints of the equal sides.

6. Given: ADE is an equilateral $\triangle$,
CFB is an equilateral $\triangle$,
$ABCD$ is a square.
Prove: $BFDE$ is a $\square$.

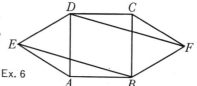

Ex. 6

NECESSARY AND SUFFICIENT CONDITIONS

All of the theorems that have been proved for parallelograms are true for rectangles, squares, and rhombuses. If a polygon is a square this is sufficient for it to be a parallelogram though not necessary. What is the difference between *necessary* conditions and *sufficient* conditions? To pass a course in geometry, it is *necessary* to do the homework but it is not *sufficient*. A person must generally also pass the tests and take part in the class discussion. A necessary condition for a parallelogram to be a rectangle is for the parallelogram to have one right angle. This is also a sufficient condition since this is the only requirement for the parallelogram to be a rectangle.

‖ Developmental Exercises

DE—1. In the statement "if the street is icy, it is slippery" determine if the condition is necessary and/or sufficient.

Solution

"If a street is icy, it is slippery" is a valid statement. Since the conclusion can be deduced from the condition, the condition is sufficient for the conclusion.

‖ **The condition is sufficient for the conclusion if the statement is valid.**

On the other hand "if the street is slippery, it is icy" is not necessarily valid. Some streets are slippery when wet. Thus, the condition is not necessary for the conclusion. Notice that to judge whether the condition was necessary for the conclusion the validity of the converse of the original statement was determined.

A condition is necessary for a conclusion if the converse of the statement is valid.

DE—2. Determine if the condition for the following statement is necessary and/or sufficient. If a quadrilateral has a pair of parallel sides it is a parallelogram.

Solution

This statement is not valid because the quadrilateral may be a trapezoid. Thus, the condition is not sufficient.

The converse of the statement, "if a quadrilateral is a parallelogram it has a pair of parallel sides," is valid. Therefore, the condition is necessary.

DE—3. Determine if the condition for the following statement is necessary and/or sufficient. If a parallelogram has a pair of equal adjacent sides it is a rhombus.

Solution

This statement is valid, therefore, the condition is sufficient. The converse "if a parallelogram is a rhombus it has a pair of adjacent sides equal" is also valid. Therefore, the condition is necessary.

Since the condition is necessary and sufficient, that is, the statement and its converse are both valid, it may be stated, "a parallelogram is a rhombus if, and only if, it has a pair of adjacent sides equal."

Exercises

Decide whether the conditions in each of the following statements are necessary, sufficient, or necessary and sufficient.

1. If a person drives in excess of the speed limit he will lose his driver's license.

2. One may lose weight by not eating for 40 days.

3. If $x = 4$, then $x = 4$.

4. If $x + 2 = 6$, then $x = 4$.

5. If the opposite sides of a quadrilateral are equal, the quadrilateral is a parallelogram.

6. If three angles of a quadrilateral are equal, the quadrilateral is a parallelogram.

7. If the base angles of a triangle are equal, the triangle is isosceles.

8. If a point is on the bisector of a given line, it is equidistant from the endpoints of that line.

9. If the angles of a triangle are equal, the triangle is equilateral.

10. Write all the statements of Exercises **1-9** with valid necessary and sufficient conditions in "if and only if" form.

PROPERTIES OF THE RECTANGLE

A *rectangle* is a parallelogram with one right angle. It has all the properties that are possessed by a parallelogram. The opposite angles are equal; the opposite sides are equal and parallel; the consecutive angles are supplementary; and the diagonals bisect each other. Because the rectangle is a special parallelogram it has additional properties not possessed by all parallelograms.

Rectangles may add interest and variety to architecture and room decoration as illustrated by this expansive pool-side deck.

Developmental Exercises

DE—1. Given: *ABCD* is a rectangle.

Prove: $\angle A = \angle B = \angle D = 90°$.

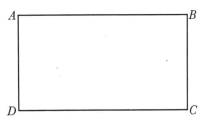

Fig. 195

Solution

Analysis:

Each angle is equal to 90° if the angles are equal. (One angle is 90° by definition.)

$\angle D = \angle B$ and $\angle A = \angle C$ if they are opposite angles of a parallelogram. Are they?

$\angle D + \angle A = 180°$ if they are consecutive angles of a parallelogram. Are they?

$\angle D = 90°$ if $\angle A = 90°$.

Since one angle is 90° (by definition) and $\angle A$ could be any vertex, $\angle A = 90°$. How many degrees are in $\angle B$? $\angle C$? $\angle D$?

Proof:

STATEMENTS	REASONS
1. *ABCD* is a rectangle.	1. Given.
2. $\angle A$ (or any other vertex angle) $= 90°$.	2. A rectangle is a parallelogram with one right angle.
3. $\angle C = \angle A$.	3. Opposite angles in a parallelogram are equal.
4. $\angle C = 90°$.	4. Quantities equal to the same quantity are equal.
5. $\angle D + \angle A = 180°$.	5. Consecutive angles of a parallelogram are supplementary.
6. $\angle D = 90°$.	6. If equals are subtracted from equals, the differences are equal.
7. $\angle D = \angle B$.	7. Reason 3.
8. $\angle B = 90°$.	8. Reason 4.

Thus, the following has been proved.

THEOREM 36

Each angle of a rectangle is a right angle.

DE—2. Given: Rectangle *ABCD*.

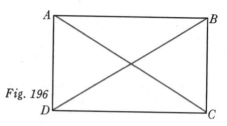

Fig. 196

      Prove: $DB = AC$.

Solution
    Analysis:
    $DB = AC$ if they are corresponding parts of congruent triangles.
    $\triangle ADC \cong \triangle DBC$ if **s.a.s. = s.a.s.**
    Proof:

STATEMENTS	REASONS
1. *ABCD* is a rectangle.	1. Given.
2. $\angle D = 90°$, $\angle C = 90°$.	2. Each angle of a rectangle is a right angle.
3. $\angle D = \angle C$.	3. All right angles are equal.
4. $AD = BC$, $DC = AB$.	4. The opposite sides of a parallelogram are equal.
5. $\triangle ADC \cong \triangle BCD$.	5. **s.a.s. = s.a.s.**
6. $AC = DB$.	6. Corresponding parts of congruent triangles are equal.

Thus, the following theorem has been proved.

║THEOREM 37
║The diagonals of a rectangle are equal.

Exercises

1. Prove Developmental Exercise **1**, assuming $\angle C = 90°$.

2. Prove Developmental Exercise **2**, using triangles *ABD* and *ABC*.

3. Given: *ABCD* a rectangle, $DE = FC$.
    Prove: $AF = BE$.

Ex. 3

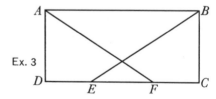

Ex. 4

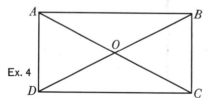

4. Given: *ABCD* a rectangle.
    Prove: $DO = CO$.

5. The diagonals of a certain rectangle intersect to form a 60° angle. State a relationship between the length of the diagonal and one of the shorter sides. Prove that relationship.

6. Prove that the bisectors of the angles of a parallelogram form a rectangle.

7. Given: $ABCD$ a $\square$,
       Diagonals $BD = AC$.

  Prove: $ABCD$ is a rectangle.

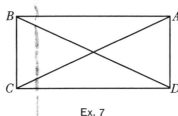

Ex. 7

8. Given: $ABCD$ a rectangle.

  Prove: $\triangle BCD \cong \triangle BAD$.

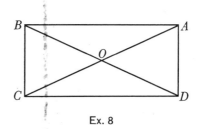

Ex. 8

9. Using the diagram and information in Exercise **8,** prove $DO = OB$ and $AO = OC$.

10. Given: $ABCD$ a rectangle,
       $\angle ADF = \angle CBE$.

  Prove: $FBED$ is a $\square$.

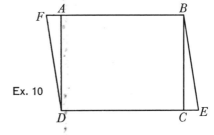

Ex. 10

SUFFICIENT CONDITIONS FOR A RECTANGLE

To prove that a parallelogram is a rectangle it is sufficient to show that the parallelogram has one right angle. This condition is based on the definition of a rectangle. There are other conditions sufficient to prove that a parallelogram is a rectangle. Study the developmental exercises below for the proofs of these conditions.

Developmental Exercises

DE—1. Given: Quadrilateral *ABCD*,
   $\angle A = \angle B = \angle C = \angle D$.

Prove: *ABCD* is a rectangle.

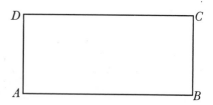

Fig. 197

Solution

Analysis:

You would know:	If you knew:
1. *ABCD* is a rectangle.	1. *ABCD* is a parallelogram with one right angle.
2. *ABCD* is a parallelogram.	2. $\angle A = \angle B = \angle C = \angle D$.
3. $\angle A = \angle B = \angle C = \angle D$.	3. Given.
4. $\angle A$(or any vertex angle) is a right angle.	4. $\angle A + \angle B + \angle C + \angle D = 360°$.
5. $\angle A + \angle B + \angle C + \angle D = 360°$.	5. The sum of the interior angles of a convex polygon of *n* sides is $(n-2)180°$. Theorem 28. $n = 4$.
6. $n = 4$.	6. If *ABCD* is a quadrilateral.
7. *ABCD* is a quadrilateral.	7. Given.

Proof:

Statements	Reasons
1. *ABCD* is a quadrilateral, $\angle A = \angle C$, $\angle B = \angle D$.	1. Given.
2. *ABCD* is a $\square$.	2. If the opposite angles of a quadrilateral are equal, the quadrilateral is a parallelogram.
3. $\angle A = \angle B = \angle C = \angle D$.	3. Given.
4. $\angle A + \angle B + \angle C + \angle D = 360°$.	4. Why?
5. $4\angle A = 360°$.	5. Why?
6. $\angle A = 90°$.	6. Why?
7. *ABCD* is a rectangle.	7. Why?

Thus, the following theorem has been proved:

THEOREM 38

If the angles of a quadrilateral are equal, the quadrilateral is a rectangle.

DE—2. Given: *ABCD* is a ▱,
AC = BD.

Prove: *ABCD* is a rectangle.

Fig. 198

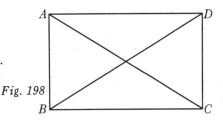

Solution

STATEMENTS	REASONS
1. *ABCD* is a ▱. AC = BD.	1. Given.
2. AB = DC.	2. The opposite sides of a parallelogram are equal.
3. BC = BC.	3. Identity.
4. △CBA ≅ △CBD.	4. s.s.s. = s.s.s.
5. ∠CBA = ∠BCD.	5. Corresponding parts of congruent triangles are equal.
6. ∠CBA + ∠BCD = 180°.	6. The consecutive angles of a parallelogram are supplementary.
7. 2∠BCD = 180°.	7. A quantity may be substituted for its equal.
8. ∠BCD = 90°.	8. If equals are divided by equals, the quotients are equal.
9. *ABCD* is a rectangle.	9. If a parallelogram contains one right angle it is a rectangle.

Thus, the following theorem has been proved.

THEOREM 39
If a parallelogram has equal diagonals, it is a rectangle.

Exercises

1. Draw a general rectangle. Bisect each angle. Prove the bisectors form a square.

2. Draw a transversal intersecting two parallel lines. Draw lines which bisect the four interior angles. Prove these lines form a rectangle.

3. Given a quadrilateral with three right angles, prove that the figure formed is a rectangle.

4. Given a parallelogram with two opposite angles supplementary, prove the parallelogram is a rectangle.

5. Given two line segments unequal in length, use one line segment as a diagonal to construct a rectangle. Use the other given line segment as a side of the rectangle.

6. Construct a rectangle with a line segment and an angle given. Use the given line segment as a diagonal and the given angle as an angle between the diagonals of the rectangle.

PROPERTIES OF THE RHOMBUS

A rhombus is a parallelogram with two equal adjacent sides. Since it is a parallelogram, it has all the properties of a parallelogram. However, a rhombus also has additional properties. Study the properties in the developmental exercises.

Developmental Exercises

DE—1. Prove the following theorem:

THEOREM 40

A rhombus is equilateral.

Solution

Given: Rhombus *ABCD*.

Prove: $AB = BC = CD = DA$.

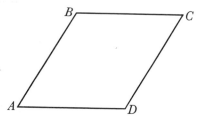

Fig. 199

Proof:

STATEMENTS	REASONS
1. $AB = AD$, $ABCD$ is a $\square$.	1. A rhombus is a parallelogram with two equal adjacent sides.
2. $AB = CD$, $AD = BC$.	2. The opposite sides of a parallelogram are equal.
3. $AB = AD = BC = CD$.	3. Quantities equal to the same or equal quantities are equal.

DE—2. Prove the following theorem:

> **THEOREM 41**
> **The diagonals of a rhombus are perpendicular.**

Solution

Given: Rhombus *ABCD*.
Prove: $AC \perp DB$.

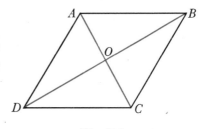

Fig. 200

Analysis:

$AC \perp DB$ if AC is the perpendicular bisector of DB. Using the Two-Point Theorem, if $AD = AB$ and $OD = OB$, $AC \perp DB$. $AD = AB$ if $ABCD$ is a rhombus. $OD = OB$ if the diagonals of a parallelogram bisect each other. Do the diagonals of a parallelogram bisect each other?

Now write a proof for this theorem.

DE—3. Prove the following theorem:

> **THEOREM 42**
> **The diagonals of a rhombus bisect the angles.**

Solution

Given: Rhombus *ABCD*.

Prove: $\angle 1 = \angle 2$,
$\angle 3 = \angle 4$,
$\angle 5 = \angle 6$,
$\angle 7 = \angle 8$.

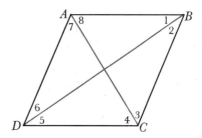

Fig. 201

Analysis:

$\angle 1 = \angle 2$ and $\angle 5 = \angle 6$ if $\triangle BAD \cong \triangle BCD$.
$\triangle BAD \cong \triangle BCD$ if $AD = DC$, $AB = BC$, and $DB = DB$.
Likewise: $\angle 3 = \angle 4$ and $\angle 7 = \angle 8$ if $\triangle ABC \cong \triangle ADC$.
$\triangle ABC \cong \triangle ADC$ if $AB = AD$, $BC = DC$, and $AC = AC$.
Now write a formal proof for this theorem.

Exercises

1. Write a formal proof for Theorem 41 using the method described in Developmental Exercise **2.**

2. Give a proof for Theorem 41 other than the one described in Developmental Exercise **2.** Hint: Use congruent triangles.

3. Using the method outlined in Developmental Exercise **3,** write a complete formal proof for Theorem 42.

4. State the properties of a rhombus.

5. Given: Rhombus *ABCD*,
         E the midpoint of *AF*,
         G the midpoint of *FC*.

     Prove: *EH = GH*.

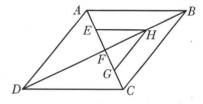

Ex. 5

6. Prove that the line segments joining the midpoints of the adjacent sides of a rhombus form a rectangle.

7. If one angle of a rhombus is 50 degrees, find the size of each angle in the triangles formed by the diagonals and the sides of the rhombus.

8. If a diagonal of a rhombus is equal to a side of the rhombus, find the number of degrees in each angle.

9. One angle of a rhombus is given as 120 degrees. The shorter diagonal is 9 inches. Find the length of one side.

10. Construct a rhombus whose sides are $2\frac{1}{2}$ inches long and whose acute angles are each 60 degrees.

11. In rhombus *ABCD* the number of degrees in $\angle A$ is 18° more than 5 times the number of degrees in $\angle B$. Find the number of degrees in each angle of the rhombus.

12. The sum of the lengths of the diagonals of a rhombus is $4\frac{1}{2}$ inches. The length of one of the diagonals is twice the length of the other. Construct the rhombus.

SUFFICIENT CONDITIONS FOR A RHOMBUS

If a quadrilateral is a parallelogram with a pair of equal adjacent sides, it is a rhombus. There are other conditions which can be proved sufficient for a quadrilateral to be a rhombus. Study the theorems below for these conditions.

Developmental Exercises

DE—1. Prove the following theorem:

THEOREM 43

If a quadrilateral is equilateral, it is a rhombus.

Solution

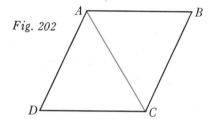

Fig. 202

Given: Quadrilateral *ABCD*,
$AB = BC = CD = AD$.

Prove: *ABCD* is a rhombus.

Analysis:

The definition of a rhombus requires that *ABCD* be a parallelogram and that any two adjacent sides are equal.

The data given includes the equal adjacent sides. It remains to be demonstrated that *ABCD* is a parallelogram. By joining *A* to *C*, you can find $AB \parallel DC$. One pair of sides will then be equal and parallel.

Now write a formal proof for this theorem.

DE—2. Prove the following theorem:

THEOREM 44

If the diagonals of a parallelogram are perpendicular, the parallelogram is a rhombus.

Solution

Given: *ABCD* is a ▱,
$AC \perp BD$.

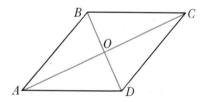

Prove: *ABCD* is a rhombus.

Fig. 203

Analysis:
ABCD is a rhombus if it is a parallelogram with two equal adjacent sides. *ABCD* is given as a parallelogram so it remains to be shown that $AB = AD$. This will be proved if $\triangle AOB \cong \triangle AOD$. $\triangle AOB \cong \triangle AOD$ by **s.a.s. = s.a.s.** if $AO = AO$, $\angle BOA = \angle AOD$, and $BO = OD$.

Now write a formal proof for this theorem.

Exercises

1. Write a formal proof for Theorem 43.

2. Write a formal proof for Theorem 44.

3. Write an analysis and formal proof for the following:

> **THEOREM 45**
> **If the diagonals of a parallelogram bisect its angles, the parallelogram is a rhombus.**

4. Given: Rhombus *ABCD* with $\angle A$ being 30° more than twice $\angle B$, find the number of degrees in each angle.

5. Given: Two unequal line segments, use them as diagonals to construct a rhombus.

6. Given: The sides of a rhombus measure $2\frac{1}{2}''$. Each acute angle of the rhombus equals 60°. Construct the rhombus.

7. From the point where the bisector of an angle in a triangle meets the opposite side, lines parallel to the other sides of the triangle are drawn. Prove that a rhombus is formed.

8. Given: The perimeter and one diagonal of a rhombus, construct the figure.

9. By joining the midpoint of the base of an isosceles triangle to the midpoints of the sides, a quadrilateral is formed. Name the quadrilateral. Prove that your classification is correct.

10. Given: *ABCD* is a rectangle. *X*, *Y*, *Z*, and *W* are midpoints.
Prove: *XYZW* is a rhombus.

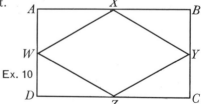
Ex. 10

THE SQUARE

A *square* is a rectangle with two equal adjacent sides. It has all the properties of the rectangle and the rhombus. Additional properties can be proved for the square. These properties are given in the developmental exercises.

‖Developmental Exercises

DE—1. Prove the following theorem:

‖THEOREM 46

‖A square is equilateral.

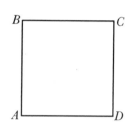

Fig. 204

Solution

Given: *ABCD* is a square.
Prove: $AB = BC = CD = DA$.
Proof:

STATEMENTS	REASONS
1. $AB = BC$.	1. A square is a rectangle with two equal adjacent sides.
2. $ABCD$ is a $\square$.	2. Statement 1 and the definition of a rectangle.
3. $AB = CD$, $BC = AD$.	3. The opposite sides of a parallelogram are equal.
4. $AB = BC = CD = DA$.	4. Quantities equal to the same or equal quantities are equal.

DE—2. Prove the following theorem:

‖THEOREM 47

‖The diagonals of a square are perpendicular.

Solution

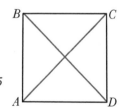

Given: *ABCD* is a square.
Prove: $AC \perp BD$.

Fig. 205

Analysis:
$AC \perp BD$ if *ABCD* is a rhombus. *ABCD* is a rhombus if any two adjacent sides are equal. Since *ABCD* is a square, are the adjacent sides equal?
The written proof is left for you.

DE—3. Prove the following theorem:

║**THEOREM 48**
║**The diagonals of a square bisect the angles.**

Solution

Given: *ABCD* is a square.

Prove: *AC* bisects ∠*DAB* and
∠*BCD*,
DB bisects ∠*ABC* and
∠*CDA*.

Fig. 206

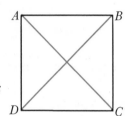

Analysis:

The diagonals bisect the angles if *ABCD* is a rhombus.
The written proof that *ABCD* is a rhombus is left to you.

Exercises

1. Write a formal proof for Theorem 47.

2. Write a formal proof for Theorem 48.

3. Draw a square with its diagonals. List as many facts as you can about the various lines and angles in the diagram.

4. Given: Square *ABCD*,
$EF = AF$,
$GH = HC$,
$AF = HC$.
Prove: $AE = GC$.

Ex. 4

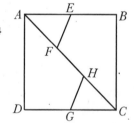

Ex. 5

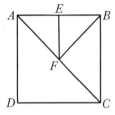

5. Given: Square *ABCD*,
$EF \perp AB$,
$AE = EB$.
Prove: $AF = BF = FC$.

6. Prove that in a rectangle that is not a square, the bisectors of the angles form a square.

7. Construct a square, given a line segment as its perimeter.

8. Construct a square, given a line segment as its diagonal.

SUFFICIENT CONDITIONS FOR A SQUARE

You have observed that the converse of certain theorems are valid. The following converses are valid and are frequently used.

Developmental Exercises

DE—1. Prove the following theorem:

> **THEOREM 49**
>
> **If the diagonals of a rectangle are perpendicular, the rectangle is a square.**

Solution

> **Given:** *ABCD* is a rectangle,
> *AC* ⊥ *BD*.

> **Prove:** *ABCD* is a square.

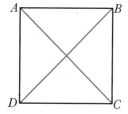

Fig. 207

Analysis:

You need only to prove that the sides are equal. *AB* = *BC* because any point on the perpendicular bisector of a line segment is equidistant from the ends of the line segment.

DE—2. Prove the following theorem:

> **THEOREM 50**
>
> **If the diagonals of a rhombus are equal, the rhombus is a square.**

Solution

> **Given:** *ABCD* is a rhombus,
> *AC* = *BD*.

> **Prove:** *ABCD* is a square.

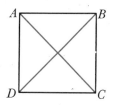

Fig. 208

Analysis:

You need only to prove that consecutive angles are equal. ∠*DAB* = ∠*CBA* because they are corresponding angles of congruent triangles.

Exercises

1. Write a formal proof for Developmental Exercises **1** and **2**.

2. Write an analysis and formal proof for the following:

┃ **THEOREM 51**
┃ **If an angle of a rhombus is 90°, the rhombus is a square.**

3. State the conditions required for a rhombus to be classified a square.

4. State the conditions required for a rectangle to be classified a square.

5. Create a design which uses squares of different sizes.

6. Construct a square given its diagonal. Show that the construction is valid.

7. Construct a square given its perimeter. Show that the construction is valid.

8. Draw a right triangle. Extend the hypotenuse in both directions. Now bisect the exterior angles formed by the hypotenuse and sides of the right angle. Label the point of intersection of the bisectors P. Extend the sides of the right angle. From P, draw two perpendicular lines to the extended sides of the right angle. Prove the perpendiculars form a square with the sides of the right angle.

9. Prove: In a rectangle which is not a square, the bisectors of the angles form a square.

10. Draw a square, $ABCD$. On the sides of $ABCD$ locate points E, F, G, and H, so that $AH = BE = CF = GD$. Connect points E, F, G, and H to form a quadrilateral. Prove $EFGH$ is a square.

USING PARALLELOGRAMS IN PROOFS

In a proof you may use any theorem that has been previously proved. Notice in the developmental exercises how established theorems on parallelograms are used to prove new theorems.

Developmental Exercises

DE—1. Given: $a \parallel b \parallel c \parallel d$
intersecting t and t',
$LM = MN = NO$.

Prove: $ST = TV = VW$.

Fig. 209

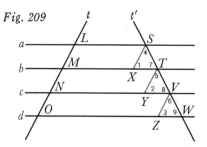

Construction: Through S, T, V, and W draw lines parallel to t.

Solution

STATEMENTS	REASONS
1. $a \parallel b \parallel c \parallel d$, $LM = MN = NO$.	1. Given.
2. $SX \parallel t$, $TY \parallel t$, $VZ \parallel t$.	2. Through a point not on a given line a line can be drawn parallel to the given line.
3. $LMXZ$ is a $\square$, $MNYT$ is a $\square$, $NOZV$ is a $\square$.	3. A quadrilateral having opposite sides parallel is a parallelogram.
4. $SX = LM$, $TY = MN$, $VZ = NO$.	4. The opposite sides of a parallelogram are equal.
5. $XS = YT = VZ$.	5. Quantities equal to the same or equal quantities are equal.
6. $SX \parallel TY \parallel VZ$.	6. Lines parallel to the same line are parallel.
7. $\angle 4 = \angle 5 = \angle 6$, $\angle 7 = \angle 8 = \angle 9$.	7. If parallel lines are cut by a transversal the corresponding angles are equal.
8. $\triangle SXT \cong \triangle TYV \cong \triangle VZW$.	8. **a.a.s. = a.a.s.**
9. $ST = TV = VW$.	9. Why?

Thus, it has been proved that:

THEOREM 52

If three or more parallel lines intercept equal segments on one transversal, they cut off equal segments on any transversal.

Corollary

A line bisecting one side of a triangle and parallel to a second side bisects the third side of the triangle.

DE—2. Divide a line segment into three equal parts.

Solution
- Draw a line and label it *AB*.
- At *A*, draw a line, *AC*, in any direction.
- With your compass lay off 3 equal lengths on *AC*. Any convenient length may be used.

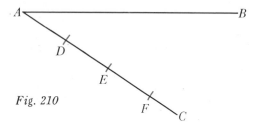

Fig. 210

- Connect points *B* and *F*. At *C* and *D*, construct lines parallel to *BF* by constructing equal corresponding angles.

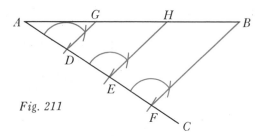

Fig. 211

Notice that transversal *AC* is divided into equal segments by the parallel lines. Therefore, any other transversal, *AB*, is also divided into equal segments by the parallel lines, Theorem 52.

Exercises

1. Prove the corollary using the diagram at the right.

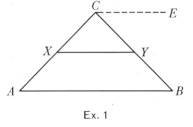

Ex. 1

2. Divide a given line segment into 7 equal parts.

3. Construct three-fifths of a line segment.

4. Construct a square whose perimeter is equal in length to a given line segment.

5. Illustrate and prove: In a right triangle, the perpendicular bisector of a leg also bisects the hypotenuse.

6. Draw a triangle. Prove that the line joining the midpoints of the two sides of the triangle bisects any line segment to the third side from the opposite vertex.

7. Draw an equilateral triangle. Trisect one side and join the two points of division to the opposite vertex. How many congruent triangles are thus formed? Why are they congruent?

8. If a line segment cuts off one-third of a side of a triangle and is parallel to a second side of the triangle, prove that it divides the third side into segments which have a 1 : 2 ratio.

DE—3. Prove the following theorem:

> ‖ **THEOREM 53**
>
> ‖ **If a line joins the midpoints of two sides of a triangle, it is parallel and equal to one-half the third side.**

Solution

Fig. 212

Given: $BY = YC$,
$AX = CX$.
Prove: $XY \parallel AB$,
$XY = \frac{1}{2} AB$.

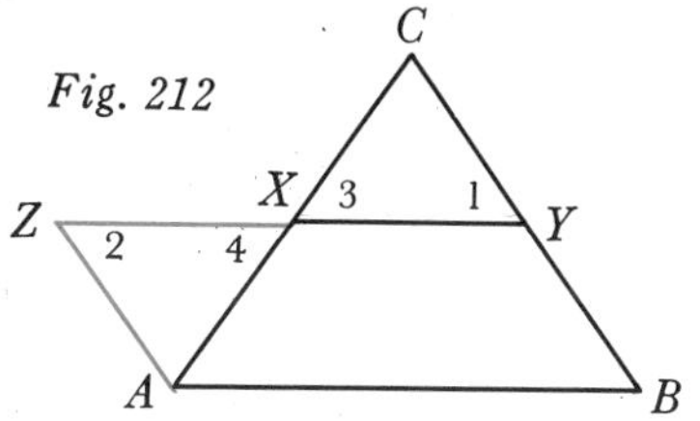

Construction: Extend XY through X its own length to Z. Join Z to A.

Analysis:

You would know:	If you knew:
1. $AB \parallel XY$, $XY = \frac{1}{2} AB$.	1. $ABYZ$ is a $\square$.
2. $ABYZ$ is a $\square$.	2. $AZ \parallel BY$, $AZ = BY$.
3. $AZ \parallel BY$.	3. $\angle 1 = \angle 2$.
4. $AZ = BY$.	4. $AZ = CY$.
5. $\angle 1 = \angle 2$, $AZ = CY$.	5. $\triangle AZX \cong \triangle CYX$.
6. $\triangle AZX \cong \triangle CYX$.	6. **s.a.s. = s.a.s.**

Proof:

STATEMENTS	REASONS
1. $AX = XC$.	1. Given.
2. $XY = XZ$.	2. A line can be extended a given distance.
3. $\angle 3 = \angle 4$.	3. Vertical angles are equal.
4. $\triangle AXZ \cong \triangle CYX$.	4. If two triangles have two sides and the included angle of one equal respectively to two sides and the included angle of the other, the triangles are congruent.
5. $\angle 1 = \angle 2$, $AZ = CY$.	5. Corresponding parts of congruent triangles are equal.
6. $AZ \parallel BY$.	6. If two lines are cut by a transversal forming equal alternate-interior angles, the lines are parallel.
7. $CY = BY$.	7. Given.
8. $AZ = BY$.	8. Quantities equal to the same or equal quantities are equal.
9. $ABYZ$ is a $\square$.	9. If a pair of opposite sides of a quadrilateral are equal and parallel, the quadrilateral is a parallelogram.
10. $XY \parallel AB$.	10. Opposite sides of a parallelogram are parallel.
11. $AB = YZ$.	11. Opposite sides of a parallelogram are equal.
12. $XZ + XY = ZY$.	12. The whole is equal to the sum of its parts.
13. $XZ + XY = AB$.	13. Quantities equal to the same or equal quantities are equal.
14. $2XY = AB$.	14. A quantity may be substituted for its equal without changing the value of the expression.
15. $XY = \frac{1}{2} AB$.	15. If equals are divided by equals the quotients are equal.

Exercises

1. The sides of a triangle are 18″, 16″, and 15″. The midpoints of the sides are joined. Find the perimeter of each triangle formed.

2. The sides of a triangle are 10″, 12″, and 18″. Lines joining the midpoints of the sides form four triangles. Which triangle has the greatest perimeter? The least perimeter?

3. Join the midpoints of the sides of an equilateral triangle. State a generalization which is consistent with the data given.

4. Prove the conclusions stated in Exercise **3.**

5. Prove that the lines connecting the midpoints of the sides of an isosceles triangle form an isosceles triangle.

6. Prove that the lines joining the midpoints of the sides of an equilateral triangle divide it into four congruent triangles.

7. Prove that the lines joining the midpoints of the opposite sides of a quadrilateral bisect each other.

8. Prove that if the midpoint of the hypotenuse of a right triangle is joined to the midpoints of the legs, a rectangle is formed.

9. Draw a triangle, *ABC*. Select a point, *X*, on *AC* and points *H*, *W*, *Z*, and *Y*, the midpoints of *AB*, *BC*, *CX*, and *AX* respectively. Prove *YHWZ* is a parallelogram.

10. Prove that the midpoint of the hypotenuse of a right triangle is equidistant from the vertices of the triangle.

11. Name the polygon formed by lines joining the midpoints of the sides of a rectangle. Prove your answer is correct.

12. Draw a quadrilateral. Join the midpoints of the successive sides. Prove that the quadrilateral formed is a parallelogram.

13. If medians to two sides of a triangle intersect the sides at points *A* and *B*, prove *AB* is one-half the base of the triangle.

14. Prove that the sum of the perpendiculars from the midpoints of two sides of a triangle to the third side is equal to the altitude on the third side.

TRAPEZOIDS

A **trapezoid** *is a quadrilateral with one, and only one, pair of parallel sides.* The parallel sides of a trapezoid are called its *bases.* The nonparallel sides of a trapezoid are called its *legs.* If the legs of the trapezoid are equal, the trapezoid is called an *isosceles* trapezoid. A *median* of a trapezoid joins the midpoints of the legs. *EF* is the median if *E* and *F* are midpoints of *AD* and *BC* respectively.

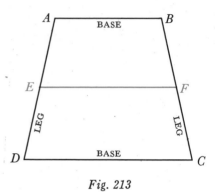

Fig. 213

Developmental Exercises

DE—1. Prove the following theorem:

‖THEOREM 54
‖ **The base angles of an isosceles trapezoid are equal.**

Solution

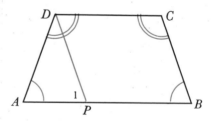

Given: $AB \parallel DC$,
$AD = BC$.

Prove: $\angle A = \angle B$,
$\angle D = \angle C$.

Fig. 214

Construction: Through *D* draw a line parallel to *BC*.

Analysis:
$\angle A = \angle B$ if $\angle A = \angle 1$ and $\angle B = \angle 1$.
$\angle A = \angle 1$ if $AD = DP$.
$\angle B = \angle 1$ if $DP \parallel BC$.
$AD = DP$ if $DP = CB$.
$DP = CB$ if $DPCB$ is a $\square$.

Write a complete proof for Theorem 54.

DE—2. Prove the following theorem:

║ **THEOREM 55**
║ **The diagonals of an isosceles trapezoid are equal.**

Solution

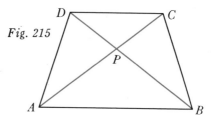

Fig. 215

Given: $AB \parallel DC$,
     $AD = BC$.

Prove: $AC = DB$.

Analysis:

$AC = DB$ if they are corresponding sides of congruent triangles.
$\triangle ABC \cong \triangle ABD$ if $AD = BC$, $\angle DAB = \angle CBA$, and $AB = AB$.

Write a formal proof for this theorem.

Exercises

1. Prove that the base angles of an isosceles trapezoid are equal.

2. Prove that the diagonals of an isosceles trapezoid are equal.

3. If an angle of an isosceles trapezoid is equal to $58°$, how large is each angle of the trapezoid?

4. One angle of an isosceles trapezoid is $x°$, the opposite angle contains $(x-33)°$. Find the number of degrees in each angle.

5. Prove: If a trapezoid has equal base angles, it is isosceles.

6. Prove: If a trapezoid has equal diagonals, it is isosceles.

7. Prove: If a trapezoid has supplementary opposite angles, it is isosceles.

8. Prove that the midpoint of either base of an isosceles triangle is equidistant from the midpoints of the legs.

9. Given three unequal line segments, construct an isosceles trapezoid having one of the line segments as altitude and the other two segments as bases.

10. Given three unequal line segments, construct an isosceles trapezoid having the given line segments as sides.

DE—3. Prove the following theorem:

> **THEOREM 56**
> **The median of a trapezoid is parallel to the bases and equal to one-half their sum.**

Solution

Given: EF is a median of trapezoid $ABCD$.

Prove: $EF \parallel DC$,
$EF \parallel AB$,
$EF = \frac{1}{2}(DC+AB)$.

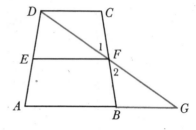

Fig. 216

Construction: Join D to F and extend the line through F to meet AB extended through B.

STATEMENTS	REASONS
1. EF is a median of trapezoid $ABCD$.	1. Given.
2. F is the midpoint of BC, E is the midpoint of AD.	2. A median of a trapezoid joins midpoints of the nonparallel sides.
3. $AB \parallel DC$.	3. Two sides of a trapezoid are parallel.
4. $\angle GBF = \angle C$.	4. Alternate-interior angles formed by parallel lines cut by a transversal are equal.
5. $\angle 1 = \angle 2$.	5. Vertical angles are equal.
6. $\triangle GBF \cong \triangle DCF$.	6. **a.s.a. = a.s.a.**
7. $DF = FG$, $DC = BG$.	7. Corresponding parts of congruent triangles are equal.
8. $EF \parallel AB$, $EF = \frac{1}{2}(AB+BG)$.	8. A line joining the midpoints of two sides of a triangle is parallel to the third side of the triangle and equal to $\frac{1}{2}$ the third side.
9. $EF = \frac{1}{2}(AB+DC)$.	9. A quantity may be substituted for its equal.
10. $EF \parallel DC$.	10. Lines parallel to the same line are parallel.

Exercises

1. The bases of a trapezoid are 6 and 10 inches respectively. Find the length of the median.

2. The sides of a trapezoid are $5''$, $6''$, $5''$, and $12''$ respectively. Find the length of the median.

3. The median of a trapezoid is 16 feet and one base is 10 feet 4 inches. Find the length of the other base.

4. Construct a trapezoid given the four sides.

5. If the bases of a trapezoid are x units and $3x$ units, express the length of the median? Illustrate your answer with a sketch.

6. If the median of a trapezoid is y units and one base is $\frac{1}{2}y$ units, express the length of the other base.

7. The line joining the midpoints of the nonparallel sides of a trapezoid is $5'8''$ and one of the parallel sides is 2.5 times the other. How long is each parallel side of the trapezoid?

8. Express the relationship proved in Theorem 56 as a formula, where M represents the length of the median and b and b' represent the lengths of the bases.

9. If the shorter base of a trapezoid is increased until it becomes equal in length to the longer base, describe the change which takes place in the form of the quadrilateral.

10. If the upper (shorter) base of a trapezoid decreases until it becomes zero, describe the resulting figure.

11. If the lower base of a trapezoid is increased by the length of the upper base and the upper base is increased by the length of the lower base, describe the resulting figure.

12. Find the length of each line segment in the adjacent sketch.

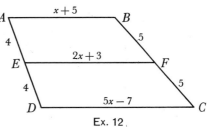

Ex. 12

SOLID GEOMETRY

The parallelogram, trapezoid, and other plane figures studied in this chapter have two dimensions. Corresponding figures in three dimensions have surfaces which are plane figures. A *polyhedron* is a surface bounded by planes. The bounding planes are called the *faces* of the polyhedron. The intersections of the faces are called the *edges*, and the intersections of the edges are called the *vertices* of the polyhedron.

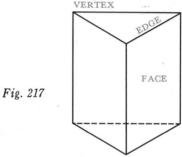

Fig. 217

POLYHEDRON

If every section made by a plane is a convex polygon, the polyhedron is called a *convex polyhedron*.

A *regular* polyhedron is one whose faces are congruent regular polygons. A regular polyhedron of four faces, four equilateral triangles, is a *tetrahedron*; of six faces, six squares, is a *hexahedron*; of eight faces, eight equilateral triangles, is an *octahedron*; of twelve faces, twelve regular pentagons, is a *dodecahedron*; and of twenty faces, twenty equilateral triangles, is an *icosahedron*. Only these five regular polyhedrons can exist.

That only the five regular polyhedrons, of four, six, eight, twelve, and twenty faces can exist may be proved as follows. Notice that each face angle of the regular polyhedron is the interior angle of a regular polygon. Hence, each face angle must contain $\left(\dfrac{n-2}{n}\right)$ 180 degrees or $180 - \dfrac{360}{n}$ degrees, where n represents the number of sides of the regular polygon. Each polyhedral angle must have at least three faces. The sum of all the face angles must be less than 360 degrees. (If the sum of the face angles equals 360 degrees, the face angles would all lie in the same plane.)

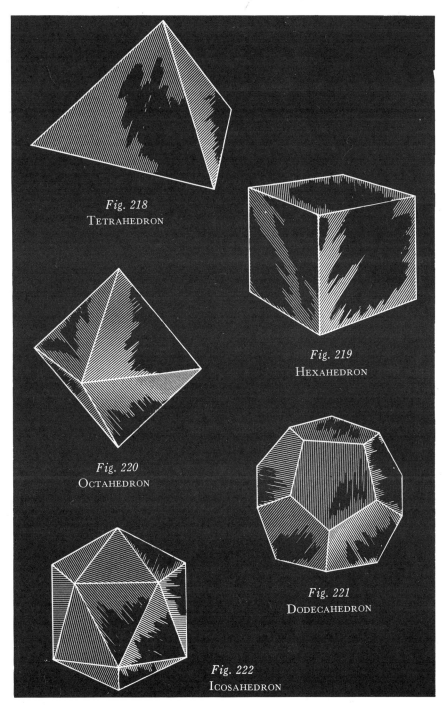

Fig. 218
TETRAHEDRON

Fig. 219
HEXAHEDRON

Fig. 220
OCTAHEDRON

Fig. 221
DODECAHEDRON

Fig. 222
ICOSAHEDRON

If there are three face angles at each vertex of the regular polyhedron, the sum of the face angles at any vertex may be written as:

$$3\left(180 - \frac{360}{n}\right) < 360$$

from which n, the number of sides of the regular polygon, can be determined.

$$3\left(180 - \frac{360}{n}\right) < 360$$

$$540 - \frac{1080}{n} < 360$$

$$3 - \frac{6}{n} < 2$$

$$1 < \frac{6}{n}$$

$$n < 6$$

Thus, n may equal 3, 4, or 5. Why are the values 1 and 2 not included for n? If $n = 3$, the polygons are equilateral triangles and the polyhedron is a tetrahedron. If $n = 4$, the polygons are squares and the polyhedron is a hexahedron. If $n = 5$, the polygons are regular pentagons and the polyhedron is a dodecahedron.

If each polyhedral angle of a regular polyhedron has four face angles, the sum of the face angles at any vertex would be written as:

$$4\left(180 - \frac{360}{n}\right) < 360'$$

and again the value or values of n, the number of sides of the regular polygons, can be determined.

$$4\left(180 - \frac{360}{n}\right) < 360$$

$$2 - \frac{4}{n} < 1$$

$$1 < \frac{4}{n}$$

$$n < 4$$

Therefore, n must equal 3. Why? The only polyhedron with four face angles at each vertex has faces that are equilateral triangles. This regular polyhedron is the octahedron.

If each polyhedral angle of a regular polyhedron has five face angles, the sum of the faces angles would be written:

$$5\left(180 - \frac{360}{n}\right) < 360$$

$$900 - \frac{1800}{n} < 360$$

$$5 - \frac{10}{n} < 2$$

$$3 < \frac{10}{n}$$

$$n < \frac{10}{3} \text{ or } 3\tfrac{1}{3}$$

Hence, $n = 3$ is the only possible value. The only regular polyhedron having five face angles at each vertex is the icosahedron.

If the number of face angles at each vertex of the polyhedron is six, the sum of the face angle is:

$$6\left(180 - \frac{360}{n}\right) < 360$$

$$1080 - \frac{2160}{n} < 360$$

$$3 - \frac{6}{n} < 1$$

$$2 < \frac{6}{n}$$

$$n < 3$$

Is $n < 3$ ever possible? Can a polygon have less than three sides? Since n must be less than three (as required by the algebraic solution) and at least three (as required by the number of sides necessary for a polygon) a contradictory conclusion has arisen. Since this conclusion was based on the assumption that a polyhedron can have six face angles at any vertex, this ambiguity implies that no regular polyhedron can have six face angles at any vertex. This same ambiguity arises for all values of six and above. Therefore, the five regular polyhedrons named are the only ones that can exist.

A *prism* is a polyhedron with two parallel faces, called its bases. It can be triangular or rectangular depending on whether the bases are triangles or rectangles, respectively. If its base is a parallelogram, the prism is called a *parallelepiped*.

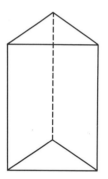

PRISMS

Fig. 223

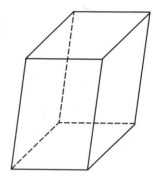

Exercises

1. Draw a cube, a rectangular solid, a parallelepiped.

    a. How many vertices has each? How many edges?

    b. List some properties of each.

2. Draw a rectangular solid. Join two opposite vertices with a dotted line. It is a diagonal of the parallelepiped.

    a. Draw additional lines to make the diagonal a common side of two right triangles.

    b. How many diagonals has a rectangular solid? Can you prove them equal?

3. What is the least number of faces

    a. a prism can have?

    b. a pyramid can have?

4. Find the sum of all the face angles of

    a. a triangular prism.

    b. a cube.

    c. a rectangular solid.

EXTEND YOUR HORIZON

People who pilot ships and airplanes often study the effect of winds crossing their path. If the airplane represented in the drawing is headed north and the wind is from 135° the plane will be blown to the west. In the navigation of ships and airplanes, as in mapping and military operations, the angle of direction is measured in clockwise direction

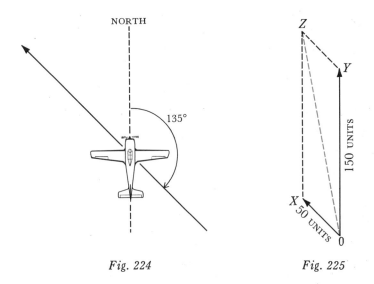

Fig. 224   Fig. 225

from North. The arrowhead on the line segment *OX* indicated the direction the wind is going, thus *OX* indicated the wind is from 135° and going toward 315°.

If the wind is 50 miles per hour, the magnitude may be represented by a line 50 units long.

A line segment, such as *OX*, that represents both direction and magnitude is called a *vector*. Observe that the arrowhead does not mean that *OX* extends indefinitely beyond *X* but shows the direction the wind is going.

Also, the direction and force of the engine driven propeller on the airplane may be represented by a vector. *OY* represents a force from the south (going north) with a speed of 150 miles per hour. (See Figure 225).

The effect of these two forces on the airplane is the geometrical sum of the two vectors. This sum is represented by the diagonal of a parallelogram formed by the two vectors. Thus, OZ represents the speed and direction of the airplane as the result of the two forces represented by OX and OY. A vector sum such as OZ is called a *resultant*.

Forces can act in the same direction and also in opposite directions. Consider a ship moving in exactly the same direction as the wind is blowing, or into a headwind. Simple addition or subtraction will then determine the resultant of two forces.

The measure of the resultant is not difficult to obtain if the forces can be represented by a rectangle or a square. Right triangles then make the solution simple.

CHAPTER SUMMARY

Polygons are classified according to
1. angles
    a. equiangular
    b. convex
    c. concave   (page 183)
2. sides
    a. equilateral
    b. the number of sides   (page 183)

Properties of a parallelogram are
1. both pairs of opposite sides are parallel.   (page 186)
2. both pairs of opposite sides are equal.   (page 189)
3. opposite angles are equal.   (page 189)
4. consecutive angles are supplementary.   (page 189)
5. the diagonals bisect each other.   (page 192)

Sufficient conditions for a quadrilateral to be a parallelogram are
1. parallel opposite sides.   (page 186)
2. equal opposite sides.   (page 193)
3. one pair of equal and parallel opposite sides.   (page 194)
4. diagonals which bisect each other.   (page 196)
5. equal opposite angles.   (page 198)
6. supplementary consecutive angles.   (page 199)

Properties of a rectangle are
1. all the properties of a parallelogram.   (page 202)
2. each angle is a right angle.   (page 203)
3. equal diagonals.   (page 204)

Sufficient conditions for a parallelogram to be a rectangle are
1. one angle to be a right angle.   (page 205)
2. equal angles.   (page 206)
3. equal diagonals.   (page 207)

Properties of a rhombus are
1. all the properties of a parallelogram.   (page 208)
2. equilateral.   (page 208)
3. diagonals which bisect the angles.   (page 209)
4. perpendicular diagonals.   (page 209)

Sufficient conditions for a parallelogram to be a rhombus are
1. equal sides.   (page 211)
2. perpendicular diagonals.   (page 211)
3. diagonals which bisect the angles.   (page 212)

Properties of a square are
1. all the properties of a rectangle.   (page 213)
2. all the properties of a rhombus.   (page 213)

Sufficient conditions for a quadrilateral to be a square are
1. a rectangle with perpendicular diagonals.   (page 215)
2. a rhombus with equal diagonals.   (page 215)
3. a rhombus with one right angle.   (page 216)

Properties of a trapezoid are
1. two, and only two, sides are parallel.   (page 222)
2. the median is parallel to the bases and equal to one-half their sum.   (page 224)

Properties of an isosceles trapezoid are
1. all the properties of a trapezoid.
2. the nonparallel sides are equal.   (page 222)
3. equal base angles.   (page 222)
4. equal diagonals.   (page 223)

CHAPTER REVIEW

Vocabulary

Match the word in the left hand column with its correct definition in the right hand column.

1. Pentagon

2. *n*-gon

3. Octagon

4. Hexagon

5. Quadrilateral

6. Trapezoid

7. Parallelogram

8. Rectangle

9. Rhombus

10. Square

a. A quadrilateral that has both pairs of opposite sides parallel.

b. A polygon of six sides.

c. A rectangle with equal adjacent sides.

d. A parallelogram with one right angle.

e. A parallelogram with two adjacent sides equal.

f. A polygon of *n*-sides.

g. A polygon of three sides.

h. A polygon of five sides.

i. A polygon of nine sides.

j. A polygon having equal angles.

k. A polygon of eight sides.

l. A polygon of four sides.

m. A quadrilateral having two, and only two, sides parallel.

Exercises

1. State six conditions which are sufficient to determine a parallelogram.

2. Draw a line segment. Construct the difference between one-half and one-third of the segment.

3. You have learned that an isosceles trapezoid has equal base angles. State and prove the converse of that idea.

4. Draw a quadrilateral so that a line joining the midpoints of two opposite sides and a diagonal bisect each other. Prove the quadrilateral is a parallelogram.

5. State the properties shared by a rhombus and a square. How do a rhombus and a square differ?

6. State the properties shared by a parallelogram and a trapezoid. How do a parallelogram and a trapezoid differ?

7. State three conditions which are necessary for a trapezoid to be isosceles.

8. List the properties shared by a parallelogram, rectangle, and square.

9. The median of a trapezoid is 28 linear units and the upper base is 20 linear units. Sketch the figure and determine the length of the lower base.

10. An exterior angle at one vertex of a parallelogram is 115°. Sketch the figure and compute the size of the angle at the vertex opposite the given exterior angle.

11. Prove that in any quadrilateral the midpoints of the diagonals and the midpoints of two opposite sides are vertices of a parallelogram.

12. Prove that line segments joining midpoints of opposite sides of any quadrilateral bisect each other. Hint: Draw a diagonal and join the midpoints consecutively.

13. Draw an isosceles trapezoid. Join the midpoints of the bases. How is the line related to the bases? Prove your answer.

14. Draw a parallelogram. Join the midpoints of two opposite sides of the parallelogram to opposite ends of a diagonal. Prove that these lines trisect the other diagonal.

15. Construct isosceles trapezoid $XYZW$, given XY, $\angle Y$, and $\angle X$. Is more than one figure determined?

16. On AC of $\triangle ABC$ locate point O so that $AO = \frac{1}{3}AC$. On BC locate point Q so that $BQ = \frac{1}{3}BC$. Join points O and Q. Prove $OQ = \frac{2}{3}AB$.

CHAPTER TEST

1. Given: $AB = BC = CD = DE = EF = FA$.

    a. Is polygon $ABCDEF$ convex or concave?

    b. Classify $ABCDEF$ according to the number of sides.

    c. Find the number of degrees in an exterior angle of $ABCDEF$.

Ex. 1

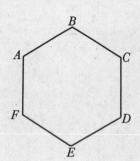

2. Given: $AB \parallel CD$, $EF \perp AB$, $GH \perp AB$.

    a. Why is $EFGH$ a parallelogram?

    b. Classify the parallelogram.

    c. If $EG = EF$, classify the parallelogram.

    d. Classify the quadrilateral $ECDG$.

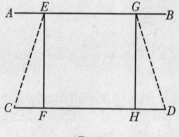

Ex. 2

3. Given: $XW = 6''$, $WZ = 9''$, $XW \parallel ZY$, $ZY = 6''$, $\angle XYZ = a°$.

    a. Classify the quadrilateral.

    b. Find the length of XY.

    c. Represent the number of degrees in $\angle XWZ$.

    d. Represent the number of degrees in $\angle WXY$.

Ex. 3

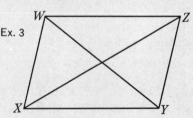

4. Given: $XP=PY$, $ZQ=QY$, $ZR=RX$, $XY=14''$, $ZY=16''$, $ZX=18''$.

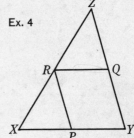

Ex. 4

a. Classify the quadrilateral *PYQR*.

b. Find the length of *RP*.

c. Find the length of *RQ*.

d. What is the perimeter of *PYQR*?

5. If one base of a trapezoid is 7 units and the median is 11 units, find the other base.

6. If the sides of a triangle are 8, 12, and 16 units respectively, find the perimeter of an inner triangle formed by joining the midpoints of three sides in order.

7. Illustrate and prove: In an isosceles trapezoid the midpoint of the base is equally distant from the midpoints of the legs.

8. Illustrate and prove: If a point is equally distant from two successive vertices of a rectangle, it is also equidistant from the other two vertices.

9. Draw two equilateral triangles with a common base. Name the figure formed. Prove your answer correct.

10. Draw an equilateral triangle, *XYZ*. Use its sides as bases of congruent isosceles triangles, *XAY*, *XZB*, *YCZ*. Select a quadrilateral in the figure, such as *XAYZ*, and prove it is a rhombus.

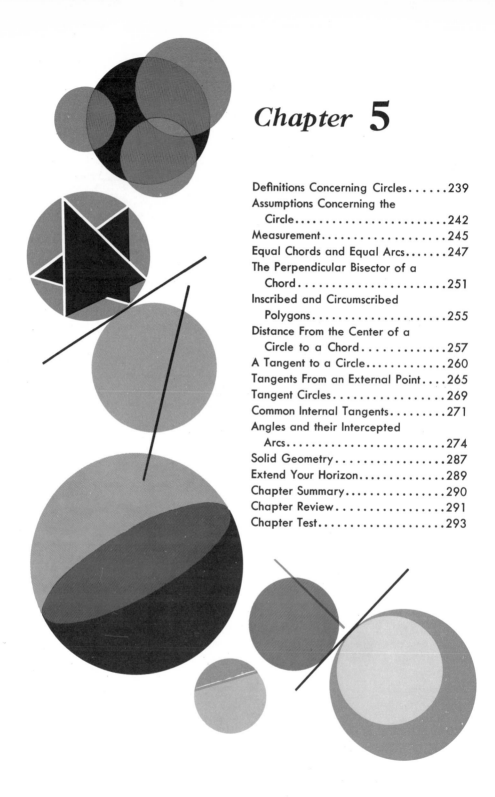

Chapter 5

CIRCLES

DEFINITIONS CONCERNING CIRCLES

The **circle** *is a closed curve, lying in a plane, all points of which are equidistant from a fixed point called the center.* Notice from the definition that a circle is a *curve* and not a *surface.* Consider, for example, a round clock. The shape of the clock is a circle; the face of the clock is the area enclosed by the circle.

The circle is the simplest and most useful plane curve. It is always perfectly symmetric. Notice how circles are used all around you. In architecture the circle is often used for design. Many tools, such as nails or screws, are circular for efficiency. Rings, hoops, and wheels are all circular. Can you list other uses of the circle?

A line which joins two points of the circle is a *chord.* In Figure 226, *PR* is a chord. A chord which passes through the center of the circle is called a diameter. *PW* is a diameter. A *radius* of a circle is a line joining the center to any point of the circle. The plural of radius is *radii.* In Figure 226, *AP, AW,* and *AQ* are radii. From the above definition it follows that a radius is one-half of a diameter. The angle formed by two radii is called a *central angle.* ∠*PAQ* is a central angle.

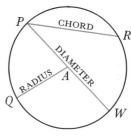

Fig. 226

A *secant* is a line that intersects the circle in two distinct points. If a line has one, and only one, point in common with a circle, the line is called a *tangent.*

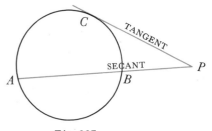

Fig. 227

An *arc* is any part of a circle. Two arcs are said to be equal if they are the same fractional part of a circle. One-half of a circle is a *semicircle*. An arc shorter than a semicircle is a *minor arc*. A *major arc* is longer than a semicircle. *AB* and *BC* are minor arcs of circle *O*. *BCD* is a major arc. The symbol for arc is ⌢. $\overset{\frown}{AB}$ is said to be intercepted by the sides of ∠*AOB*.

Fig. 228

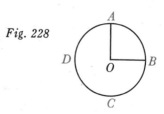

If two or more circles have the same center but have unequal radii, they are called *concentric* circles. A circle is usually named by its center point. The symbol for circle is ⊙. Thus, the circle in Figure 228 is ⊙*O*.

Exercises

1. If *O* is the center of the circle, name all the chords, diameters, and radii.

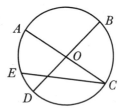

Ex. 1

Ex. 2

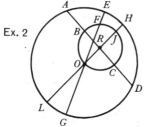

2. If *O* is the center of the larger circle and *R* is the center of the smaller circle, name all the chords, diameters, radii, and secants.

In Exercises **3** *and* **4,** *O is the center of the circle. Name all major and minor arcs and semicircles.*

3.

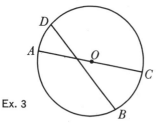

Ex. 3

4.

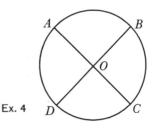

Ex. 4

5. If the radius of a circle is $1\frac{3}{4}''$, how long is the diameter?

6. If the diameter of a circle is *h* inches long, express the length of a radius of the circle.

7. Draw a circle with a radius of 2″. Estimate the position of a point $1\frac{3}{8}$″ from the center; 3″ from the center.

8. In a circle having a radius of 2″, draw two perpendicular diameters. Explain how they seem to divide the circle.

9. Draw two intersecting diameters in a circle. Do they seem to intercept equal arcs? What relationship would you need to know to support your answer?

10. Draw a circle with a $\frac{7}{8}$″ radius. Draw a diameter of the circle. At each end of the diameter draw a circle with a $\frac{7}{8}$″ radius.

11. Use a compass to construct a circle having its center at a given point, *O*, and also passing through a given point, *P*.

12. Use a compass to construct a circle containing two given points, *A* and *B*.

13. Construct two equal circles. Draw a right central angle in each. Draw the chords of the central angles. Compare their lengths.

Explain the relationship of the parts in each of the diagrams in Exercises **14-18.**

14.

15.

16.

17.

18.

ASSUMPTIONS CONCERNING THE CIRCLE

In order to prove conclusions about the circle, the following assumptions are made.

Assumption 23

In a given plane one, and only one, circle can be drawn with any given point as the center and the length of any given line segment as the radius.

Assumption 24

Circles are equal if their radii or diameters are equal.

Assumption 25

A diameter bisects a circle.

Assumption 26

If a line bisects a circle and is terminated by it, the line is a diameter.

Assumption 27

Radii of the same or of equal circles are equal.

Assumption 28

A line cannot intersect a circle in more than two points.

Assumption 29

A point is inside, on, or outside a circle according to whether its distance from the center is respectively less than, equal to, or greater than the radius of the circle.

Illustration:

$AO > n$, therefore A is outside $\odot O$.
$BO = n$, therefore B is on $\odot O$.
$CO < n$, therefore C is inside $\odot O$.

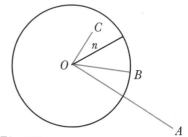

Fig. 229

Assumption 30

In the same circle or in equal circles, equal central angles intercept equal arcs.

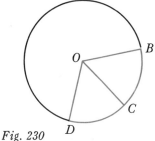

In Figure 230, if $\angle BOC = \angle DOC$ then $\overset{\frown}{BC} = \overset{\frown}{DC}$.

Fig. 230

Assumption 31

In the same circle or in equal circles, equal arcs are intercepted by equal central angles.

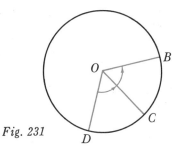

In Figure 231, if $\overset{\frown}{DC} = \overset{\frown}{BC}$, then $\angle DOC = \angle BOC$.

Fig. 231

‖ Developmental Exercises

DE—1. In the circle below, name the equal line segments.

Solution

Since radii of the same circle are equal (Assumption 27), $GO = EO = OD = OC = OA$.

Diameters of the same circle are also equal. Why? Thus, $EA = GD$.

DE—2. Which points in Figure 232 lie

    a. inside the circle?
    b. on the circle?
    c. outside the circle?

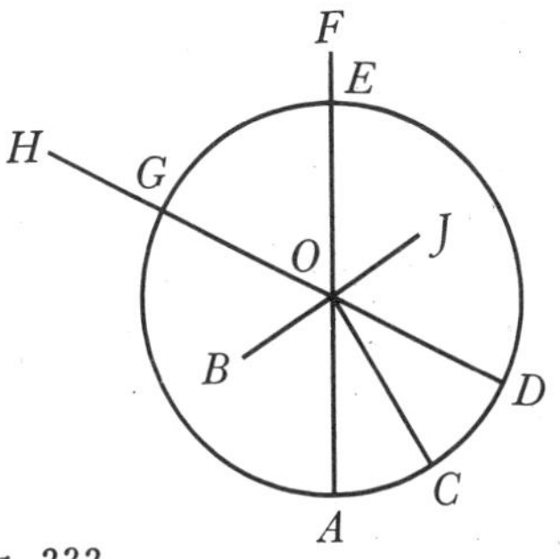

Fig. 232

Solution

    a. Points B and J lie inside the circle.
    b. Points A, C, D, E, and G lie on the circle.
    c. Points F and H lie outside the circle.

DE—3. a. With a given point, *O*, as the center and a given distance, *d*, as the radius, construct a circle.

b. How many circles are determined by the given data?

Solution

a. ● Open the compass so that the distance between the points is equal to the length of the given distance, *d*.

Fig. 233

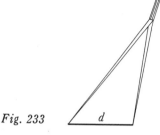

● With *d* as radius and the steel point of the compass at point *O*, draw a circle.

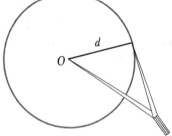

Fig. 234

b. Assumption 23—In a given plane, one and only one circle can be drawn with any given point as the center and the length of any given line segment as the radius.

Exercises

1. With a given point, *O*, as the center and a radius of 1″, construct a circle.

2. With a given radius of 1″, how many circles can be drawn through a given point, *Y*?

3. Through two given points, *M* and *N*, how many circles can be drawn?

4. In a circle with a radius of 18″, a chord is drawn joining ends of radii which form a 60° angle. How long is the chord?

5. Construct two equal circles. Draw central angles of 45° in each. Draw the chords of the central angles. Prove the chords are equal.

6. In ⊙*O*, diameter *AB* is perpendicular to chord *CD*. Prove $\overset{\frown}{CB} = \overset{\frown}{BD}$. Hint: Draw radii *OC* and *OD*. Prove congruent triangles.

7. *AB* is a diameter of circle *O*. *CO* and *DO* are radii. Chord *AD* is parallel to *CO*. Prove $\overset{\frown}{DC} = \overset{\frown}{CB}$.

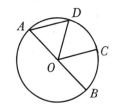

Ex. 7

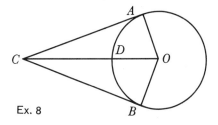

Ex. 8

8. In the diagram at the right, *AO*, *DO*, and *BO* are radii. *AC* ⊥ *AO*, *CB* ⊥ *OB*. Prove $\overset{\frown}{AD} = \overset{\frown}{DB}$.

MEASUREMENT

In Chapter One you learned that the unit for measuring an angle is the *degree*. One angular degree is $\frac{1}{360}$ of a revolution. Thus, around a point it is possible to have 360 degree angles.

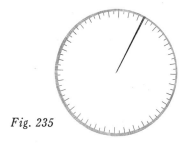

Fig. 235

Each division is one arc degree.

With this point as the center, draw a circle. Notice that each angle is a central angle of the circle. Each central angle intercepts an equal arc on the circle. Since there are 360 equal central angles, there are 360 equal arcs intercepted on the circle. Each of these arcs is measured as *one arc degree*. One arc degree is $\frac{1}{360}$ of a circle.

Assumption 32

A central angle is measured by its intercepted arc.

In order to express this relationship the symbol $\overset{\circ}{=}$ is used. $\overset{\frown}{AB} \overset{\circ}{=} \angle AOB$ is read "arc *AB* is equal in degrees to angle *AOB*."

Developmental Exercises

DE—1. If a central angle of a circle is 90°, what fractional part of the circle does it intersect?

Solution

The measure of the central angle is equal in degrees to the measure of its intercepted arc. Thus, the arc also measures 90°. The entire circle is 360°. The arc is $\frac{90}{360}$ or $\frac{1}{4}$ of the circle.

DE—2. Using the diagram at the right, find the number of degrees in $\overset{\frown}{AB}$ of $\odot O$, if $\angle ABO = 75°$.

Fig. 236

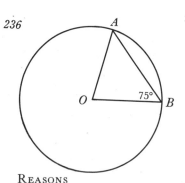

Solution

Proof:

STATEMENTS	REASONS
1. OA and OB are radii of circle O.	1. Given.
2. $OA = OB$.	2. Radii of the same or of equal circles are equal.
3. $\angle ABO = \angle BAO$.	3. In a triangle angles opposite equal sides are equal.
4. $\angle ABO = 75°$.	4. Given.
5. $\angle BAO = 75°$.	5. Quantities equal to the same or equal quantities are equal.
6. $\angle ABO + \angle BAO + \angle AOB = 180°$.	6. The sum of the interior angles of a triangle is 180°.
7. $75° + 75° + \angle AOB = 180°$.	7. A quantity may be substituted for its equal without changing the value of the expression.
8. $\angle AOB = 30°$.	8. If equals are subtracted from equals the differences are equal.
9. $\overset{\frown}{AB} = 30°$.	9. A central angle is measured by its intercepted arc.

Exercises

1. If a central angle of a circle is 15°, what fractional part of the circle does it intercept?

2. *AC* and *BD* are diameters in a circle. $\stackrel{\frown}{BC} = 120°$. How large is $\stackrel{\frown}{AB}$? $\stackrel{\frown}{CD}$? $\stackrel{\frown}{AD}$?

3. Draw two perpendicular diameters. Prove the circle is divided into four equal parts.

4. Draw two diameters in a circle. Prove they intercept two pairs of equal arcs.

5. Draw a central angle in a circle. Join the midpoint of the intercepted arc to the center of the circle. Prove the line bisects the given central angle.

6. Draw three diameters so as to divide a circle into six equal arcs. Prove the central angles each measure 60°.

EQUAL CHORDS AND EQUAL ARCS

Previously it was assumed that in the same or in equal circles, equal central angles intercept equal arcs. It is now going to be proved that in the same or in equal circles equal chords have equal arcs.

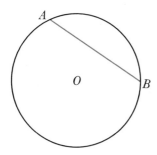 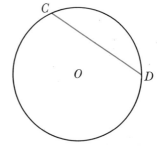

Fig. 237

Given that $\odot O = \odot Q$ and $AB = CD$, it is to be proved that $AB = CD$. Thus far the only method to establish equal arcs is through equal central angles. Central angles *AOB* and *CQD* must therefore be constructed. Study the proof of this theorem in the developmental exercises.

Developmental Exercises

DE—1. Prove the following theorem:

|| **THEOREM 57**
|| **In the same or in equal circles, equal chords have equal arcs.**

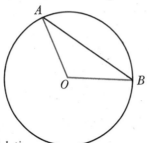

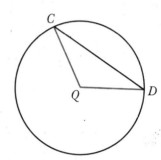

Fig. 238

Solution

Given: $AB = CD$,
   $\odot O = \odot Q$.
Prove: $\overset{\frown}{AB} = \overset{\frown}{CD}$.

Construction: Draw radii OA and OB in $\odot O$ and CQ and DQ in $\odot Q$.

Proof:

STATEMENTS	REASONS
1. $\odot O = \odot Q$, $\quad AB = CD$.	1. Given.
2. Draw OA, OB, OC, OD.	2. Through two points one and only one a straight line may be drawn.
3. $OA = OB = QC = QD$.	3. Radii of the same or of equal circles are equal.
4. $\triangle AOB \cong \triangle CDQ$.	4. s.s.s. = s.s.s.
5. $\angle AOB = \angle CQD$.	5. Corresponding angles of congruent triangles are equal.
6. $\overset{\frown}{AB} = \overset{\frown}{CD}$.	6. In equal circles, equal central angles intercept equal arcs.

Thus, Theorem 57 has been proved if the chords are in equal circles. Now prove Theorem 57 if the chords are in the same circle.

Given: $AB = CD$.

Prove: $\overset{\frown}{AB} = \overset{\frown}{CD}$.

Is $\triangle AOB \cong \triangle COD$?

Is $\angle AOB = \angle COD$?

Why is $\overset{\frown}{AB} = \overset{\frown}{CD}$?

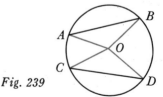

Fig. 239

DE—2. Prove the following theorem:

> **THEOREM 58**
>
> **In the same or in equal circles, equal arcs have equal chords.**

Solution

Using Figure 238 in **DE—1**

Given: $\odot O = \odot Q$ and $\overset{\frown}{AB} = \overset{\frown}{CD}$.

Prove: $AB = CD$.

Proof:

STATEMENTS	REASONS
1. $\odot O = \odot Q$, $\overset{\frown}{AB} = \overset{\frown}{CD}$.	1. Given.
2. $\angle AOB = \angle CQD$.	2. In the same or in equal circles, equal arcs have equal central angles.
3. $OA = OB = QC = QD$.	3. Radii of the same or equal circles are equal.
4. $\triangle AOB \cong \triangle CQD$.	4. **s.a.s. = s.a.s.**
5. $AB = CD$.	5. Corresponding sides of congruent triangles are equal.

Exercises

1. Write a proof for Theorem 57 assuming the chords are in the same circle.

2. Write a proof for Theorem 58 assuming the arcs are in the same circle.

3. Given: $\overset{\frown}{AD} = \overset{\frown}{BC}$ in $\odot O$.
Prove: $AC = BD$.

4. Given: $AC = BD$ in $\odot O$.
Prove: $AD = BC$.

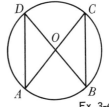

Ex. 3-4

5. Given: AOC is a diameter of $\odot O$,
$AB = AD$.
Prove: $\overset{\frown}{DC} = \overset{\frown}{BC}$.

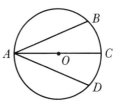

Ex. 5

6. Given: *DOB* is a diameter of
⊙*O*,
$\overset{\frown}{AB} = \overset{\frown}{BC}$.
Prove: *DA* = *DC*.

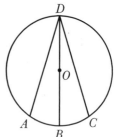

Ex. 6

7. Two equal circles intersect at *X* and *Y*. Prove the minor arcs, *XY*, in the two circles are equal.

8. Draw two unequal circles, *O* and *Q*, intersecting at *X* and *Y*. Prove the line segment *OQ* is the perpendicular bisector of *XY*.

9. In circle *O*, *OP* is a radius perpendicular to chord *XY*. Prove ∠*PXY* = ∠*PYX*.

10. In circle *O*, *XY* is a diameter. Radius *OW* is parallel to chord *XZ*. Prove $\overset{\frown}{ZW} = \overset{\frown}{WY}$.

11. The vertices of equilateral triangle *ABC* lie on a circle. Prove the points *A*, *B*, and *C* divide the circle into three equal arcs.

12. Prove that if diameter *AOB* bisects central angle *COD*, it bisects major arc *CAD*.

13. Given: *AOB* is a diameter in
⊙*O*.
∠1 = ∠2.
Prove: *CE* = *DF*.

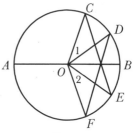

Ex. 13

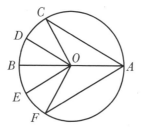

Ex. 14

14. Given: *AOB* is a diameter in
⊙*O*,
DO ⊥ *OF*,
CO ⊥ *OE*,
$\overset{\frown}{DB} = \overset{\frown}{BE}$.
Prove: *AC* = *AF*.

THE PERPENDICULAR BISECTOR OF A CHORD

A *perpendicular bisector* of a chord of a circle is a line which forms right angles with the chord at its midpoint. Study the developmental exercises for the properties of such a bisector.

Developmental Exercises

DE—1. Draw several chords in a large circle. Construct the perpendicular bisectors of each chord. What do you observe?

Solution

The perpendicular bisectors of the chords pass through the center of the circle.

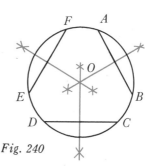

Fig. 240

DE—2. Prove the following theorem:

THEOREM 59
The perpendicular bisector of a chord passes through the center of the circle.

Solution

> **Given:** $\odot O$ with chord AB,
> $CD \perp AB$,
> $AE = EB$.
> **Prove:** CD is a diameter of
> $\odot O$.

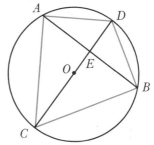

Fig. 241

Analysis:

CD is a diameter if $\overset{\frown}{CAD} = \overset{\frown}{CBD}$. $\overset{\frown}{CAD} = \overset{\frown}{CBD}$ if $\overset{\frown}{CA} + \overset{\frown}{AD} = \overset{\frown}{CB} + \overset{\frown}{BD}$. This will be true if $\overset{\frown}{CA} = \overset{\frown}{CB}$, $\overset{\frown}{AD} = \overset{\frown}{BD}$. $\overset{\frown}{CA} = \overset{\frown}{CB}$ and $\overset{\frown}{AD} = \overset{\frown}{BD}$ if their respective chords are equal. The chords may be proved equal by proving $\triangle ADE \cong \triangle DBE$ and $\triangle AEC \cong \triangle EBC$.

Now write a proof for this theorem.

DE—3. Through three points not in a straight line, construct a circle. Prove that one and only one circle can be drawn through the three points.

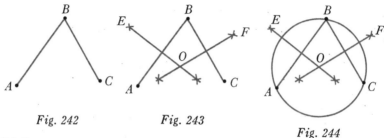

Fig. 242 *Fig. 243*

Fig. 244

Solution

● Given the points A, B, and C, draw lines AB and BC. AB and BC will be chords of the constructed circle. (Figure 242)

● Construct the perpendicular bisectors of AB and BC. Their point of intersection, O, is the center of the circle. Why? (Figure 243)

● With the length of AC as radius and O as the center, construct a circle. (Figure 244)

Proof:

Between two points one and only one straight line may be constructed. The lines AB and BC are therefore unique. The perpendiculars, OE and OF, of AB and BC respectively were constructed (a possible construction). Since AB and BC are neither parallel nor in the same straight line (given), these perpendicular bisectors will intersect. If OE and OF did not intersect, they would be parallel; BC would be perpendicular to OE; and points A, B, and C would lie in the same straight line. Why? The point O is the intersection of these perpendiculars. O is on the perpendicular bisector of AB and is therefore equidistant from A and B. O is on the perpendicular bisector of BC and is thus equidistant from B and C. $AO = BO$, $BO = CO$; therefore, $AO = BO = CO$. Thus, O is equidistant from A, B, and C. A circle described about O with OA as radius will pass through A, B, and C. Thus, at least one circle can be constructed through the three given points.

The center of any circle that passes through A, B, and C must be on both of the perpendicular bisectors of AB and BC, and, therefore, on their intersection. Since two straight lines intersect in one and only one point, O is a unique point and thus the center of the only circle that can be drawn through A, B, and C.

Thus, the following theorem has been proved.

‖ **THEOREM 60**

‖ **Three noncollinear points determine a circle.**

DE—4. Prove the following theorem:

THEOREM 61

If a line through the center of a circle is perpendicular to a chord, it bisects the chord and the major and minor arcs of the chord.

Solution

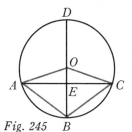
Fig. 245

Given: DB is a diameter of
$\odot O$.
$DB \perp AC$.

Prove: $AE = EC$,
$\overparen{AB} = \overparen{BC}$,
$\overparen{AD} = \overparen{CD}$.

Proof:

STATEMENTS	REASONS
1. Draw lines OA, OC, AB, and BC.	1. Between two points one and only one line can be drawn.
2. $DB \perp AC$.	2. Given.
3. $\angle DEC$ and $\angle DEA$ are right angles.	3. Why?
4. $\angle DEC = \angle DEA$.	4. All right angles are equal.
5. $OA = OC$.	5. Radii of the same circle are equal.
6. $OE = OE$.	6. Identity.
7. $\triangle OEA \cong \triangle OEC$.	7. Why?
8. $AE = EC$.	8. Corresponding sides of congruent triangles are equal.
9. $\triangle AEB \cong \triangle CEB$.	9. Supply the missing steps.
10. $AB = BC$.	10. Same as Reason 8.
11. $\overparen{AB} = \overparen{BC}$.	11. In the same circle equal chords have equal arcs.
12. DB is a diameter of $\odot O$.	12. Given.
13. $\overparen{BAD} = \overparen{BCD}$.	13. A diameter bisects the circle.
14. $\overparen{BAD} = \overparen{BA} + \overparen{AD}$, $\overparen{BCD} = \overparen{BC} + \overparen{CD}$.	14. The whole is equal to the sum of its parts.
15. $\overparen{BA} + \overparen{AD} = \overparen{BC} + \overparen{CD}$.	15. Why?
16. $\overparen{AD} = \overparen{CD}$.	16. Why?

Corollary

A line through the center of a circle and bisecting any chord not a diameter, is perpendicular to it.

Exercises

1. Given a circle, determine its center.

2. In Developmental Exercise **3,** what would have happened if the three points were collinear (on the same straight line)?

3. Write a formal proof for Theorem 60.

4. Complete the proof for Theorem 61.

5. Illustrate and prove the corollary.

6. In a circle draw a diameter. From one end of the diameter draw two equal chords. Prove the equal chords make equal angles with the diameter.

7. Draw two concentric circles. Draw a line segment so that all of it is a chord of the larger circle and part of it is a chord of the smaller circle. Prove the segments between the circles are equal.

8. If a diameter bisects a minor arc, *AB*, prove it also bisects the major arc, *AB*.

9. Show a construction for bisecting an arc of a circle when the center is unknown.

10. If two chords bisect each other, prove they are diameters.

11. Given: $\odot O$ with radii *OB* and *OA*, $PE = PF$, $PC \perp OB$, $PD \perp OA$.
 Prove: $\overset{\frown}{BP} = \overset{\frown}{PA}$.

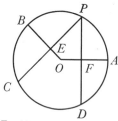

Ex. 11

12. Given: $\odot O$ with chords *AB*, *BC*, and *CA*. $\angle BAC = \angle BCA$.
 Prove: $\overset{\frown}{AB} = \overset{\frown}{BC}$.

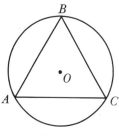

Ex. 12

INSCRIBED AND CIRCUMSCRIBED POLYGONS

The word "scribe" means "to write or draw." "Inscribe" means "to draw in." A polygon is said to be *inscribed* (drawn in) in a circle if the sides of the polygon are chords of the circle, that is, if all the vertices of the polygon lie on the circle. The circle is said to be *circumscribed* about (drawn about) the circle.

A polygon is circumscribed about a circle if the sides of the polygon are tangents to the circle. The circled is then inscribed in the polygon.

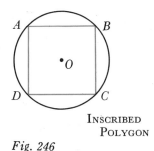

INSCRIBED
POLYGON

Fig. 246

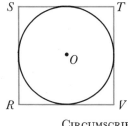

CIRCUMSCRIBED

Fig. 247 POLYGON

▌*Developmental Exercises*

DE—1. Inscribe a square within a given circle.

Solution

● In the given circle construct a diameter, *AB*.

● On *AB* at *O* construct *CD* ⊥ *AB*.

● Join *C*, *B*, *D*, and *A*.

CBDA is the required square.

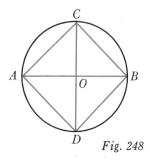

Fig. 248

DE—2. Circumscribe a square about a circle.

Solution

● In the given circle construct a diameter, *AB*.

● At the points *A*, *O*, and *B*, construct perpendiculars to *AB*.

● At the points *C* and *D* construct perpendiculars to *CD*.

SYZW is the circumscribed square.

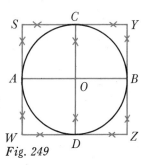

Fig. 249

DE—3. Inscribe an equilateral hexagon in a circle.

Solution

A *hexagon* is a six-sided polygon. Thus, the circle will be divided into six equal arcs. Each arc will measure $\frac{360}{6}$ arc degrees or 60 degrees. The central angle intercepting such an arc will also measure 60 degrees. Why? Why is the chord of such an arc equal in length to the radius of the circle?

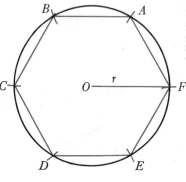

Using the length of the radius of the circle, mark off equal arcs on the circle. Label these points *A*, *B*, *C*, *D*, *E*, and *F*.

ABCDEF is the required hexagon.

Fig. 250

Exercises

1. An equilateral polygon is inscribed in a circle. If each arc of the circle contains 36°, how many sides has the polygon?

2. Draw a circle. Inscribe an equilateral triangle in the circle.

3. Draw a circle. Inscribe an equilateral dodecagon in the circle.

4. Prove the construction in Developmental Exercise **3**.

5. Circumscribe an equilateral hexagon about a circle.

6. Show that a circumscribed equilateral hexagon is regular.

7. Circumscribe an equilateral quadrilateral about a circle.

8. Inscribe an equilateral octagon in a circle.

9. Circumscribe a circle about a given square.

10. Circumscribe a circle about a given rectangle.

11. Prove that the line connecting the centers of two intersecting circles bisects the common chord of the circles.

12. Prove that the line connecting the midpoints of two parallel chords passes through the center of the circle.

DISTANCE FROM THE CENTER OF A CIRCLE TO A CHORD

The distance from a point to a line is the length of the perpendicular from the point to the line. Hence, the distance from the center of a circle to a chord is the length of the perpendicular from the center to the chord.

Developmental Exercises

DE—1. Prove the following theorem:

> **THEOREM 62**
> **In the same or in equal circles, equal chords are equally distant from the center.**

Solution

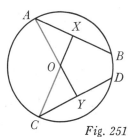

Case I
Given: In $\odot O$, $AB=CD$.
   $OX \perp AB$,
   $OY \perp CD$.
Prove: $OX=OY$.

Construction: Draw lines OA and OC.

Fig. 251

Proof:

STATEMENTS	REASONS
1. $AB=CD$, $OX \perp AB$, $OY \perp CD$.	1. Given.
2. $\frac{1}{2}AB=\frac{1}{2}CD$.	2. If equals are divided by equals, the quotients are equal.
3. $AX=\frac{1}{2}AB$, $CY=\frac{1}{2}CD$.	3. A line through the center of a circle perpendicular to a chord bisects the chord.
4. $AX=CY$.	4. Quantities equal to the same or equal quantities are equal.
5. $OA=OC$.	5. Radii of the same circle are equal.
6. $\triangle AOX \cong \triangle COY$.	6. Why?
7. $OX=OY$.	7. Corresponding sides of congruent triangles are equal.

Now prove this theorem for Case II "in equal circles."

DE—2. Prove the following theorem:

> **‖THEOREM 63**
> **‖ In the same circle or in equal circles, chords equally distant from the**
> **‖ center are equal.**

Solution

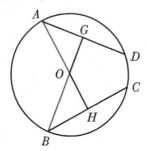 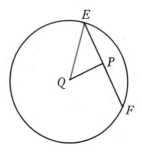

Fig. 252

Given: $\odot O = \odot Q$, $OG = OH = PQ$.
Prove: $AD = BC = EF$.

Analysis:

$OG \perp AD$, $OH \perp BC$, $PQ \perp EF$ since distance is measured along the perpendicular. $AD = BC = EF$ if $AG = BH = EP$ and H, G, and P are their respective midpoints. $AG = BH = EP$ if lines OA, OB, and QE are constructed and triangles AGO, BHO, and EQP are congruent.

Now write a complete proof for this theorem.

Exercises

1. Write a formal proof for Theorem 62, Case II.

2. Write a formal proof for Theorem 63.

3. In a circle chords are drawn from the ends of an arc to the midpoint of the arc. Prove that the chords are equal.

4. In the diagram at the right, $\overset{\frown}{AC} = \overset{\frown}{BD}$, $OE \perp AB$, $OF \perp CD$. Prove $OE = OF$.

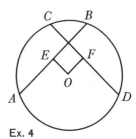

Ex. 4

5. Given chord AB of circle O and chord CD of circle O', prove that if the chords are equal and are equally distant from the center, the circles are equal.

6. Prove that if a parallelogram is inscribed in a circle, the opposite sides are equally distant from the center.

7. An equilateral polygon is inscribed in a circle. If the midpoint of two sides are joined in order and also joined to the center of the circle, prove that an isosceles triangle is formed.

8. Prove that the perpendiculars from the center of a circle to the sides of a regular inscribed polygon are equal.

9. Prove that the diagonals of an inscribed isosceles trapezoid are equally distant from the center of the circle.

10. Given equal circles O and Q intersecting at A and B, prove $QBOA$ is a rhombus.

11. Construct a chord equal and perpendicular to a given chord in a circle. Prove your construction.

12. Construct a chord equal and parallel to another chord in the same circle. Prove your construction.

13. If the center of a circle is located on the bisector of an angle, prove the circle intercepts equal chords, if any, from the sides of the angle. Is the phrase "if any" necessary in this exercise?

14. Draw two equal circles and a line segment joining their centers. Draw a line parallel to their line of centers and intersecting each circle in two points. Prove the chords intercepted in the circles are equal.

15. Given: AC and BE are equal chords,
OD is a radius.
Prove: $\angle APO = \angle BPO$.

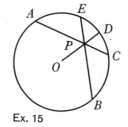

Ex. 15

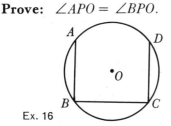

Ex. 16

16. Given: $AB \perp BC$,
$DC \perp BC$.
Prove: $AB = DC$.

A TANGENT TO A CIRCLE

Figure 253 shows how a secant to a circle can rotate about a point until the line and circle have but one point in common. In that position the line is a *tangent* to the circle. The circle is also said to be *tangent* to the line. Point *A* is called the *point of tangency*, or *point of contact*.

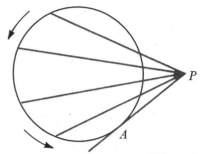

Fig. 253

This intricate cut glass design is composed of concentric circles and many intersecting tangents to each circle.

Developmental Exercises

DE—1. Draw a circle having a diameter of at least two inches. Lay a pencil in the same plane as the circle but not in contact with it. Think of the pencil as a straight line segment. Describe the relationship between the pencil and the circle as you slide the pencil toward the circle, keeping it parallel to its original position.

Solution

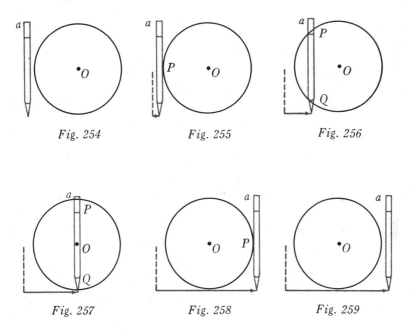

Fig. 254   Fig. 255   Fig. 256

Fig. 257   Fig. 258   Fig. 259

Figure 254—The line and the circle have no points in common.

Figure 255—The line and the circle first have one point in common; line *a* is a tangent.

Figure 256—The line and the circle have two points in common; line *a* is a secant. A segment of the secant, *PQ*, is a chord.

Figure 257—Chord *PQ* becomes a diameter as secant *a* moves through the center of the circle.

Figure 258—Line *a* again becomes a tangent.

Figure 259—The line and the circle have no points in common.

DE—2. Prove the following theorem:

THEOREM 64

If a line is perpendicular to a radius at its outer end, it is tangent to the circle.

Solution

Given: OA is a radius of $\odot O$.
Prove: $OA \perp BC$ at A,
BC is tangent to $\odot O$
at A.

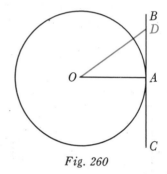

Fig. 260

Construction: Draw OD, D being any point on BC other than A.

Proof:

STATEMENTS	REASONS
1. $OA \perp BC$.	1. Given.
2. OA is the shortest distance from O to BC.	2. The length of the perpendicular is the shortest distance from a point to a line.
3. OD is not perpendicular to BC.	3. From a point to a line one, and only one, perpendicular can be constructed. In this case OA is that unique perpendicular.
4. OD is greater than OA.	4. Same as Reason 2.
5. D lies outside $\odot O$.	5. A point is inside, on, or outside a circle according to whether its distance from the center is respectively less than, equal to, or greater than the radius of the circle.
6. All points of BC except A are outside $\odot O$.	6. D was any point on BC other than A.
7. A is on circle O.	7. Same as Reason 4.
8. BC is tangent to $\odot O$.	8. If a line and a circle have but one point in common, the line is tangent to the circle.

DE—3. Prove the following theorem:

THEOREM 65

A tangent to a circle is perpendicular to a radius drawn to the point of contact.

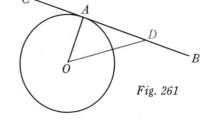

Solution

> **Given:** BC is tangent to $\odot O$
> at A.
> **Prove:** $BC \perp OA$ at A.

Fig. 261

Construction: Draw OD, D being any point on BC other than A.

Proof:

BC is tangent to $\odot O$ at A; therefore, A is the only point BC and $\odot O$ have in common. All other points on BC lie outside $\odot O$. OD is greater than OA for if a point is outside a circle its distance from the center is greater than a radius.

Since D is any point on BC other than point A, OA is the shortest distance from O to BC, and thus is the length along the perpendicular from O to BC. It is proved, therefore, that OA is perpendicular to BC at A.

DE—4. Prove the following theorem:

THEOREM 66

If a line through the center of a circle is perpendicular to a tangent, it passes through the point of tangency.

Solution

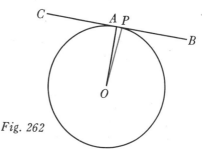

> **Given:** BC is tangent to $\odot O$
> at P,
> $OA \perp BC$ at A.
> **Prove:** P and A coincide.

Construction: Draw OP.   *Fig. 262*

Proof:

BC is perpendicular to OP (Theorem 65).

BC is given as perpendicular to OA. Since only one perpendicular can be constructed from a point to a line, OA must coincide with OP. Two lines can intersect in one, and only one, point; thus, points P and A must coincide.

DE—5. Prove the following theorem:

> ‖**THEOREM 67**
>
> ‖**If a line is perpendicular to a tangent at the point of contact, it passes through the center of the circle.**

Solution

Fig. 263

Given: *BC* is tangent to ⊙*O* at *A*,

$DA \perp BC$.

Prove: *DA* passes through *O*.

Construction: Draw *OA*.

Proof:

BC is perpendicular to *OA* (Theorem 65).

BC is given as perpendicular to *DA*. Hence, both *DA* and *OA* are perpendicular to *BC* at *A*. But in a plane through a point on a line one, and only one, perpendicular can be constructed. Thus, *OD* and *OA* must coincide. Line *OD* passes through *O*.

Exercises

1. Draw a circle and locate a point, *P*, on it. Plan a method for constructing a tangent to the circle at *P*. Test your plan.

2. Devise a method to construct two parallel tangents to a circle. Test your plan, leaving all construction lines on your paper.

3. Draw a circle and a given line which does not have any point in common with the circle. To the circle construct a tangent which is parallel to the given line.

4. Construct a tangent to a circle so that it is parallel to a given chord.

5. *A* and *B* are points of tangency of tangents *PA* and *PB*. *OA* and *OB* are radii. $\angle O = 115°$. How many degrees are in $\angle P$?

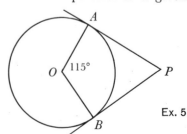

Ex. 5

Ex. 6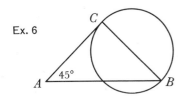

6. Given: *CB* is a diameter,
$$AC = CB,$$
$$\angle A = 45°.$$
Prove: *AC* is a tangent.

7. At *P*, the midpoint of $\overset{\frown}{XY}$, construct a tangent to the circle. Prove the tangent parallel to chord *XY*.

8. Draw a chord of a circle. Construct two tangents to the circle which are both parallel to the given chord.

9. Draw a circle and a given line which does not have any point in common with the circle. To the circle construct a tangent which is perpendicular to the given line.

10. Given two circles tangent to the same line, draw radii to the points of contact. Prove the radii are parallel. Arrange the circles in more than one position. Are the radii always parallel?

TANGENTS FROM AN EXTERNAL POINT

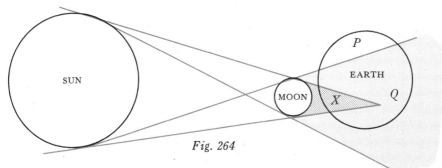

Fig. 264

Our earth, moon, and sun are in approximately the positions shown above during an eclipse of the sun. An astronomer notes four common tangents to the sun and moon as he studies the

    a. total eclipse at *X*.
    b. partial eclipse at *Q*.
    c. well-lighted area, *P*.

Can you prepare a sketch of an eclipse of the moon? The earth must then prevent rays of sunlight from reaching the moon.

Developmental Exercises

DE—1. Select three points outside and at different distances from a given circle. Construct two tangents to the circle from each point. Measure the length of each tangent. What generalization about two tangents from a common point seems reasonable?

Solution

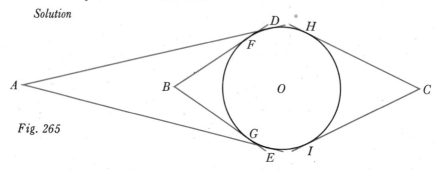

Fig. 265

$AD = AE$; $BF = BG$; and $CH = CI$. It seems reasonable to state the following theorem:

THEOREM 68

The lengths of tangents to a circle from a point outside the circle are equal.

DE—2. Prove that the lengths of tangents to a circle from a point outside the circle are equal.

Solution

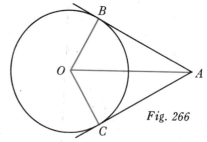

> **Given:** Tangents AB and AC to $\odot O$.
> **Prove:** $AB = AC$.

Fig. 266

Construction: Radii OB and OC and line OA.

Analysis:

$AB = AC$ if they are corresponding parts of congruent triangles.

$\triangle ABO \cong \triangle ACO$ if $\angle ABO$ and $\angle ACO$ are right angles, $OB = OC$, and $OA = OA$.

Now write a proof for this theorem.

Exercises

1. Write a formal proof for Theorem 68.

2. Prove the following theorem:

> **THEOREM 69**
>
> **If two tangents are drawn to a circle from a common point, the line from the point to the center of the circle bisects the angle between the tangents.**

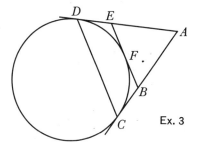

3. Given: AD and AC are tangents,

$\qquad$ F is any point on $\overset{\frown}{DC}$,

$\qquad$ BE tangent at F.

$\quad$ **Prove:** $AD + AC = AB + BE + AE$.

Ex. 3

4. From an external point a tangent is drawn to each of two circles. If the lengths of the tangents are equal and the lines from the external point to the center of the circles are equal, prove the circles are equal.

5. Construct a circle and then construct three points A, B, and C that divide the circle into three equal parts. Construct tangents to the circle at A, B, and C.

6. Prove that the tangents constructed in Exercise **5** form an equilateral triangle.

7. Two tangents from a point to a circle form equal angles with the chord which joins the points of contact.

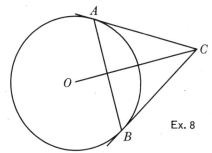

8. AC and BC are tangent to circle O. Prove CO is the perpendicular bisector of AB.

Ex. 8

Ex. 9

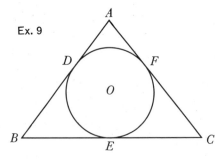

9. Given: $AB = AC$,
       AB, BC, and AC are
       tangents.
   Prove: E is the midpoint of
       BC.

10. AB and AC are tangents to
$\odot O$, $\angle BAC = 50°$. How many degrees are in each angle in the diagram?

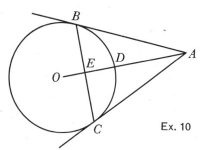

Ex. 10

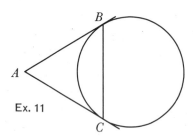

Ex. 11

11. Given: AB and AC are tan-
       gents,
       $\angle BAC = 60°$.
   Prove: $\triangle ABC$ is equilateral.

12. Draw two chords intersecting in a circle. Given that a diameter
through their point of intersection bisects the angle between the chords,
prove the chords are equal.

13. Draw AB and CD as nonparallel line segments, construct a circle
tangent to AB and CD.

14. Given: PA and PB are tangents,
       OA and OB are radii,
       AB is a chord.
   Prove: $\angle OAC = \angle OBC$.

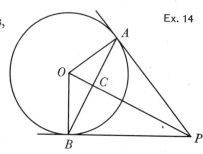

Ex. 14

TANGENT CIRCLES

Two circles are tangent to each other if they are tangent to the same line at the same point. If their centers lie on the same side of their common tangent, they are tangent *internally*. See Figure 267. If their centers are on opposite sides of their common tangent, they are tangent *externally*. See Figure 268.

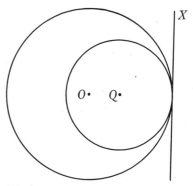

Fig. 267

Developmental Exercises

DE—1. Prove that if two circles are tangent externally, their line of centers passes through the point of contact.

Solution

> **Given:** $\odot O$ and $\odot Q$ tangent externally at C to AB. Line OQ is the line of center.
>
> **Prove:** C is on OQ.

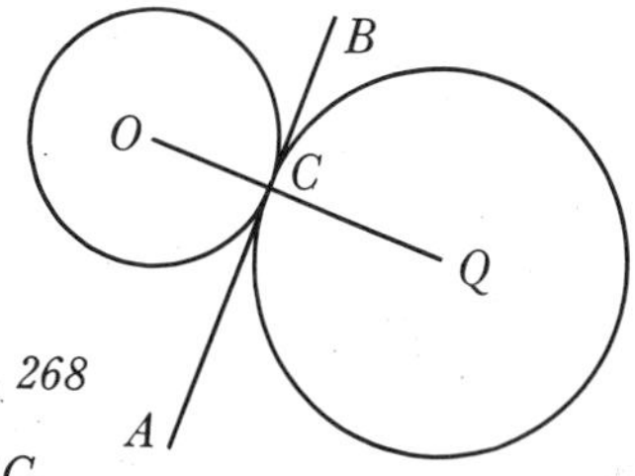

Fig. 268

Construction: Draw radii OC and QC.

Proof:

STATEMENTS	REASONS
1. AB is tangent to $\odot O$ and $\odot Q$ at C.	1. Given.
2. QC is a radius of Q, OC is a radius of O.	2. Construction.
3. $QC \perp AB$, $OC \perp AB$.	3. A tangent to a circle is perpendicular to a radius drawn to the point of contact.
4. QCO is a straight line.	4. Through a given point there is one and only one perpendicular to a given line.
5. OQ is a straight line.	5. Given.
6. $\therefore QCO$ and OQ coincide.	6. Between two points one and only one straight line can be drawn.
7. C is on OQ.	7. Why?

DE—2. Prove that if two circles are tangent internally, their line of centers (extended if necessary) passes through the point of contact.

Solution

Given: $\odot O$ and $\odot Q$ tangent internally at C to AB. Line OQ is the line of centers.

Prove: C is on OQ.

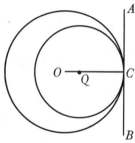

Fig. 269

Construction: Draw radii OC and QC.

Analysis:

The proof is similar to the proof in Developmental Exercise 1. $OC \perp AB$ at C, $QC \perp AB$ at C. (A tangent to a circle is perpendicular to a radius drawn to the point of contact.) Since through point C there is one and only one perpendicular to line AB, QOC is a straight line. QOC is the line of centers extended since between two points one, and only one, straight line can be drawn and any line segment can be extended in either direction.

As a result of Developmental Exercises **1** and **2** the following theorem has been proved.

THEOREM 70

If two circles are tangent, their line of centers (extended if necessary) passes through the point of contact.

Exercises

*Which of Exercises **1-3** are valid? Give a proof for any valid propositions and use a drawing to illustrate the lack of validity of the others.*

1. Two circles tangent to the same line are tangent to each other.

2. If three circles are tangent to each other, their centers lie in a straight line.

3. If two circles are tangent to the same circle, they are tangent to each other.

4. Circles O and O' are tangent externally at B. Prove that any point on their common tangent through B is equidistant from points O and O'.

5. *AC*, *AF*, *BD*, and *BG* are tangents and the circles are tangent at *E*. If *AF* = *BG*, prove *AC* = *BD*.

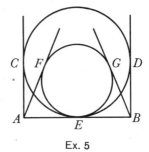

Ex. 5

6. Three circles are tangent so that each is tangent to each of the other two. The lines of centers are 18″, 16″, and 1 foot. Compute the radius of each circle.

COMMON INTERNAL TANGENTS

The *line of centers* of two circles is the line segment that joins their centers. Lines that are tangent to two circles and intersect their line of centers are called *common internal tangents*. In Figure 270, *AB* is a common internal tangent of circles *O* and *P* and of circles *O* and *Q*. *Common external tangents* to two circles are lines tangent to both circles and not intersecting their line of centers. *AB* is a common external tangent to circles *P* and *Q*.

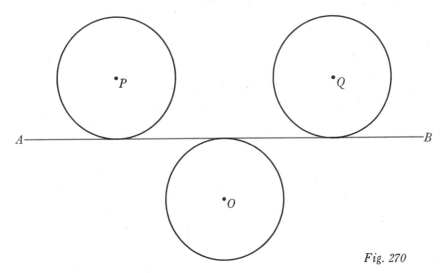

Fig. 270

Developmental Exercises

DE—1. If common internal tangents are drawn to two circles, prove the tangents are of equal length.

Solution

The exercise does not state whether the circles are equal or unequal. Equal circles may have properties not possessed by unequal circles, but the relationships which exist for unequal circles will also exist if the circles are equal. Hence, the more general case, and the one to be considered here, is when the circles are unequal.

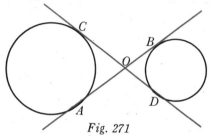

Given: Two circles with common internal tangents *AB* and *CD*.
Prove: *AB*=*CD*.

Fig. 271

Proof:

STATEMENTS	REASONS
1. $AO=CO$, $OB=OD$.	1. Why?
2. $AO+OB=CO+OD$.	2. Why?
3. $AB=AO+OB$, $CD=CO+OD$.	3. Why?
4. $AB=CD$.	4. Why?

DE—2. Prove that if two circles are tangent externally, the common internal tangent bisects the common external tangent.

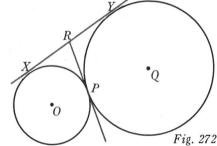

Solution

Given: $\odot O$ tangent to $\odot Q$ at *P*.
XY a common external tangent.
PR a common internal tangent.
Prove: $XR=RY$.
Analysis:

Tangents to a circle from a point outside the circle are equal. Thus, $XR=RP$ and $RP=RY$. Therefore, $XR=RY$. Does it matter if $\odot O$ does equal $\odot Q$?

Fig. 272

Exercises

1. If quadrilateral *ABCD* is circumscribed about a circle with *AB*, *BC*, *CD*, and *DA* tangent at *H*, *G*, *F*, and *E* respectively, prove *BH*+ *CF* = *BC* and *AH*+*DF* = *AD*.

2. Given: *AD* and *BC* are chords of one of two concentric circles and tangents of the other.
Prove: *AD* = *BC*.

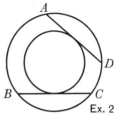
Ex. 2

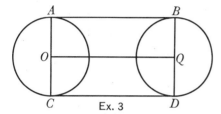
Ex. 3

3. Given: *AB* and *CD* are external tangents to circles *O* and *Q*.
Prove: *AB* = *CD*.

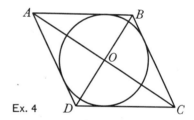
Ex. 4

4. *AB*, *BC*, *CD*, and *AD* are tangents to the circle with center *O*. Prove ∠*BOC*+ ∠*AOD* = 180°.

5. Construct two circles making the sum of their radii equal to the length of their line of centers. Construct common external and common internal tangents.

6. Draw tangents *PA* and *PB* to circle *O*. Draw diameter *AOC*. Join *O* to *P*, *C* to *B*, and *A* to *B*. Prove *PO* ∥ *BC*.

7. Draw two externally tangent circles. Through their common point draw any line which terminates in the circles. Prove that tangents to the circles at those points are parallel.

8. *A*, *B*, and *C* are the points of tangency. Prove ∠*ACB* is a right angle.

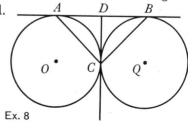
Ex. 8

ANGLES AND THEIR INTERCEPTED ARCS

An *inscribed angle* is an angle whose vertex is on the circle and whose sides are chords of the circle. An inscribed angle may be drawn in several positions in relation to the center of the circle. The center of the circle may lie on the angle, inside the angle, or outside the angle. A proof must consider each of these positions before it can be accepted as valid.

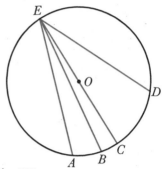

Fig. 273

There is a relationship between the size of the angle formed by intersecting lines in a circle and the size of the arcs intercepted by these lines. Each possibility will be studied in the following theorems. After you have carefully studied each theorem, perhaps you can make a generalization to cover all the possibilities.

Developmental Exercises

DE—1. Prove the following theorem:

THEOREM 71
An inscribed angle is measured by one-half its intercepted arc.

Solution

Given: $\angle ABC$ is inscribed in $\odot O$.

Prove: $\angle ABC \stackrel{\circ}{=} \frac{1}{2}\widehat{AC}$.

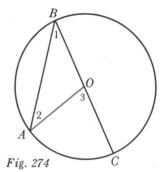

Fig. 274

Case I. One side of the inscribed angle is a diameter.

STATEMENTS	REASONS
1. Join A to O.	1. Two points in a plane determine a line.
2. $AO = BO$.	2. Radii of a circle are equal.
3. $\angle 3 \overset{\circ}{=} \widehat{AC}$.	3. A central angle is measured by its intersected arc.
4. $\angle 1 = \angle 2$.	4. Angles opposite equal sides of a triangle are equal.
5. $\angle 3 = \angle 2 + \angle 1$.	5. An exterior angle of a triangle is equal to the sum of the remote interior angles.
6. $\angle 3 = 2 \angle 1$.	6. A quantity may be substituted for its equal.
7. $\dfrac{\angle 3}{2} = \angle 1$.	7. If equals are divided by equals the quotients are equal.
8. $\angle 1 \overset{\circ}{=} \dfrac{\widehat{AC}}{2}$.	8. Same as Reason 6.

Case II. The center of the circle lies within the inscribed angle.

Fig. 275

STATEMENTS	REASONS
1. From B to O construct line segment BOD.	1. Two points in a plane determine a line.
2. $\angle 1 \overset{\circ}{=} \dfrac{\widehat{AD}}{2}$, $\angle 2 \overset{\circ}{=} \dfrac{\widehat{DC}}{2}$.	2. Case I.
3. $\angle 1 + \angle 2 \overset{\circ}{=} \dfrac{\widehat{AD}}{2} + \dfrac{\widehat{DC}}{2}$ or $\frac{1}{2}(\widehat{AD} + \widehat{DC})$.	3. If equals are added to equals the sums are equal.
4. $\angle 1 + \angle 2 = \angle ABC$, $\widehat{AD} + \widehat{DC} = \widehat{AC}$.	4. The whole is equal to the sum of its parts.
5. $\frac{1}{2}(\widehat{AD} + \widehat{DC}) = \frac{1}{2}\widehat{AC}$.	5. If equals are divided by equals the quotients are equal.
6. $\angle ABC \overset{\circ}{=} \frac{1}{2}\widehat{AC}$.	6. A quantity may be substituted for its equal.

Case III. The center of the circle lies outside the angle.

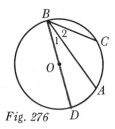

Fig. 276

STATEMENTS	REASONS
1. From B to O construct line segment BOD.	1. Two points in a plane determine a line.
2. $\angle DBC \overset{\circ}{=} \frac{1}{2}\overset{\frown}{DC}$, $\angle 1 \overset{\circ}{=} \frac{1}{2}\overset{\frown}{DA}$.	2. Case I.
3. $\angle DBC = \angle 1 + \angle 2$.	3. Why?
4. $\frac{1}{2}\overset{\frown}{DC} \overset{\circ}{=} \frac{1}{2}\overset{\frown}{DA} + \angle 2$.	4. Why?
5. $\angle 2 \overset{\circ}{=} \frac{1}{2}\overset{\frown}{DC} - \frac{1}{2}\overset{\frown}{DA}$.	5. If equals are subtracted from equals the differences are equal.
6. $\overset{\frown}{DC} = \overset{\frown}{DA} + \overset{\frown}{AC}$.	6. Reason 3.
7. $\frac{1}{2}\overset{\frown}{DC} = \frac{1}{2}\overset{\frown}{DA} + \frac{1}{2}\overset{\frown}{AC}$.	7. Why?
8. $\frac{1}{2}\overset{\frown}{DC} - \frac{1}{2}\overset{\frown}{DA} = \frac{1}{2}\overset{\frown}{AC}$.	8. Reason 5.
9. $\angle 2 \overset{\circ}{=} \frac{1}{2}\overset{\frown}{AC}$.	9. Reason 4.

The proof is general since all possible positions of an inscribed angle have been considered.

Corollary 1
Any angle inscribed in a semicircle is a right angle.

Corollary 2
Two inscribed angles whose sides intercept the same arc or equal arcs of a circle are equal.

Corollary 3
A circle which has the hypotenuse of a right triangle as a diameter passes through the vertex of the right angle.

Corollary 4
The opposite angles of an inscribed quadrilateral are supplementary.

Corollary 5
Parallel lines intercept equal arcs on a circle.

Exercises

1. Prove Corollary 1.

2. Prove Corollary 2.

3. Prove Corollary 3.

4. Prove Corollary 4.

5. Prove Corollary 5.

6. a. Name the inscribed angles in the diagram.

    b. Identify any angles which are inscribed in the same arc.

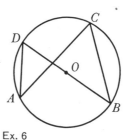

Ex. 6

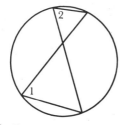

Ex. 7

7. State the relationship between angles 1 and 2. Give a reason for your answer.

8. Given that quadrilateral *ABCD* is inscribed in a circle and ∠*C* = 110°, find the number of degrees in ∠*A*.

9. Use a triangle inscribed in a circle to prove that the sum of the angles of a triangle is 180°.

10. Given that the angles of a triangle inscribed in a circle are 2*x*, *x*, and *x*+5. Find the number of degrees in each arc of the circle.

11. Given: △*ABC* is inscribed in ⊙*O*; ∠*A* = 2 ∠*B*; and $\overset{\frown}{AB}$ = 72°. Find the number of degrees in $\overset{\frown}{CB}$.

12. Given: *AB* ∥ *DC*,
        AC ∥ *DE*,
        $\overset{\frown}{BC}$ = 30°.
Find the number of degrees in $\overset{\frown}{CE}$.

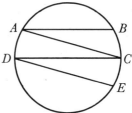

Ex. 12

13. Given: Inscribed quadrilateral *ABCD*,
$\overset{\frown}{DC} = 82°$,
$\angle BDC = 56°$.
Prove: $\angle DCB = ?°$.

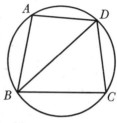

Ex. 13

14. If one of the legs of an isosceles triangle is a diameter of a circle, prove the base of the triangle is bisected by the circle.

15. Prove that if any two equal chords of a circle intersect, their corresponding segments are equal.

16. Explain how a right angle can be constructed, using only compasses and straightedge.

17. Explain how an inscribed angle varies as its intercepted arc changes from about 20° to about 300°.

18. Prove that a parallelogram inscribed in a circle is a rectangle.

19. Given: *AB* ∥ *DC*,
DB bisects $\angle ABE$.
Prove: *BE* = *DC*.

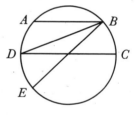

Ex. 19

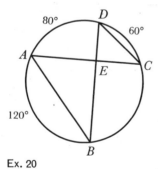

Ex. 20

20. Find the number of degrees in
a. $\angle ABC$ **b.** $\angle ACD$
c. $\angle DBC$ **d.** $\angle ACB$
e. $\overset{\frown}{BC}$ **f.** $\angle BAC$
g. $\angle AED$ **h.** $\angle DEC$
i. $\angle AEB$
j. Can you find any relationship between the number of degrees in $\overset{\frown}{AB} + \overset{\frown}{DC}$ and $\angle AEB$ or $\angle DEC$?

DE—2. Prove the following theorem:

> **THEOREM 72**
>
> **An angle formed by a tangent and a chord at the point of contact is measured by one-half the intercepted arc.**

Solution

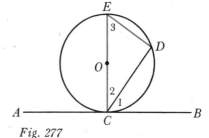

Fig. 277

Given: AB is tangent to
$\odot O$ at C,
CD is a chord.

Prove: $\angle DCB \overset{\circ}{=} \frac{1}{2}\widehat{DC}$.

Construction: Join C to O and extend CO to make a diameter of circle O.

Proof:

STATEMENTS	REASONS
1. AB is tangent to $\odot O$ at C, CD is a chord.	1. Given.
2. Draw COE and DE.	2. Between two points one and only one line can be constructed.
3. $\angle D = 90°$.	3. An angle inscribed in a semicircle is a right angle.
4. $\angle D + \angle 2 + \angle 3 = 180°$.	4. The sum of the interior angles of a triangle is 180°.
5. $\angle 2 + \angle 3 = 90°$.	5. Why?
6. $EC \perp AB$.	6. A tangent to a circle is perpendicular to a radius drawn to the point of contact.
7. $\angle BCE = 90°$.	7. Why?
8. $\angle BCE = \angle 1 + \angle 2$.	8. The whole is equal to the sum of its parts.
9. $\angle 1 + \angle 2 = 90°$.	9. Why?
10. $\angle 1 = \angle 3$.	10. Complements of the same angle are equal.
11. $\angle 3 \overset{\circ}{=} \frac{1}{2}\widehat{DC}$.	11. An inscribed angle is measured by one-half its intercepted arc.
12. $\angle 1 \overset{\circ}{=} \frac{1}{2}\widehat{DC}$.	12. Quantities equal to the same quantity are equal.

Exercises

1. In the diagram, what is the measure of $\angle 1$ if
   a. $\overset{\frown}{CD} = 116°$.
   b. $\overset{\frown}{CD} = 99°$.
   c. $\overset{\frown}{ED} = 40°$.
   d. $\angle 3 = 57°$.

2. In the diagram, how many degrees are in $\overset{\frown}{DC}$ if
   a. $\angle 1 = 88°$.
   b. $\angle 1 = 25°$.
   c. $\angle 2 = 19°$.

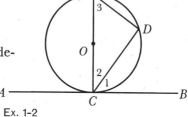

Ex. 1-2

3. Given: AB tangent to $\odot O$ at C,
      DE tangent to $\odot O$ at F,
      $\overset{\frown}{CN} = \overset{\frown}{MF}$,
      $\overset{\frown}{FMC} = \overset{\frown}{CNF}$.
Prove: $\angle 1 = \angle 2$.

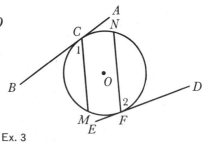

Ex. 3

4. Prove that a tangent through the vertex of an inscribed isoceles triangle is parallel to the base.

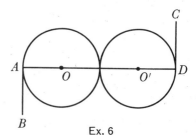

5. In the diagram, r is tangent to $\odot O$ at A. Prove that $\angle 3$ is the supplement of $\angle(1+2)$.

Ex. 5

6. Given: $\odot O$ and $\odot O'$ tangent at X.
      AB and CD are tangents.
Prove: $AB \parallel CD$.

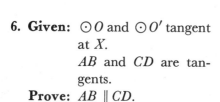

Ex. 6

DE—3. Prove the following theorem:

> **THEOREM 73**
>
> **An angle formed by two intersecting chords is measured by one-half the sum of the arcs intercepted by the angle and by its vertical angle.**

Solution

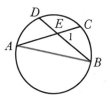

Given: *AC* and *DB* are chords of the circle intersecting at *E* forming $\angle 1$.

Prove: $\angle 1 \stackrel{\circ}{=} \frac{1}{2}(\overset{\frown}{BC}+\overset{\frown}{DA})$.

Fig. 278

Proof:

STATEMENTS	REASONS
1. Draw *AB*.	1. Between two points one and only one line segment can be drawn.
2. $\angle 1 = \angle A + \angle B$.	2. The exterior angle of a triangle is equal to the sum of the two nonadjacent interior angles.
3. $\angle A \stackrel{\circ}{=} \frac{1}{2}\overset{\frown}{BC}$, $\angle B \stackrel{\circ}{=} \frac{1}{2}\overset{\frown}{AD}$.	3. An inscribed angle is measured by one-half its intercepted arc.
4. $\angle 1 \stackrel{\circ}{=} \frac{1}{2}\overset{\frown}{BC}+\frac{1}{2}\overset{\frown}{DA}$ or $\frac{1}{2}(\overset{\frown}{BC}+\overset{\frown}{DA})$.	4. A quantity may be substituted for its equal.

Exercises

1. Angles formed by two intersecting chords intercept consecutive arcs of 54°, 106°, 110°, and 90°. Find the number of degrees in the angles formed by the chords.

2. An angle of 75° is formed by two intersecting chords. One of the intercepted arcs is 105°. How many degrees are in the other?

3. Given: *AC* and *BD* are chords.

Prove: $\angle AEB = \angle P + \angle Q$.

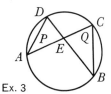

Ex. 3

4. Prove that if two chords in a circle are perpendicular, the sum of two opposite intercepted arcs is 180°.

5. Inscribe in a circle a quadrilateral with two equal adjacent sides. From their common point draw a diagonal. Prove that the diagonal bisects the angle to whose vertex it is drawn.

6. Prove that chords, which are perpendicular to a third chord at its endpoints, are equal.

7. Form an inscribed angle by drawing a diameter and a chord. Draw a radius parallel to the chord and prove that it bisects the arc intercepted by the diameter and chord.

8. Prove that if the diagonals of an inscribed quadrilateral are diameters of the circle, the quadrilateral is a rectangle.

DE—4. Prove the following theorem:

> **THEOREM 74**
>
> **If two secants are drawn to a circle from an external point, the angle formed is measured by one-half the difference between the intercepted arcs.**

Solution

Given: AC and AD are secants.

Prove: $\angle A \overset{\circ}{=} \frac{1}{2}(\overset{\frown}{DC} - \overset{\frown}{BE})$.

Construction: Join E to C.

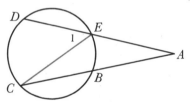

Fig. 279

Proof:

STATEMENTS	REASONS
1. AC and AD are secants.	1. Given.
2. $\angle 1 = \angle A + \angle BCE$.	2. The exterior angle of a triangle is equal to the sum of the two nonadjacent interior angles.
3. $\angle A = \angle 1 - \angle BCE$.	3. If equals are subtracted from equals the differences are equal.
4. $\angle 1 \overset{\circ}{=} \dfrac{\overset{\frown}{DC}}{2}$, $\angle BCE \overset{\circ}{=} \dfrac{\overset{\frown}{BE}}{2}$.	4. An inscribed angle is measured by one-half its intercepted arc.
5. $\angle A \overset{\circ}{=} \frac{1}{2}\overset{\frown}{DC} - \frac{1}{2}\overset{\frown}{BE}$, or $\angle A \overset{\circ}{=} \frac{1}{2}(\overset{\frown}{DC} - \overset{\frown}{BE})$.	5. A quantity may be substituted for its equal.

Exercises

1. In Figure 279, how many degrees are in $\angle A$ if
   a. $\overset{\frown}{DC} = 160°$, $\overset{\frown}{EB} = 40°$.   **b.** $\overset{\frown}{DC} = 117°$, $\overset{\frown}{BE} = 52°$.
   c. $\overset{\frown}{DC} = 78°10'$, $\overset{\frown}{BE} = 34°50'$.   **d.** $\angle 1 = 70°$, $\overset{\frown}{BE} = 22°20'$.

2. In Figure 279, how many degrees are in $\overset{\frown}{DC}$ if
   a. $\angle A = 50°$, $\overset{\frown}{BE} = 26°$.   **b.** $\angle A = 37°10'$, $\overset{\frown}{BE} = 13°$.

3. In Figure 279, how many degrees are in $\overset{\frown}{BE}$ if
   a. $\angle A = 30°$, $\overset{\frown}{DC} = 116°$.   **b.** $\angle A = 10°20'$, $\overset{\frown}{DC} = 62°$.

4. Given: $AB = BC$,
            $\angle C = 10°$.
Find the number of degrees in $\overset{\frown}{AE}$.

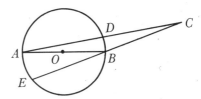

Ex. 4

DE—5. Prove the following theorem:

|| **THEOREM 75**
|| If two tangents are drawn to a circle from an external point, the angle
|| formed is measured by one-half the difference between the inter-
|| cepted arcs.

Solution

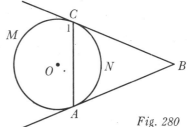

    Given: BC and BA are tan-
          gents to the circle.
    Prove: $\angle B \overset{\circ}{=} \frac{1}{2}(\overset{\frown}{CMA} - \overset{\frown}{CNA})$.

Fig. 280

    Analysis:
    $\angle B \overset{\circ}{=} \frac{1}{2}(\overset{\frown}{CMA} - \overset{\frown}{CNA})$ if $\angle B = \angle 1 - \angle BAC$; $\angle 1 \overset{\circ}{=} \frac{1}{2}\overset{\frown}{CMA}$ and $\angle BAC$
$\overset{\circ}{=} \frac{1}{2}\overset{\frown}{CNA}$.

    Now write a formal proof for the theorem.

|| **Corollary**
|| If a tangent and a secant are drawn to a circle from an external point,
|| the angle formed is measured by one-half the difference between the
|| intercepted arcs.

Exercises

1. Prove Theorem 75.

2. Prove the corollary.

In Exercises **3-5** *refer to Figure 280.*

3. By what arc is $\angle CAB$ measured? $\angle ACB$? What is your conclusion? Compare AB and CB.

4. How many degrees are in $\angle B$ if
    a. $\widehat{CMA} = 260°$.   **b.** $\widehat{CNA} = 112°$.   **c.** $\angle 1 = 107°$.

5. How many degrees are in $\widehat{CMA}$ and $\widehat{CNA}$ if
    a. $\angle B = 80°$.   **b.** $\angle B = 67°20'$.

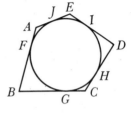

6. Given: $\widehat{JF} = 54°$,
             $\widehat{JI} = 56°$,
             $\widehat{IH} = 88°$,
             $\widehat{FG} = 105°$.

Find the number of degrees in $\angle A$, $\angle B$, $\angle C$, $\angle D$, and $\angle E$.

Ex. 6

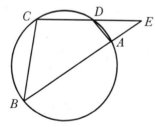

Ex. 7

7. Given: $ABCD$ is an inscribed
            quadrilateral,
            BA and CD extend to
            meet at E,
            $\widehat{BC} = 98°$,
            $\angle E = 34°$,
            $\widehat{DC} = 64°$.

Find the number of degrees in $\angle B$, $\angle C$, and $\widehat{AD}$.

8. AB and AC are tangents to the circle O. Compare the measure of $\angle D$ with $\angle A$.

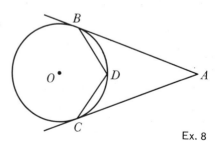

Ex. 8

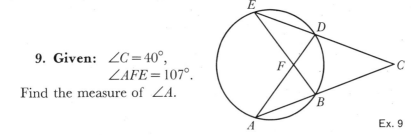

9. Given: $\angle C = 40°$,
$\qquad\angle AFE = 107°$.
Find the measure of $\angle A$.

Ex. 9

10. If tangents are drawn to a circle from a common point so that the length of the chord joining the points of tangency is equal to the length of the tangents, determine the measure of each intercepted arc.

11. From point A, tangents AB and AC are drawn to circle O. Q is any point on minor arc CB. Prove that $\angle ABC$ is equal to the sum of $\angle ABQ$ and $\angle ACQ$.

12. Given: $\angle C \stackrel{\circ}{=} \widehat{AD}$,
$\qquad\widehat{BD}$ is 5° less than $\widehat{AD}$.
Find the number of degrees in $\widehat{AB}$.

Ex. 12

Carefully review the theorems and corollaries which show the relationship between the arc or arcs of a circle and (**a**) a central angle, (**b**) an inscribed angle, (**c**) an angle formed by a tangent and a chord, (**d**) an angle formed by two intersecting chords, (**e**) an angle formed by two secants at a common point, (**f**) an angle formed by two tangents at a common point, and (**g**) an angle formed by a tangent and a secant at a common point. Summarize these relationships into one statement. After you have written a generalization, compare it with the following statement.

An angle formed by lines which intersect or are tangent to a circle is measured by one-half the algebraic sum of the intercepted arcs. The value of the smaller arc is assumed to be negative when the vertex of the angle is outside the circle.

Solve the next set of exercises using this generalization.

Exercises

1. Given: BC and BA meet at an
angle of $42°$.
$\overset{\frown}{DC} = 100°$,
$\overset{\frown}{AC} = ?$, $\overset{\frown}{AD} = ?$

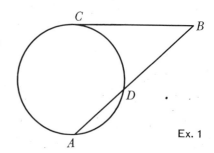

Ex. 1

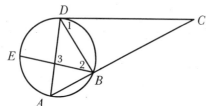

Ex. 2

2. Given: $\overset{\frown}{EA} = 78°$,
$\overset{\frown}{ED} = 88°$,
$\angle 3 = 84°$.

Find the number of degrees in $\angle C$
and $\angle A$.

3. If two tangents to a circle are drawn from an external point and form an angle of $70°$, the larger intercepted arc is what fractional part of the circle?

4. Prove that the angle between two tangents to a circle has a measure equal to $180°$ minus the measure of the smaller of the intercepted arcs.

5. If two tangents to a circle are perpendicular, how many degrees are contained in each intercepted arc?

6. Given: $\angle 1 = 20° = \overset{\frown}{BF}$,
$\overset{\frown}{AB} = 120°$.
Find the number of degrees in $\angle E$,
$\angle A$, and $\angle EDC$.

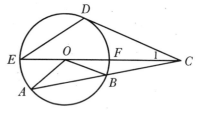

Ex. 6

7. Sides of two angles intercept the same arc of a circle. One angle is inscribed; the other angle is formed by two tangents drawn from the same external point. The inscribed angle has a measure of $50°$. What is the measure of the angle made by the tangents?

8. Two secants intersect at an external point making an angle of $a°$. If the larger arc is $b°$, express in terms of $a°$ and $b°$ the smaller intercepted arc.

SOLID GEOMETRY

A **sphere** *is a surface each point of* *which is the same distance from a given* *point called the center.* Compare this definition with that of a circle.

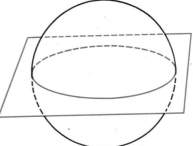

Fig. 281

The intersection of a plane and sphere is always a circle. If the plane passes through the center of the sphere, the intersection is called a *great circle*. Each sphere may have an unlimited number of great circles. Each point on the sphere is a given distance from the center of the sphere. In Figure 282, $OA = OE = OB$. Each point on a great circle is the same given distance from the center of the circle. Thus, the sphere and its great circles have the same center and radius.

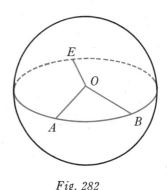

Fig. 282

The shortest distance between two points on a sphere is the length of the minor arc of a great circle containing these two points. In Figure 282, minor arc AB is the shortest distance between A and B. For all practical purposes the earth is considered to be a sphere. When flying from Chicago to London the shortest route follows the arc of the great circle passing through Chicago and London. Try to trace such a route on a globe. Does it appear to be the shortest route?

On the earth the great circle formed by passing an imaginary plane through the center of the sphere perpendicular to the diameter connecting the poles is called the *equator*. The intersections of planes parallel to the plane of the equator are called the *parallels of latitude*. Each great circle through the north pole is known as a *meridian of longitude*.

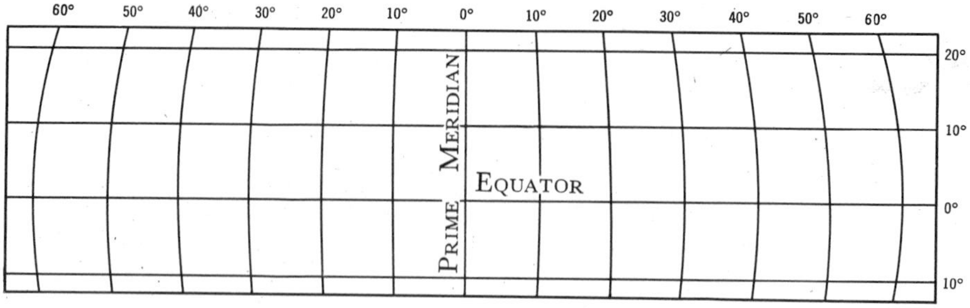

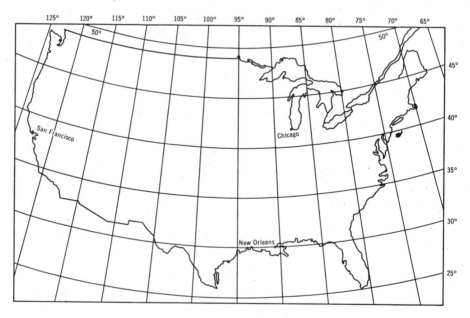

Fig. 283

Every point of the globe can be located by an ordered pair of real numbers corresponding to its exact latitude and longitude. The zero parallel of latitude is the equator. The zero meridian of longitude is called the *prime meridian*. It passes through the poles and Greenwich, England.

Fig. 284

Can you identify the latitude and longitude of New Orleans? Of Chicago? Of San Francisco? Find the approximate longitude and latitude of your city.

Exercises

1. How many lines can be tangent at a point on a sphere at the same time?

2. How many planes can be tangent at a point on a sphere at the same time?

3. Make a sketch to show how two spheres intersect.

4. If a diameter of a sphere is perpendicular to a plane, at an end of the diameter, how are the sphere and plane related?

5. Two TV stations on the same meridian have latitudes of $18°$N and $33°$N. How far apart are they?

6. Why are all great circles of a sphere equal?

EXTEND YOUR HORIZON

Circles help to create other curves which may be new to you. One such curve is the *cycloid*. It is the curve traced by a point on a circle as the circle rolls along a straight line. The length of each of the series of arches is four times the diameter of the circle. The height (amplitude) of each arch is also equal to the diameter of the circle.

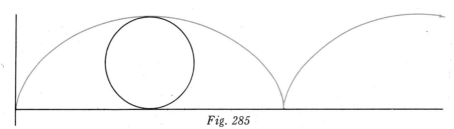

Fig. 285

Teeth of heavy gears are frequently cut so that their faces are arcs of cycloids. When such gears are meshed there is rolling contact between gear teeth instead of grinding contact, thus prolonging the life of the gears many times.

A sliding particle, free from friction, will travel from X to Y along the cycloid in less time than along any other curved line. The cycloid has long been known as "the curve of quickest descent."

CHAPTER SUMMARY

A circle is determined by
1. three noncollinear points.   (page 252)
2. a given point as center and the length of any given line segment as radius.   (page 242)

Two circles are equal if
1. their radii are equal.   (page 242)
2. their diameters are equal.   (page 242)

Two line segments are equal if
1. they are radii of the same or of equal circles.   (page 242)
2. they are diameters of the same or of equal circles.   (page 242)
3. they are chords subtending equal arcs in the same or equal circles. (page 249)
4. they are chords equally distant from the center of the same or of equal circles.   (page 258)
5. they are common internal tangents to two circles.   (page 272)
6. they are tangents to a circle from a common point outside the circle.   (page 266)

Arcs of a circle, or of equal circles, are equal if
1. they are intercepted by equal central angles.   (page 243)
2. they are subtended by equal chords.   (page 248)

A line passing through the center of a circle
1. and terminated by it is a diameter.   (page 242)
2. divides the circle into two equal arcs.   (page 242)
3. and perpendicular to a chord, bisects the chord and the major and minor arcs of the chord.   (page 253)
4. and bisecting any chord, not a diameter, is perpendicular to it. (page 253)
5. and perpendicular to a tangent passes through the point of tangency.   (page 263)

CHAPTER REVIEW

Vocabulary

Match the word in the left hand column with its correct definition in the right hand column.

1. Circle

    a. A line segment which joins two points of a circle.

    b. A line segment that intersects the circle in two points.

2. Chord

    c. A line segment that intersects the circle in one, and only one, point.

3. Secant

    d. A line segment joining the center of a circle to any point of the circle.

4. Tangent

    e. A chord which passes through the center of the circle.

5. Radii

    f. An angle formed by two radii.

    g. An angle formed by two chords.

6. Diameter

    h. A surface each point of which is the same distance from a fixed point called the center.

7. Central Angle

    i. A curve, in a plane, all points of which are equidistant from a fixed point called the center.

8. Concentric Circles

    j. Circles having equal radii but different centers.

9. Inscribed Polygon

    k. Circles having the same center but unequal radii.

10. Circumscribed Polygon

    l. A polygon whose sides are tangents of a circle.

    m. A polygon whose sides are chords of a circle.

11. Sphere

Exercises .

1. Draw a chord in a circle so that it is equal to a radius. How many degrees are in the major arc of the chord?

2. Construct a circle which is tangent to the sides of a given angle and has its center equally distant from two given points.

3. Given that CD is a tangent at A to circle O, draw diameter AB. Draw chord $RS \parallel CD$. Prove AB bisects RS.

4. Given an angle and a line, construct an isosceles triangle having its vertex angle equal to the given angle and the line equal to the radius of the circumscribed circle.

5. Inscribe an equilateral octagon in circle O. YZ is a side of the octagon. How many degrees are in $\angle YOZ$?

6. At B and C, AB and AC respectively are tangent to circle O. Prove that OA is the perpendicular bisector of BC.

7. Draw diameter BC in circle O. Chord AC makes a $33°$ angle with the diameter. How many degrees are in AC?

8. Construct a triangle with a side, an adjacent angle, and a radius of an inscribed circle given.

9. Construct two parallel and equal chords in a circle.

10. Given two parallel lines and a point between them, construct a circle through the given point and also tangent to the parallel lines. .

11. Inscribe isosceles triangle ABC in a circle, making $AB = BC$. Draw diameter BD. Prove $AD = DC$.

12. A right triangle whose sides are 3, 4, and 5 linear units is inscribed in a circle. Determine the radius of the circle.

13. Two sides of an inscribed triangle have arcs of $110°$ and $140°$. How many degrees has each angle of the triangle?

14. Given two externally tangent, equal circles, draw two line segments through the point of contact with their endpoints on the circles. Draw chords joining the endpoints of the line segments. Prove these chords are equal.

CHAPTER TEST

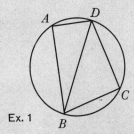

1. In the diagram at the right, $\overset{\frown}{CD} = 100°$ and $\overset{\frown}{BC} = 80°$. Find the number of degrees of $\angle A$ and $\angle DBC$.

Ex. 1

2. An isosceles triangle, ABC, has as its base, AB, a chord of circle O. The legs AC and BC of the triangle intersect the circle at two points, X and Y, respectively. Prove $AX = BY$.

3. In a circle, diameter AB is perpendicular to chord CD. How many degrees are in $\angle ADC$ if $\angle BAC = 80°$.

4. In $\odot O$, AB and AD are chords on opposite sides of diameter AC. Prove $\angle BAD + \angle BCD = 180°$.

5. BC is tangent to $\odot O$ at A. If $\angle ABO = 35°$, how large is $\angle AOB$?

6. AB is tangent to circle O, CD is a diameter. Find the measure of $\overset{\frown}{AC}$, $\angle C$, and $\angle CAB$.

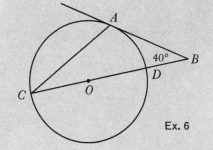

Ex. 6

7. Prove that the corresponding segments of two common internal tangents to two circles are equal.

8. How many degrees are contained in the major arc of a chord if the chord is equal in length to the radius of the circle?

9. Draw a chord in a circle, construct a second circle which is concentric to the first and tangent to the chord.

10. In a circle of radius $4''$, inscribe an isosceles triangle with base angles of $30°$. Determine the length of each side of the triangle.

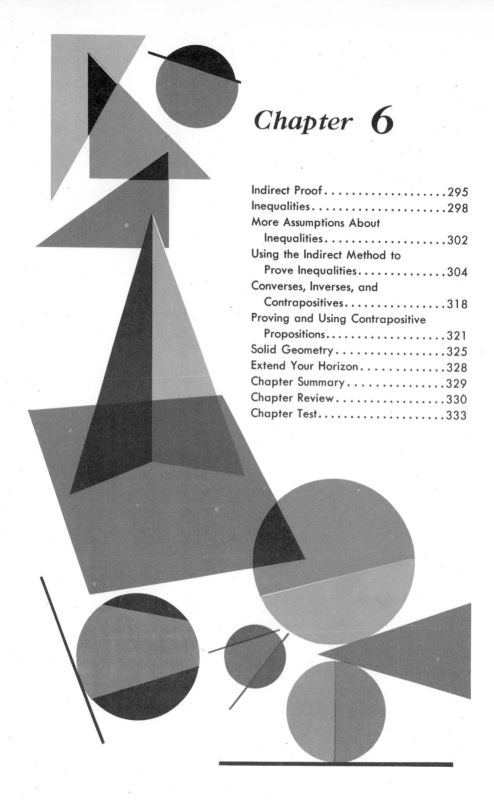

Chapter 6

INDIRECT PROOF AND INEQUALITIES

INDIRECT PROOF

In many states an automobile driver's license must be renewed two years after it is issued. Mr. Ayers carried his driver's license for almost two years. Before leaving with his family for a vacation tour on June 28 for two weeks, it occurred to him to check the expiration date of his driver's license. When he unfolded it he found that the month of issue was made unreadable by a crease in the paper. It read, in part, ". . . ISSUED JU   31. EXPIRES TWO YEARS FROM DATE." Did Mr. Ayers have to renew his license before his vacation?

Mr. Ayers may have reasoned in the following way:

(*1*) The license expires in a month whose first two letters are *JU*. Only two months satisfy this condition, June and July.

(*2*) The license expires on the thirty-first, therefore, the month of expiration has thirty-one days.

(*3*) Since June has only thirty days while July has thirty-one days, the license must expire in July.

On the basis of this reasoning, Mr. Ayers did not have to renew his license before his vacation.

This conclusion was not deduced directly but indirectly. This method of reasoning is called an *indirect proof*. Although the month was illegible, the conclusion formed by this indirect method was certain.

|| **Conclusions may be established by indirect proof.**

If a conclusion established through proper reasoning is false then any one or all of the assumptions from which the conclusion follows also must be false. If Mr. Ayer's license was not due for renewal, then his assumption that it must be renewed every two years is false.

Developmental Exercises

DE—1. One summer evening Henry was installing a small electric motor in his workshop for temporary use. His father told him to connect it to the furnace circuit since the furnace would not be used for several weeks. There were three circuits identified by a blue tag, a white tag, and a yellow tag. Henry knew that the washer, furnace, and lights were on the different circuits. He did not know which circuit went to the furnace. How could Henry discover which circuit to use?

Solution

Henry thought, "Since the furnace is not operating, if I disconnect the furnace circuit nothing will happen." He started the washer and turned on the lights. He disconnected the yellow circuit and the lights went out. He disconnected the blue circuit and the washer stopped. He concluded that the furnace operated as part of the white circuit.

This method of reasoning is a form of indirect reasoning where elimination is used. All possible alternatives must be known in advance. Observe that Henry proved directly that the lights were on the yellow circuit and the washer was on the blue circuit, but his proof that the furnace was on the white circuit was indirect. Observe that all circuits except one were eliminated before he drew his conclusion.

> To establish a conclusion using an indirect proof through elimination, all possibilities must be considered and all but one of the possibilities must be eliminated.

DE—2. Prove that in equal circles unequal arcs have unequal chords.

Solution

Given: $\odot O = \odot Q$, $\overset{\frown}{AB} \neq \overset{\frown}{RS}$. (Read arc AB is not equal to arc RS.)
Prove: Chord $AB \neq$ chord RS.

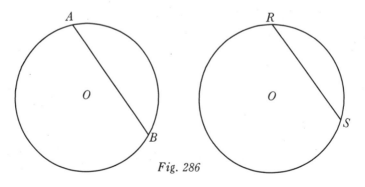

Fig. 286

Proof:

STATEMENTS	REASONS
1. Either $AB = RS$, or $AB \neq RS$.	1. These are the only possibilities.
2. If $AB = RS$, then $\overarc{AB} = \overarc{RS}$.	2. In equal circles, equal chords have equal arcs.
3. But $\overarc{AB} \neq \overarc{RS}$.	3. Given.
4. Therefore, $AB \neq RS$.	4. Only remaining possibility.

The steps in an indirect proof are generally the following:

(*1*) State all the possibilities.

(*2*) Assume a possibility that you expect to be false.

(*3*) Show that a conclusion based on the assumption in Step 2, through logical reasoning, contradicts a given fact, another assumption, a definition, or a theorem previously proved. Since the conclusion has been proved false the assumption upon which it was based must be false.

(*4*) Repeat this process with the other possibilities except the one which you are trying to establish.

(*5*) Conclude that, after all other possibilities have been proved false, the remaining possibility must be true.

Exercises

1. Jan, Lynn, and Mary went shopping. They each bought two articles. They bought a hat, a brown dress, brown shoes, a ring, a book, and a purse. The girl who bought the shoes bought the book. The girl who bought the dress bought the hat to match. Jan never wears brown. Lynn asked if she could borrow the book. What did each of the girls buy?

2. Six men sat down to dinner at a round table. One was bald, one was very brilliant, one was slightly deaf, one was a cynic, one was a millionaire, and one was a man of leisure. The millionaire sat opposite Mr. Gray and next to the man of leisure. The man who was slightly deaf sat opposite Mr. Bates, who sat between the brilliant man and the millionaire. The bald man sat opposite Mr. Hicks, next to the slightly deaf man and to the left of the millionaire. Mr. Jones sat next to Mr. Gray and to the left of Mr. Mills. Mr. Roberts sat next to Mr. Bates. Can you identify each of these men?

Prove Exercises **3-8** *by the indirect method.*

3. A line perpendicular to one of two intersecting lines is not perpendicular to the other.

4. If the sum of the angles of a polygon is not 180°, the polygon is not a triangle.

5. If the diagonals of a parallelogram are not equal, the parallelogram is not a rectangle.

6. If the base angles of a trapezoid are unequal, the trapezoid is not isosceles.

7. If a line is not perpendicular to the base of an isosceles triangle, then it does not join the vertex of the triangle to the midpoint of the base.

8. A median to a side of a scalene triangle is not an altitude.

INEQUALITIES

In most of your work so far, you have been limited to equality relationships. You have proved that the opposite sides of a parallelogram are equal, that the chords opposite equal arcs in the same or equal circles are equal, and many other relationships of equality. Not all relationships express equality. A relationship which does not express an equality is called an *inequality*. In Figure 287 line segments *a* and *b* are unequal, have unequal measures, $(a \neq b)$. Line segment *a* is greater than line segment $b(a > b)$. Line segment *b* is less than line segment *a* $(b > a)$. These three relationships are examples of inequalities.

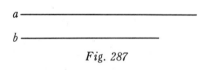

Fig. 287

Two inequalities are said to be of the same order if the symbols point in the same direction and in the opposite order if the symbols point in opposite directions.

Same Order

a. $7 > 5$	**b.** $-2 > -5$	**c.** $8 < 9$	**d.** $-8 < -6$
$3 > 1$	$-2 > -4$	$6 < 10$	$-5 < -2$

Opposite Order

a. $5 < 7$	**b.** $-2 > -6$	**c.** $9 > 8$	**d.** $6 > -1$
$3 > 1$	$0 < 3$	$6 < 10$	$2 < 4$

The proofs in connection with equalities were based on a group of assumptions. In order to develop proofs dealing with inequalities, additional assumptions must be stated.

Assumption 33

Addition:

a. If equals are added to unequals, the sums are unequal in the same order.

b. If unequals are added to unequals of the same order, the sums are unequal in the same order.

In the examples which follow letters of the alphabet stand for real numbers:

Add:

a. $5>3$	$a>b$	$2<4$	$r<s$
$2=2$	$c=c$	$5=5$	$x=y$
$7>5$	$a+c>b+c$	$7<9$	$r+x<s+y$

b. $5>3$	$m>n$	$3<4$	$g<h$
$2>1$	$p>r$	$5<7$	$e<f$
$7>4$	$m+p>n+r$	$8<11$	$g+e<h+f$

Assumption 34

Subtraction:

a. If equals are subtracted from unequals, the differences are unequal in the same order.

b. If unequals are subtracted from equals, the differences are unequal in the opposite order.

Examples:

Subtract:

a. $5>3$	$a>b$	$7<9$	$m<n$
$2=2$	$r=s$	$3=3$	$h=h$
$3>1$	$a-r>b-s$	$4<6$	$m-h<n-h$

b. $5=5$	$x=y$	$7=7$	$g=g$
$3>1$	$w>z$	$4<6$	$e<f$
$2<4$	$x-w<y-z$	$3>1$	$g-e>g-f$

Assumption 35

Multiplication:

a. If unequals are multiplied by positive equals, the products are unequal in the same order.

b. If unequals are multiplied by negative equals, the products are unequal in the opposite order.

Examples:

Multiply:

a. $5>3$	$2<4$	**b.** $5>3$	$2<4$
$2=2$	$6=6$	$-2=-2$	$-6=-6$
$10>6$	$12<24$	$-10<-6$	$-12>-24$

Assumption 36

Division:

a. If unequals are divided by positive equals, the quotients are unequal in the same order.

b. If unequals are divided by negative equals, the quotients are unequal in the opposite order.

Examples:

Divide:

a. $10>6$	$8<12$	**b.** $10>6$	$8<12$
$2=2$	$4=4$	$-2=-2$	$-4=-4$
$5>3$	$2<3$	$-5<-3$	$-2>-3$

Assumption 37

If two quantities are unequal, then either the first is greater than the second or the second is greater than the first.

Example:

If $a\neq b$ then $a>b$ or $b>a$.

Assumption 38

If the first of three quantities is greater than the second and the second is greater than the third, then the first is greater than the third.

Examples:

If $6>3$ and $3>1$, then $6>1$.

If $a>b$ and $b>c$, then $a>c$.

Exercises

Perform the indicated operations and state the assumptions used.

1. Divide: $34 > 14$
$$\underline{2 = 2}$$

2. Divide: $16 > 4$
$$\underline{2 = 2}$$

3. Divide: $44 < 66$
$$\underline{2 = 2}$$

4. Add: $18 > 13$
$$\underline{2 = 2}$$

5. Subtract: $45 > 15$
$$\underline{5 = 5}$$

6. Multiply: $7 > 2$
$$\underline{5 = 5}$$

7. Multiply: $7 < 8$
$$\underline{9 = 9}$$

8. Multiply: $7 < 9$
$$\underline{6 = 6}$$

9. Multiply: $9 > 6$
$$\underline{8 = 8}$$

10. Multiply: $8 = 8$
$$\underline{9 = 9}$$

11. Subtract: $45 > 16$
$$\underline{5 = 5}$$

12. Subtract: $15 < 18$
$$\underline{9 = 9}$$

13. Subtract: $18 = 18$
$$\underline{9 = 9}$$

14. Subtract: $24 = 24$
$$\underline{7 < 14}$$

15. Add: $85 < 99$
$$\underline{10 = 10}$$

16. Add: $96 > 81$
$$\underline{27 = 27}$$

17. Multiply: $8 > 4$
$$\underline{-3 = -3}$$

18. Multiply: $16 < 20$
$$\underline{-5 = -5}$$

19. Divide: $8 < 20$
$$\underline{-4 = -4}$$

20. Divide: $15 > 9$
$$\underline{-3 = -3}$$

Answer each question and state the assumption which applies.

21. John has more money than Henry. Which will have the greater amount if each receives two dollars more?

22. Bill is taller than Mary. Mary is taller than June. Is Bill taller than June?

23. Jack is twice as old as Dick. In six years which will be the oldest?

24. Sue had more money than Lynn. If each spent one-half of their money, which had the most left?

MORE ASSUMPTIONS ABOUT INEQUALITIES

Remember that assumptions are accepted by common agreement. They are necessary as a foundation for the system of logical reasoning. The examples are intended only to aid your understanding of the meaning of the assumptions and in no way should they be considered as proofs.

Assumption 39

A straight line segment is the shortest line segment that can be drawn between two points.

A special case of this assumption is the following:

In a triangle the sum of the lengths of two sides of a triangle is greater than the length of the third side.

Example:

In triangle ABC, CB is the shortest line segment joining C and B. $(CA+AB)>CB$.

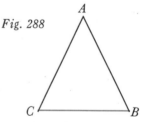

Fig. 288

Assumption 40

A quantity may be substituted for its equal in a statement of inequality.

Example:

If $a=c$ and $a+b>d+e$, then $c+b>d+e$.

A previously stated assumption which concerns inequalities is the following:

Assumption 9

The whole is equal to the sum of its parts and is greater than any of them.

Example:

$AB=AC+CB$.
$AB>AC$.
$AB>CB$.

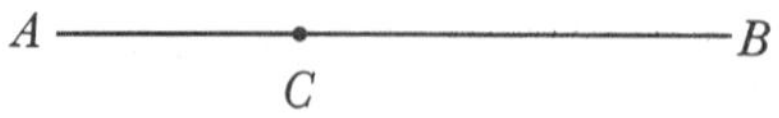

Fig. 289

Exercises

1. **Given:** The diagram at the right.

   Prove: $\angle ABC = \angle 1 + \angle 2.$

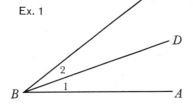

Ex. 1

2. **Given:** Segment ABC.

   Prove: $AC > BC.$

Ex. 2

3. **Given:** $\angle A > \angle B,$
   $\angle B = \angle 1.$

   Prove: $\angle A > \angle 1.$

4. Given three line segments with measures of $1.2'$, $3.7'$, and $.5'$, prove that a triangle cannot be made with these segments.

5. **Given:** $AB < CD,$
   $X = AB,$
   $Y = CD.$

   Prove: $X < Y.$

Consider each of the following statements and state whether you think all possibilities are taken into account.

6. Of two angles, one is smaller than, equal to, or larger than the other.

7. Two straight lines either intersect or are parallel.

8. A triangle is either isosceles or scalene.

9. A straight line intersects a circle in one or two points.

10. Three cards are drawn from a box containing five white cards and five red ones. The cards drawn are (*1*) all red, (*2*) all white, (*3*) two red and one white.

11. You are in your room studying with just one lamp turned on. Suddenly that lamp goes out. List as many possible reasons for the light failure as you can. Tell how you would test each possibility.

12. Prove that supplements of unequal angles are unequal.

USING THE INDIRECT METHOD TO PROVE INEQUALITIES

In many instances a theorem can be proved more readily if you use an indirect method of proof rather than a direct method of proof. Remember that in employing the indirect method, you must be careful to consider all of the possible conclusions and to eliminate all but the one that you wish to prove. Your final statement should be the proved relationship.

Notice in the following theorems how the indirect method of proof is used to prove inequality relationships.

Developmental Exercises

DE—1. Prove the following theorem:

> **THEOREM 76**
> **If one angle of a triangle is larger than a second angle, the side opposite the first angle is longer than the side opposite the second angle.**

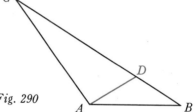

Solution
   Given: $\triangle ABC$,
               $\angle A > \angle B$.
   Prove: $BC > AC$.

   Analysis:
   There are two possibilities:
   Either (1) $BC = AC$, or   *Fig. 290*
           (2) $BC \neq AC$.

   If it can be shown that, by assuming BC and AC to be equal, a conclusion contrary to a proved statement is obtained, then the assumption $BC = AC$ is false.

   Proof:

STATEMENTS	REASONS
1. Either $BC = AC$, or $BC \neq AC$.	1. Only possibilities.
2. If $BC = AC$, then $\angle A = \angle B$.	2. If two sides of a triangle are equal, the angles opposite those sides are equal.
3. But $\angle A > \angle B$.	3. Given.
4. Hence, $BC \neq AC$.	4. The only remaining possibility.

Having established that BC is not equal to AC does not mean that BC is necessarily greater than AC. If BC and AC are not equal, there are the following two possibilities:

(*1*) $BC > AC$.

(*2*) $BC < AC$.

Construct AD making $\angle BAD$ equal to $\angle B$.

STATEMENTS	REASONS
1. $(DC + AD) > AC$.	1. The sum of two sides of a triangle is greater than the third.
2. $\angle BAD = \angle B$.	2. Construction.
3. $AD = BD$.	3. Sides opposite equal angles of a triangle are equal.
4. $(BD + DC) > AC$.	4. A quantity may be substituted for its equal in a statement of inequality.
5. $(BD + DC) = BC$.	5. The whole is equal to the sum of its parts.
6. $BC > AC$.	6. Same as Reason 4.

DE—2. Prove the following theorem:

┃┃THEOREM 77

┃┃If two sides of a triangle are unequal, the angle opposite the longer side is larger than the angle opposite the shorter side.

Solution

Given: $\triangle ABC$,
$\qquad BC > AC$.

Prove: $\angle A > \angle B$.

Analysis:

There are three possibilities.

(*1*) $\angle A = \angle B$.

(*2*) $\angle A > \angle B$.

(*3*) $\angle A < \angle B$.

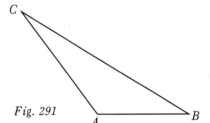

Fig. 291

If $\angle A = \angle B$, then $BC = AC$. (If two angles of a triangle are equal, the sides opposite those angles are equal.) But this is contrary to fact, since $BC > AC$. Hence, $\angle A = \angle B$. Possibility (1) is eliminated.

If $\angle A < \angle B$, then $BC < AC$ from Theorem 75. But this is contrary to fact, since $BC > AC$. Hence, $\angle A$ is not less than $\angle B$. Possibility (3) is eliminated.

The remaining possibility is the second one listed. Therefore, $\angle A > \angle B$.

Exercises

1. In triangle ABC, $\angle A$ is $62°$, $\angle B = 57°$. Which side of the triangle is the shortest?

2. Prove indirectly that a triangle can have only one obtuse angle.

3. On line $ABCD$ construct $\triangle BCE$. If exterior angle $EBA = 120°$ and exterior angle $DCE = 115°$, compare the length of BE to the length of CE.

4. Prove that if two angles of a triangle are not equal, the median to their common side is not perpendicular to that side.

5. In triangle ABC, $AB = 6.2''$, $BC = 5.8''$, $CA = 6.7''$. Name the largest angle of the triangle. Name the smallest angle.

6. Prove indirectly that if a quadrilateral is not a parallelogram, it is not a rhombus.

7. Given: $AD = BD$,
$\qquad BC > AB$.
Prove: $\angle 2 > \angle 3$.

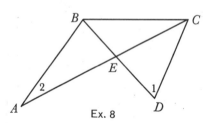

Ex. 7

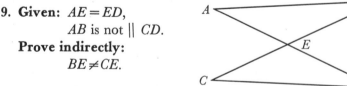

Ex. 8

8. Given: $AB = BC = BD$.
Prove: $\angle 1 > \angle 2$.

9. Given: $AE = ED$,
$\qquad AB$ is not $\parallel CD$.
Prove indirectly:
$\qquad BE \neq CE$.

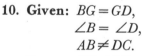

Ex. 9

Ex. 10

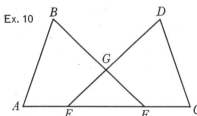

10. Given: $BG = GD$,
$\qquad \angle B = \angle D$,
$\qquad AB \neq DC$.
Prove: $GE \neq CF$.

DE—3. Prove the following theorem:

> ┃**THEOREM 78**
>
> ┃If two triangles have two sides of one respectively equal to two sides
> ┃of the other but the included angle of the first greater than the in-
> ┃cluded angle of the second, then the third side of the first is greater
> ┃than the third side of the second.

Solution

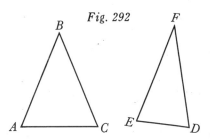

Fig. 292

Given: △*ABC* and △*EFD*,
  AB = *EF*,
  BC = *FD*,
  ∠*B* > ∠*F*.
Prove: *AC* > *ED*.

Analysis:

To compare *AC* with *ED*, construct △*ABD* ≅ △*EFD* and compare *AC* with *AD*.

Why is *AD* = *ED*?

If *AC* > *AD*, how do ∠*ACD* and ∠*CDA* compare?

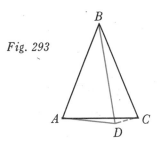

Fig. 293

If *BC* = *BD*, how do ∠*BCD* and ∠*CDB* compare?

If ∠*CDB* = ∠*BCD*, how do ∠*ACD* and ∠*CDB* compare? Why?

If ∠*CDB* > ∠*ACD*, how does ∠*ACD* compare with ∠*ADC*? Why?

Proof:

STATEMENTS	REASONS
1. △*ABD* ≅ △*EFD*.	1. Possible construction.
2. *ED* = *AD*.	2. Corresponding sides of congruent triangles are equal.
3. ∠*CDB* = ∠*BCD*.	3. Angles opposite equal sides of a triangle are equal.
4. ∠*BCD* > ∠*ACD*.	4. Why?
5. ∠*CDB* > ∠*ACD*.	5. Why?
6. ∠*CDA* > ∠*CDB*.	6. Why?
7. ∠*CDA* > ∠*ACD*.	7. Name the assumption.
8. *AC* > *AD*.	8. Why?
9. *AC* > *ED*.	9. Substituting *ED* for its equal, *AD*.

Exercises

1. Complete the proof for Theorem 78.

2. Prove that if $ab = -8$ and a is positive, then b is negative.

3. Prove that if $x^2 - 16 = 0$, then $x \neq 6$.

4. Prove that if $x^2 + 6 = 7x$, then $x \neq -1$.

5. In triangle ABC median CD is drawn making $\angle BDC > \angle CDA$. Prove $CB > CA$.

6. In isosceles triangle ABC (with AB as the base) a line segment is drawn from point D on the base to vertex C making $\angle DCB > \angle ACD$. Prove $AD < DB$.

7. Given: $AC = AD$.
Prove: $BC > BD$.

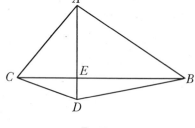

Ex. 7

8. A rectangular field contains an area of 300 square yards. Find the dimensions if the length exceeds the width by 20 yds. Explain how indirect reasoning was used to determine your answer.

9. The area of a right triangle is 4 square units. If one leg is 2 units shorter than the other, find the dimensions. (Area = $\frac{1}{2}$ base $\times$ altitude.) Explain how indirect reasoning was used to determine the correct answer.

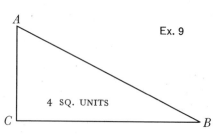

Ex. 9

4 SQ. UNITS

10. If an acute triangle has two of its sides equal in length to the legs of the triangle in Exercise **9,** compare the length of the third side to the hypotenuse of the other triangle. Compare their areas. Now repeat this for an obtuse triangle. Explain how indirect reasoning was used to determine the correct answer in each case.

DE—4. Prove the following theorem:

THEOREM 79

If two triangles have two sides of one respectively equal to two sides of the other and the third side of the first greater than the third side of the second, the angle opposite the third side of the first is greater than the angle opposite the third side of the second.

Solution

Given: $\triangle ABC$ and $\triangle FGH$, $AC=FH$, $BC=GH$, $AB>FG$.

Prove: $\angle C > \angle H$.

Fig. 294

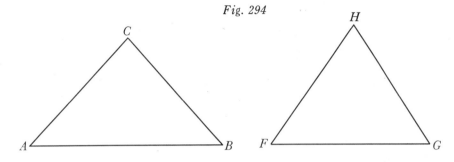

Analysis:

The only possibilities are $\angle C < \angle H$, $\angle C = \angle H$, or $\angle C > \angle H$. If $\angle C$ is less than $\angle H$, then AB is less than FG (Theorem 77).

But AB is greater than FG (given). Hence, $\angle C$ is not less than $\angle H$.

If $\angle C$ equals $\angle H$, then the segments AB and FG would be corresponding parts of congruent triangles; therefore equal.

But AB is greater than FG (given). Hence, $\angle C$ is not equal to $\angle H$.

Now write the proof for this theorem.

Exercises

1. Prove that the perpendicular from a point to a line is the shortest line segment that can be drawn from the point to the line.

2. In triangle ABC, AB measures 15 inches, BC measures 14 inches, and AC measures 13 inches. List the angles in order of size, naming the largest first.

3. Prove that if two lines are drawn from any point on the perpendicular to a line cutting off unequal distances from the foot of the perpendicular, the more remote is the greater.

4. In a right triangle, *ABC*, $\angle C$ measures 90 degrees. If $\angle B$ measures 35 degrees and *AC* measures 12 inches, what conclusion can you draw concerning the length of *BC*?

5. Prove that the hypotenuse of a right triangle is longer than either leg.

6. Prove the diagonal of a rectangle does not bisect the angles.

7. If triangle *ABC* is isosceles, prove that *AB* is greater than any other line joining the vertex *A* to a point in the base.

8. Prove that the perimeter of a quadrilateral is greater than the sum of its diagonals.

9. In the quadrilateral *ABCD*, *AD* is the longest and *BC* the shortest side. Prove $\angle B > \angle D$ and $\angle C > \angle A$.

10. Prove that the angles of a scalene triangle are unequal.

11. Prove that the diagonals of rhombus that is not a square are unequal.

12. In the diagram below the circles are equal and $\angle F > \angle A$. Prove $BC < GH$.

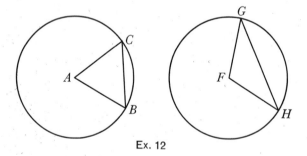

Ex. 12

13. Point *K* is taken in the base *AB* of isosceles triangle *ABC* so that $AK < BK$. Prove $\angle 2 > \angle 1$.

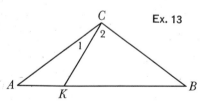

Ex. 13

14. *AB* and *BC* are equal sides of triangle *ABC*. *BC* is extended to the point *K*, and *KA* is drawn. Prove $\angle BAK > \angle AKB$.

15. In the parallelogram at the right, it is given that $\angle AOB$ equals $120°$. Prove $AB > AD$.

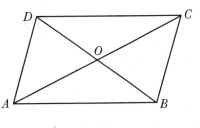

Ex. 15

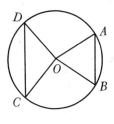

Ex. 16

16. In the circle at the right, $DC > AB$. Prove $\angle DOC > \angle AOB$.

DE—5. Prove the following theorem:

║**THEOREM 80**
║**In the same circle or in equal circles, the greater of two unequal central angles has the greater arc.**

Solution

    Given: P and Q are equal circles, $\angle P > \angle Q$.
    Prove: $\overset{\frown}{AB} > \overset{\frown}{CD}$.

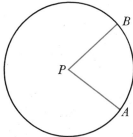 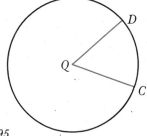

Fig. 295

    Analysis:
    In attempting to establish this theorem, the following may be stated:
$\angle P > \angle Q$. Why?
$\overset{\frown}{AB}$ is equal in measure to $\angle P$. Why?
Arc $\overset{\frown}{CD}$ is equal in measure to $\angle Q$. Why?
$\overset{\frown}{AB} > \overset{\frown}{CD}$. What assumption is applied here? Would it hold for "in the same circle"?

    Now write a proof for this theorem.

DE—6. Prove the following theorem:

> **THEOREM 81**
>
> **In the same circle or in equal circles, the greater of two unequal arcs has the greater central angle.**
> *Solution*

Analysis:

Since these last two theorems are converse statements, the illustrations for them may be identical in appearance. Use a figure similar to the one for the preceding theorem and write an analysis of the proof. Would your proof hold for "in the same circle" if you make no other change in your illustration?

The hands of the world-famed Big Ben form a central angle. As the position of the hands changes, the arc intercepted by the hands changes — the greater the central angle, the greater the intercepted arc.

Exercises

1. Write the proof for Theorem 80.

2. Write the proof for Theorem 81.

3. In the same circle do any two arcs have the same ratio as their central angles?

4. Given: $AB = CD$.
   Prove: $\angle COD > \angle BOE$.

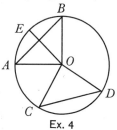

Ex. 4

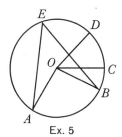

Ex. 5

5. Given: $\angle E = \angle DOC$.
   Prove: $\overarc{AB} > \overarc{DC}$.

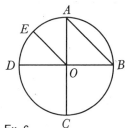

Ex. 6

6. Given: $AB \parallel EO$,
   O is the center of the circle.
   Prove: $\overarc{BC} > \overarc{ED}$.

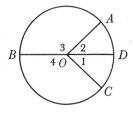

Ex. 7

7. Given: $\overarc{BCD} > \overarc{CDA}$,
   O is the center of the circle.
   Prove: $\angle 4 > \angle 2$.

8. Given: $\overarc{AC} = \overarc{AB}$ in $\odot$ O,
   A, O, X lie in a straight line.
   Prove: OX bisects $\angle BOC$.

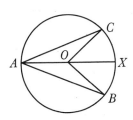

Ex. 8

DE—7. Prove the following theorem:

THEOREM 82

In the same circle or in equal circles, if two arcs are unequal the greater arc has the greater chord.

Solution

   Given: P and Q are equal circles, $\overset{\frown}{AB} > \overset{\frown}{CD}$.
   Prove: $AB > CD$.

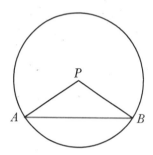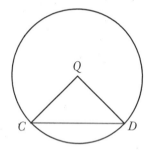

Fig. 296

Analysis:

Draw radii AP, PB, QC, and QD.

Examine triangles ABP and CDQ. Since $\overset{\frown}{AB} > \overset{\frown}{CD}$, what can you say about angles APB and CQD? The proof is left to you.

Illustrate this theorem with one circle.

DE—8. Prove the following theorem:

THEOREM 83

In the same circle or in equal circles, if two chords are unequal the greater chord has the greater arc.

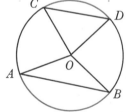

Solution

   Given: $AB > CD$.
   Prove: $\overset{\frown}{AB} > \overset{\frown}{CD}$.

Fig. 297

Analysis:

After drawing radii AO, BO, CO, and DO, can you show that $\angle AOB > \angle COD$? Why then is $\overset{\frown}{AB} > \overset{\frown}{CD}$? The proof is left to you.

Illustrate this theorem with two circles.

Exercises

1. Prove Theorem 82.

2. Prove Theorem 83.

3. Prove that in a circle the chord of an arc of 180° is twice as long as the chord of an arc of 60°.

4. Do chords have the same ratios as their central angles? Refer to Exercise 3.

5. Triangle MNO is inscribed in a circle and $\overarc{MN} = 80°$ and $\overarc{ON} = 140°$. Name the angles and sides of the triangle in order of size. Give reasons for your answers.

6. Triangle ABC is inscribed in a circle with $\overarc{AB} > \overarc{BC}$. Prove $\angle C > \angle A$.

7. Given: AC and DB are diameters of $\odot O$,
$\angle 1 > \angle 2$.
Prove: $BC > AB$.

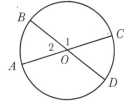

Ex. 7

8. In parallelogram $WXYZ$ the diagonals intersect at O. If $WX > WZ$ prove $\angle WOX > \angle WOZ$.

9. Secants AB and AC are drawn to circle O so that AB passes through O. Prove $\angle ABC < \angle ACB$.

10. Given: AC, a secant through the center of $\odot O$.
Prove: $AB > AK$.

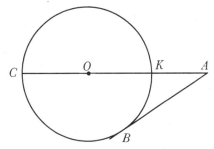

Ex. 10

DE—9. Prove the following theorem:

> ## THEOREM 84
> In the same circle or in equal circles, if two chords are unequal the longer chord is nearer the center of the circle.

Solution

Given: $AB > CD$.

Prove: $OF > OG$.

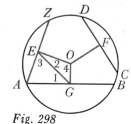

Fig. 298

Analysis:

Construct AZ equal to chord CD. Construct OG, OF, and OE perpendicular to AB, CD, and AZ, respectively.

Draw EG.

$AB > CD$ (given), AZ equals CD (constructed), hence, $AB > AZ$. AG is $\frac{1}{2}AB$, AE is $\frac{1}{2}AZ$, and $AG > AE$. Why?

$\angle 3 > \angle 1$, $\angle 4 > \angle 2$. Why?

$OE > OG$, $OE = OF$, $OF > OG$.

The formal proof is left for you.

DE—10. Prove the following theorem:

> ## THEOREM 85
> In the same circle or in equal circles, if two chords are not equally distant from the center, the chord nearer the center is the longer chord.

Solution

Analysis:

A diagram similar to the one used in Theorem 84 may be used. Using the indirect method of proof, there are three possibilities. List them, select the one that you wish to establish, and show, by assuming the truth of each of the other two possibilities, that a contradiction with the hypothesis results. The possibility that you selected is thus established.

Exercises

1. Prove Theorem 84.

2. Prove Theorem 85.

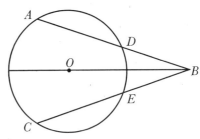

3. In the diagram, if $\angle ABO = \angle OBC$ prove that $\overset{\frown}{AD} = \overset{\frown}{CE}$.

4. In the diagram, if $\angle ABO > \angle OBC$ prove that $\overset{\frown}{AD} < \overset{\frown}{CE}$.

Ex. 3-4

5. Two parallel chords are drawn in a circle three inches and five inches from the center. What do you know about the chords? Give a reason for your answer.

6. Given a circle with two unequal chords, compare their distances from the center of the circle.

7. If a minor arc of less than 90° is doubled, what effect does it have on its central angle? On its chord?

8. If a minor arc of more than 90° is doubled, what effect does it have on its central angle? Its chord?

9. An equilateral triangle and a square are inscribed in a circle. Prove that the sides of the triangle are nearer the center of the circle.

10. If the sides of an equilateral triangle are doubled, what effect, if any, does it have on the size of the angles?

11. Two unequal chords intersect on a circle. Prove that the longer chord makes the smaller angle with the diameter through the point of intersection.

12. Given: A circle with center O,
          $AB = CD$,
          $OF \perp AB$,
          $OE \perp CD$.
   Prove: $\triangle EOF$ is isosceles.

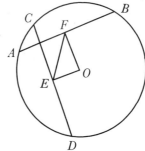

Ex. 12

CONVERSES, INVERSES, AND CONTRAPOSITIVES

Each of the *if-then* propositions considered in this textbook can be transformed into a new proposition by interchanging the data given (or one of the datum) with the conclusion (or one part of the conclusion). A *converse* proposition results. The data given is often called the *hypothesis*.

If the hypothesis and conclusion (or parts of them) are transformed so that both of them are denied (negated), the new proposition is an *inverse* of the first. However, if the original proposition is transformed so that the hypothesis and conclusion (or parts of each) are denied and interchanged, the new proposition is a *contrapositive* of the original statement. *The* **contrapositive** *then, is the inverse of the converse of the original statement.*

Observe in the following examples how each new proposition is obtained from the original proposition.

(*1*) If two lines are perpendicular to a third line, then they are parallel. *Direct proposition.*

(*2*) If two lines are parallel, then they are perpendicular to a third line. *Converse proposition.*

(*3*) If two lines are not perpendicular to a third line, then they are not parallel. *Inverse proposition.*

(*4*) If two lines are not parallel, then they are not perpendicular to a third line. *Contrapositive proposition.*

Note the interrelationships among the four statements. The third and fourth are also inverses, and the fourth is also the converse of the third statement.

You will recall that the converse of any definition is valid. However, a converse of a direct proposition is not necessarily true. It must be proved independently.

An inverse of a direct proposition is not necessarily true. It is true or false according to whether the converse is true or false. Likewise, the direct proposition and its contrapositive are either both true or both false.

‖Developmental Exercises

DE—1. Write the contrapositive of "If the corresponding angles formed by two lines cut by a transversal are equal, the lines are parallel."

Solution

    Data: Corresponding angles formed by two lines cut by a transversal are equal.

    Conclusion: Lines are parallel.

    Contrapositive: Exchange and negate as follows:

    Data: Lines are not parallel.

    Conclusion: Corresponding angles formed by the two lines cut by a transversal are not parallel.

    "If two lines are not parallel, the corresponding angles formed when the lines are cut by a transversal are not equal."

DE—2. Given: Line *a* is not parallel to line *b*. Line *c* is a transversal.

    Prove: $\angle 1 \neq \angle 2$.

Solution

    Analysis:
    $\angle 1 = \angle 2 + \angle 3$. Why? Therefore, $\angle 1 \neq \angle 2$. Why?

    Observe that this exercise is the proof of the contrapositive stated in Exercise **1**. This contrapositive may be proved but it is not necessary since it can be proved that all contrapositives of valid propositions are valid.

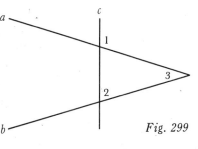

Fig. 299

‖THEOREM 86

‖**If two nonparallel lines are cut by a transversal, then the corresponding angles are not equal.**

DE—3. Write the contrapositive of "If a line bisects the vertex angle of an isosceles triangle, then it is perpendicular to the base."

Solution

    If a direct proposition contains more than one condition in its hypothesis, the negative of any one such condition interchanged with the negative of the conclusion will furnish a contrapositive proposition. Therefore, a direct proposition may have more than one contrapositive.

    a. If a line is not perpendicular to the base of an isosceles triangle, then it does not bisect the vertex angle.

b. If a line bisects an angle of a triangle and is not perpendicular to the opposite side, then the sides of the angle bisected are not equal.

Each of these contrapositives is true if the direct proposition is true; if the direct proposition is false, the contrapositives are false. This is often referred to as the **Law of Contrapositives.**

Exercises

Write the converse, inverse, and contrapositive of each of the following propositions. Discuss the validity of each proposition thus formed.

1. If a quadrilateral is a rhombus, then its diagonals are perpendicular.

2. When two parallel lines are cut by a transversal, equal corresponding angles are formed.

3. If the sum of the angles of a polygon is $360°$, the polygon is a quadrilateral.

4. Vertical angles are equal.

5. If a triangle is equilateral, it is isosceles.

6. In the same or equal circles, if two arcs are equal their chords are equal.

7. If $3x + 1 = 13$, then $x = 4$.

8. An acute triangle contains an acute angle.

9. If $x - 6 = 3$, then $x \neq 5$.

10. If a figure is not a quadrilateral, then it is not a trapezoid.

Write two converse, inverse, and contrapositive propositions for each of the following and discuss the validity of each proposition formed.

11. If $x = 3$ and $m = 7$, then $xm = 21$.

12. If a diameter of a circle is perpendicular to a chord, it bisects the chord.

13. If a quadrilateral is an isosceles trapezoid, the diagonals are equal.

14. If two isosceles triangles have the same vertex angle, then their bases are parallel.

PROVING AND USING CONTRAPOSITIVE PROPOSITIONS

While in more advanced courses it is proved that the contrapositives of a valid proposition are always valid, it will not be proved here. This statement will be accepted and used without proof.

▌Developmental Exercises

DE—1. Prove the following theorem:

▌THEOREM 87
If two straight lines are cut by a transversal so that interior angles on the same side of the transversal are not supplementary, then the lines are not parallel.

Solution

The contrapositive proposition of this theorem is the following: If two lines are parallel, the interior angles on the same side of a transversal are supplementary.

Since the contrapositive proposition has been established, the theorem is also valid.

DE—2. Prove the following corollary:

▌Corollary 1
The bisectors of two angles of a triangle intersect.

Solution

Given: AE bisects $\angle BAC$,
BF bisects $\angle CBA$.

Prove: AE intersects BF.

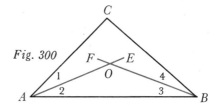

Fig. 300

Analysis:

Since AE and BF are in the same plane, AE intersects BF if AE and BF are not parallel. According to Theorem 87, if it can be shown that $\angle 2 + \angle 3 \neq 180°$, then BF intersects AE. Since $\angle C + \angle 1 + \angle 2 + \angle 3 + \angle 4 = 180°$ (the sum of the angles of a triangle is 180°) and $\angle C + \angle 1 + \angle 2 + \angle 3 + \angle 4 > \angle 2 + \angle 3$ (the whole is greater than any of its parts), $\angle 2 + \angle 3 < 180°$. Thus, $\angle 2 + \angle 3 \neq 180°$. Hence, it has been shown that AE and BF must intersect.

Be able to write a formal proof for this corollary at the request of your teacher.

DE—3. Prove the following corollary:

║**Corollary 2**
║**If two given lines are respectively perpendicular to two nonparallel**
║**lines, the given lines intersect.**

Solution

Fig. 301

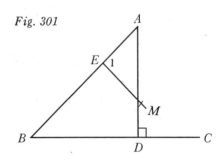

Given: AB intersects BC,
$EM \perp AB$,
$AD \perp BC$.
Prove: EM intersects AD.

Proof:

STATEMENTS	REASONS
1. Either $EM \parallel AD$ or EM intersects AD.	1. Only possibilities for two lines lying in the same plane.
2. If $EM \parallel AD$ then $\angle 1 + \angle A = 180°$.	2. If two parallel lines are cut by a transversal, the interior angles on the same side of the tranversal are supplementary.
3. $\angle 1 = 90°$.	3. Why?
4. $\angle A = 90°$.	4. If equals are subtracted from equals, the differences are equal.
5. $AD \perp BA$.	5. Why?
6. $AD \perp BC$.	6. Given.
7. $BC \parallel AB$.	7. Two lines perpendicular to the same line are parallel.
8. But AD intersects BC.	8. Given.
9. Hence, EM intersects AD.	9. Only remaining possibility.

Exercises

1. Use the Law of Contrapositives to prove that if two nonparallel lines are cut by a transversal the alternate-exterior angles are not equal.

2. Prove that if two intersecting lines are cut by a transversal the exterior angles on the same side of the transversal are not supplementary.

3. Prove the converse of Exercise **1.**

4. Prove the converse of Exercise **2.**

5. Prove that the bisector of an exterior angle of a triangle intersects the bisector of a nonadjacent interior angle of the triangle.

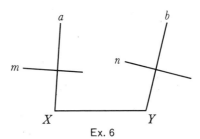

6. Given: $\angle X = 86°$,
$\angle Y = 104°$,
$m \perp a$,
$n \perp b$.

Prove: m and n intersect.

Ex. 6

7. Prove that if a line is perpendicular to one of two intersecting lines, then it is not perpendicular to the other.

8. Use the Law of Contrapositives to prove that if a quadrilateral has one acute angle it cannot be a rectangle.

Write the hypothesis and conclusion for the converse, inverse, and contrapositive of each problem illustrated below. Then prove each original conclusion by establishing the contrapositive.

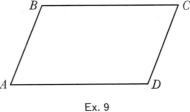

9. Given: $ABCD$ is a $\square$.
$\angle A \neq \angle B$.

Prove: $\angle C \neq \angle D$.

Ex. 9

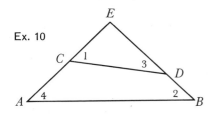

Ex. 10

10. Given: $\angle 1 \neq \angle 2$.
Prove: $\angle 3 \neq \angle 4$.

Ex. 11

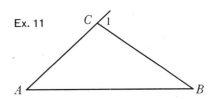

11. Given: $\angle 1 \neq 2\angle A$.
Prove: $AC \neq BC$.

12. Prove the converse of Exercise **11.**

DE—4. Prove the following theorem:

THEOREM 88

If, from a point in a perpendicular to a line, two lines are drawn so as to cut off unequal segments from the foot of the perpendicular, they are unequal and the more remote is the greater.

Solution   *Fig. 302*

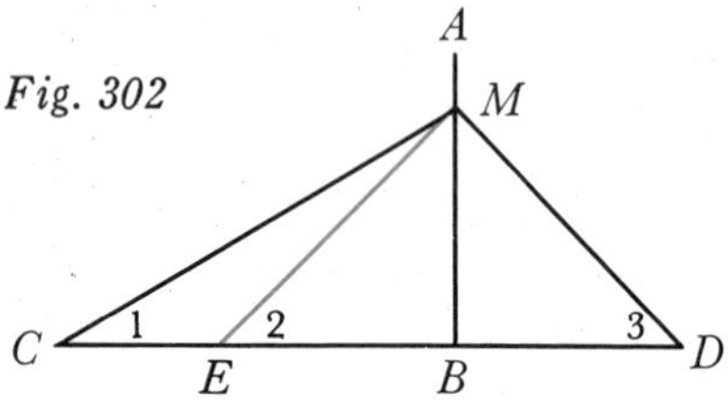

Given: $AB \perp CD$,
        $CB > BD$.

Prove: $MC > MD$.

Construction: On CB make $BE = BD$. Join E to M.

Proof:

STATEMENTS	REASONS
1. $BM \perp CD$, $BC > BD$.	1. Given.
2. $BE = BD$.	2. Possible construction.
3. MB is the perpendicular bisector of ED.	3. Definition of perpendicular bisector.
4. $\angle 2 = \angle 3$.	4. Angles opposite equal sides of a triangle are equal.
5. $\angle 2 > \angle C$.	5. The exterior angle of a triangle is greater than either nonadjacent interior angle.
6. $\angle 3 > \angle C$.	6. In an inequality a quantity may be substituted for its equal.
7. $MC > MD$.	7. If two angles of a triangle are unequal, the sides opposite are unequal in the same order.

In the illustration for this theorem, MC and MD can be drawn on the same side of BM. Make such a sketch and outline a plane of proof for that case.

Corollary

The perpendicular is the shortest distance from a point to a line.

Illustrate and prove this corollary.

Exercises

Prove each of the following by establishing the contrapositive.

1. Given: $\angle 1 = \angle 2$,
　　　　$AC \neq AD$.
Prove: $BC \neq BD$.

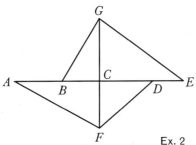

Ex. 1

Ex. 2

2. Given: $BG = DF$,
　　　　$GE = FA$,
　　　　$GC \neq FC$.
Prove: $AB \neq DE$.

3. Prove that if the opposite angles of a trapezoid are not supplementary, the trapezoid is not isosceles.

4. If a line passes through the center of a circle intersecting but not bisecting a given chord, the line is not perpendicular to the chord.

5. If one angle of a triangle is not equal to the sum of the other two angles, it is not a right triangle.

6. Prove the converse of Exercise **3.**

7. Prove the converse of Exercise **4.**

8. Prove the converse of Exercise **5.**

SOLID GEOMETRY

Geometric plane figures may be congruent even though they do not lie in the same plane. While congruency can be extended to have application in three-dimensional geometry, other relationships, which are true for figures in one plane, are not always true in solid geometry. Before applying theorems from plane geometry to solid geometry, be sure that a plane is determined or that the relationship can be used.

Developmental Exercises

DE—1. Prove the following theorem:

> ## THEOREM 3₈
>
> **If, from a point in a perpendicular to a plane, line segments cut off unequal distances in the plane from the foot of the perpendicular, then the line segments are unequal in the same order as the unequal distances cut off in the plane.**

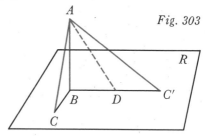

Fig. 303

Solution

Given: $AB \perp$ plane R,
$\qquad BC' > BC$.
Prove: $AC' > AC$.

Construction: In plane ABC' construct $BD = BC$.

STATEMENTS	REASONS
1. $BC = BD$.	1. Possible construction.
2. $BA = BA$.	2. Identity.
3. $AB \perp$ plane R.	3. Given.
4. $AB \perp BD$.	4. If a line is perpendicular to a plane it is perpendicular to every line in the plane passing through its foot.
5. $\triangle ABC \cong \triangle DBA$.	5. Why?
6. $BC' > BC$.	6. Given.
7. $BC' > BD$.	7. A quantity may be substituted for its equal in an inequality.
8. $AB \perp BC'$.	8. Reason 4.
9. $AC = AD$.	9. Corresponding sides of congruent triangles are equal.
10. $AC' > AD$.	10. If, from a point in a perpendicular to a line, two lines are drawn so as to cut off unequal segments from the foot of the perpendicular, they are unequal and the more remote is the greater.
11. $AC' > AC$.	11. Reason 7.

DE—2. Prove the following theorem:

‖ THEOREM 4ₛ

If unequal line segments are drawn from a point in a perpendicular to a plane, then they intersect the plane at unequal distances from the foot of the perpendicular in the same order.

Solution

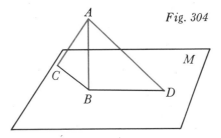

Fig. 304

Given: $AB \perp$ plane M,
$\qquad AD > AC$.
Prove: $BD > BC$.

Analysis:

$BD = BC$, or $BD < BC$, or $BD > BC$.

If $BD = BC$, then $\triangle ABC \cong \triangle ADB$. Why? As a result of the congruent triangles $AD = AC$. But $AD > AC$ is given, hence $BD \neq BC$.

If $BD < BC$, then $AD < AC$. Why? But $AD > AC$ is given, hence, BD cannot be less than BC.

The only remaining possibility is $BD > BC$.

‖ Corollary

The shortest line segment which can be drawn from an external point to a plane is the perpendicular from the point to the plane.

Exercises

1. Write a formal proof for Theorem 4_s.

2. Illustrate and prove the corollary.

3. A line is perpendicular to the plane of a circle at its center. In the plane a secant and tangent are drawn to the circle from the same point. Lines are drawn from any point on the perpendicular to the point of tangency and to the point from which the tangent and secant were drawn. Compare the lengths of those lines.

4. In Exercise **3** if two oblique lines are drawn perpendicular to the secant and tangent from a point in the perpendicular to the plane, compare the lengths of those lines.

EXTEND YOUR HORIZON

Place a drop of ink or paint in the crease of a folded paper. Press the paper to distribute the ink. Unfold the paper. Is the design made by the ink symmetric?

A figure is symmetrical with respect to a center if every straight line through the center cuts the figure in two points equally distant from the given point. A circle is symmetrical with respect to any straight line through its center. The line about which the design can be turned so that a new position coincides with the original position is called the *axis of symmetry.*

Two common assumptions related to symmetry are

(*1*) The axis of symmetry is the perpendicular bisector of the line segment which joins any two corresponding points.

(*2*) Any part of a symmetric design is congruent to its corresponding part. In respect to which points and lines are these diagrams symmetric?

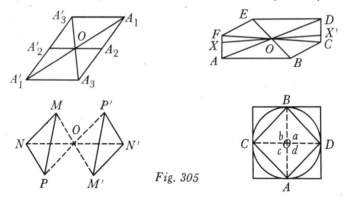

Fig. 305

Show that the bisector of the vertex angle of an isosceles triangle is an axis of symmetry of the triangle.

Sketch a geometric figure which possesses an axis of symmetry and a center of symmetry, too.

Construct a design which has a center of symmetry.

How many axes of symmetry has an equilateral triangle? A square? A regular pentagon?

Use an isosceles triangle to create a design having an axis of symmetry.

Does an isosceles trapezoid have an axis of symmetry? Two axes of symmetry? A center of symmetry? Submit sketches to explain your answers.

CHAPTER SUMMARY

The steps in an indirect proof are generally the following:

1. State all the possibilities.

2. Assume a possibility that you expect to be false.

3. Show that a conclusion based on the assumption in step 2 through logical reasoning contradicts a given fact, another assumption, a definition, or a theorem previously proved. Since the conclusion has been proved false the assumption upon which it was based must be false.

4. Repeat this process with the other possibilities except the one which you are trying to establish.

5. Conclude that, after all other possibilities have been proved false, remaining possibility must be true.   (page 297)

Angles are unequal when

1. they are corresponding angles of lines not parallel.   (page 319)

2. they are in the same circle or in equal circles and are central angles of two unequal arcs.   (page 312)

3. they are opposite unequal sides of a triangle.   (page 305)

4. they are opposite unequal sides of two triangles that have two sides equal respectively.   (page 309)

Arcs are unequal when (in the same circle or in equal circles)

1. they have unequal central angles.   (page 311)

2. they have unequal chords.   (page 314)

Line segments are unequal when

1. they are opposite unequal angles in a triangle.   (page 304)

2. they are opposite unequal angles of two triangles that have two sides respectively equal.   (page 307)

3. they are in a circle or in equal circles and are chords of unequal arcs.   (page 314)

4. they are chords in the same circle or in equal circles and are unequally distant from the center of the circle(s).   (page 316)

5. they are in the same circle or in equal circles and are perpendiculars to unequal chords.   (page 316)

6. they intercept unequal segments from the foot of a perpendicular to a line.   (page 324)

CHAPTER REVIEW

Vocabulary

Match the word or symbol in the left hand column with its correct definition in the right hand column.

1. Hypothesis

    a. The conclusion of a proposition.

    b. The given data of a proposition.

2. Proposition

    c. a is not equal to b.

    d. a is greater than b.

3. Converse

    e. a is less than b.

    f. a is not parallel to b.

4. Inverse

    g. An implicative statement to be proved.

    h. A statement accepted without proof.

5. Contrapositive

    i. A proposition formed by negating the data and conclusion of another proposition.

6. Inequalities

    j. A proposition formed by negating and interchanging the data and conclusion of another proposition.

7. Order of an inequality

    k. A proposition formed by interchanging the data and conclusion of another proposition.

8. $a > b$

    l. Refers to the direction of the inequality symbol.

9. $a < b$

    m. A family of relationships which do not express equality.

10. $a \neq b$

Exercises

Perform the indicated operations in Exercises **1-4.** *Assume letters of the alphabet represent positive integers.*

1. Add:

   a. $3 = 3$
      $\underline{4 > 3}$

   b. $6 < 7$
      $\underline{6 = 6}$

   c. $3 < 5$
      $\underline{8 < 9}$

   d. $c > n$
      $\underline{s > t}$

2. Subtract:

   a. $3 < 5$
      $\underline{2 = 2}$

   b. $5 = 5$
      $\underline{4 > 3}$

   c. $8 > 6$
      $\underline{7 = 7}$

   d. $c = d$
      $\underline{e < f}$

3. Multiply:

   a. $5 > 3$
      $\underline{2 = 2}$

   b. $6 < 8$
      $\underline{5 = 5}$

   c. $5 > 2$
      $\underline{-3 = -3}$

   d. $a < e$
      $\underline{-4 = -4}$

4. Divide:

   a. $18 > 3$
      $\underline{3 = 3}$

   b. $10 < 12$
      $\underline{4 = 4}$

   c. $15 > 3$
      $\underline{-3 = -3}$

   d. $15 < 17$
      $\underline{-5 = -5}$

5. In triangle ABC, $\angle B$ is 70 degrees. $\angle C$ is 30 degrees. Which is the longest side of the triangle?

6. Prove that if two chords drawn from one end of a diameter make unequal angles with it, the chord making the larger angle is the shorter.

7. In triangle ABD, AB and BD are equal. C is a point of BD. Prove that AC is greater than CD.

8. In the diagram $\overparen{AB} > \overparen{BC}$, $AD \perp AB$, and $DC \perp CB$. Prove that $DC > AD$.

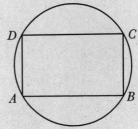

Ex. 8

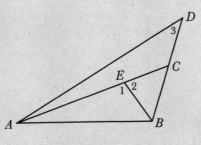

Ex. 9

9. In the diagram $AB > AE$, EB bisects $\angle DBA$, $EB = EC$. Prove $\angle 1 > \angle 3$.

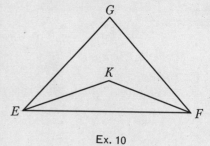

Ex. 10

10. K is any point within $\triangle EFG$. Prove that $\angle EKF > \angle G$.

11. Draw triangle ABC making $AB > BC > AC$. Prove $\angle C > \angle A > \angle B$.

12. In triangle ABC, angle A is bisected by a line meeting BC at K. Prove $AB > BK$ and $AC > CK$.

Ex. 13

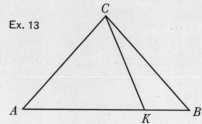

13. In the adjacent figure, AC and BC are equal. K is any point on AB. Prove $CK < AC$, $CK < BC$.

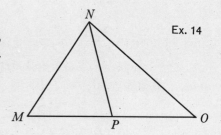

Ex. 14

14. In triangle MNO, $NO > MN$, and NP is a median drawn to MO. Prove that $\angle NPO > \angle NPM$.

15. In triangle ABC, $BC < BA$. Points E and D are located on BA and BC respectively, so that $EA = DC$. Prove $EC < DA$.

16. Inscribe a regular polygon in a circle. Prove that the perpendicular bisectors of the sides of the polygon are concurrent.

17. Given that DA is the median to BC in triangle ABC. Prove that the angles at D are unequal in the same order as the sides of the triangle opposite them.

18. Given that the sides of a quadrilateral are not equal. Use the Law of Contrapositives to prove that the diagonals are not perpendicular.

CHAPTER TEST

1. Perform the indicated operation.

a. Add:	**b.** Subtract:	**c.** Multiply:	**d.** Divide
$3 = 3$	$9 = 9$	$6 > 3$	$7 > 5$
$5 < 7$	$5 < 7$	$-2 = -2$	$-5 = -5$

2. Write the inverse, converse, and contrapositive statements related to the following: If a parallelogram is not equilateral then the diagonals are not perpendicular.

3. In circle O a diameter AB is drawn. Points C and D are located on opposite sides of AB. Join points C and D to points A and B. If chord AC is greater than chord AD, prove that chord CB is less than chord DB.

4. Triangle ABC is scalene. BC is extended through C and AB is extended through A. The bisectors of the exterior angles at C and A meet at D. If $BC > AB$, prove that $CD < AD$.

5. XZ and XY are the arms of an isosceles triangle, XYZ. XY is extended through Y to W. ZW is drawn joining points Z and W. Prove that ZW is longer than XZ.

6. Prove that supplements or complements of unequal angles are unequal in the opposite order.

7. Show that if a triangle is not isosceles the bisector of an angle is not perpendicular to the opposite side.

8. Show that a point unequally distant from the ends of a line segment cannot lie on the perpendicular bisector of the line segment.

9. Prove that the hypotenuse of a right triangle is greater than either leg.

10. Given: $ABCD$ is not a rectangle.

Prove: $DB < CA$.

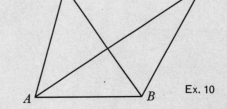

Ex. 10

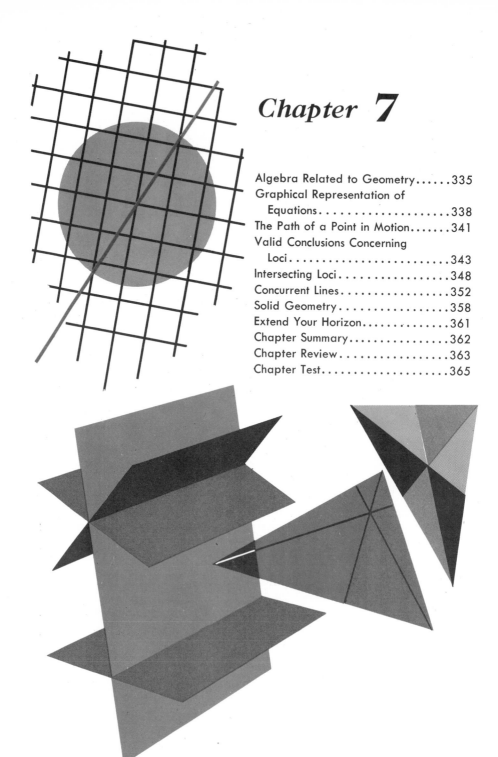

Chapter 7

LOCUS

ALGEBRA RELATED TO GEOMETRY

In the seventeenth century mathematicians first linked geometry to algebra. By assuming that all real numbers could be represented by points on a line, they developed a method of geometrically expressing algebraic relationships.

An arrangement of points which correspond to numbers is called a *number scale*. It is formed by arbitrarily designating a zero point on a line. The points which correspond to all the positive integers are located at equally spaced intervals to the right of the zero point; the points which correspond to all the negative integers are located at equally spaced intervals to the left of the zero point. The length of the line segment between any two points which correspond to consecutive integers is called *one unit length*. The points which are to be associated with fractions are located by using the appropriate fractional parts of the unit length.

The following assumptions can be made.

ASSUMPTION 41

For every real number there is one, and only one, point.

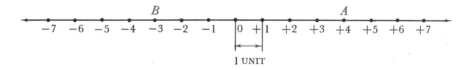

Fig. 306

Conversely, for every point there is one, and only one, real number. Point A is four units to the right of zero and is, therefore, identified as $+4$. Point B is three units to the left of the zero point and is, therefore, identified as -3.

In order to identify points in a plane, a pair of perpendicular number scales are used. The plane is, therefore, divided into four sections called *quadrants*. These quadrants are numbered counterclockwise. See Figure 307. The horizontal number scale is usually identified as the *x*-axis; the vertical number scale is usually called the *y*-axis. The point of intersection on the axes is called the *origin*. On the *x*-axis points to the right of the origin have positive values; points to the left of the origin have negative values. On the *y*-axis points above the origin have positive values; points below the origin have negative values.

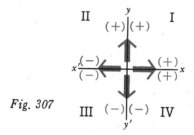

Fig. 307

Developmental Exercises

DE—1. On the axes at the right, what pair of real numbers identifies

    a. point *A*,

    b. point *B*,

    c. point *C*,

    d. point *D*,

    e. point *E*.

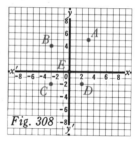

Fig. 308

Solution

    a. Point *A* is 3 units to the right of the origin and 5 units above the origin. This point is identified by the pair of numbers (3,5). The distance measured along the *x*-axis, 3, is called the *abscissa*. The distance measured along the *y*-axis, 5, is called the *ordinate*. The abscissa and ordinate together are the *coordinates* of the point. In stating these values the abscissa is written first, then followed by the ordinate. For this reason the pair of numbers which identifies a point is called an *ordered pair*. Observe that (3,5) and (5,3) do not identify the same point.

    b. Point *B* is 3 units to the left of the origin and 4 units above the origin. The coordinates of point *B* are (−3,4).

    c. Point *C* is 3 units to the left of the origin and 2 units below the origin. The coordinates of point *C* are (−3,−2).

    d. Point *D* is 2 units to the right of the origin and 2 units below the origin. The coordinates of point *D* are (2,−2).

    e. Point *E* is at the origin. Thus, the coordinates of *E* are (0,0).

DE—2. On an axes locate points having the following coordinates:

    a. (3,2)   **b.** (−3,4)   **c.** (0,1)

    d. (−4,−3)   **e.** (−2,0)   **f.** (0,−2)

Solution

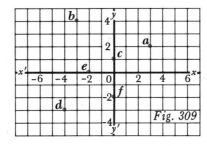

Fig. 309

    The process of locating a point on an axes is called *plotting a point.*

Exercises

    1. In the diagram what are the coordinates of points *A*, *B*, *C*, *D*, *E*, *F*, *G*, and *H*.

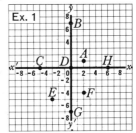

Ex. 1

    2. Draw coordinate axes and plot the following points:

    a. (2,4)   **b.** (0,3)   **c.** (−2,3)   **d.** (−4,−2)

    e. (−1,0)   **f.** (0,−3)   **g.** (4,−2)   **h.** (0,2)

    3. Draw a triangle whose vertices are (3,5), (−4,−3), and (3,−3).

    4. Draw a quadrilateral whose vertices are (2,3), (−5,3),(−5,−1), and (2,−1). Classify the quadrilateral.

    5. Estimate the coordinates of the midpoints of the legs of the triangle in Exercise **3.**

    6. Plot the following points. Connect them in order.

    a. (10,10)   **b.** (0,5)   **c.** (5,0)   **d.** (10,10)

    e. (10,10)   **f.** (5,0)   **g.** (0,−5)   **h.** (−10,10)

    i. (−10,−10)   **j.** (0,−5)   **k.** (−5,0)   **l.** (−10,−10)

    m. (−10,10)   **n.** (−5,0)   **o.** (0,5)   **p.** (−10,10)

    q. (10,10)   **r.** (0,15)   **s.** (−10,10)   **t.** (−15,0)

    u. (−10,−10)   **v.** (0,−15)   **w.** (10,−10)   **x.** (15,0)

    y. (10,10)

GRAPHICAL REPRESENTATION OF EQUATIONS

You have seen how a system of coordinates is used to plot individual points. Such a system may also be used to represent graphically the solutions of algebraic equations.

Developmental Exercises

DE—1. Locate all the points whose coordinates (x and y values) satisfy the equation $y = 2x$.

Solution

As a value is assigned to x in the equation $y = 2x$, a corresponding value for y is determined.

If $x =$	-1	0	1	2
Then $y =$	-2	0	2	4

Each pair of corresponding values of x and y that satisfy the equation may be used as the coordinates of a point. Thus, $(-1, -2)$ identifies a point which is one unit to the left of the origin and two units below the origin.

By plotting the four points, it appears that a straight line can be drawn through them. In fact, *every point whose coordinates satisfy the equation lies on the same line.* Check this by plotting another pair of values that satisfy the equation, such as $x = 3$, $y = 6$. Is the point $(3, 6)$ on the line?

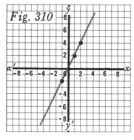

Fig. 310

Also, *the coordinates of every point on the line satisfy the equation.* Choose any point on the line. Determine its coordinates. Suppose these are $(-2, -4)$, do the values $x = -2$, $y = -4$ satisfy the equation?

This line is called the locus of the points which satisfy the equation or simply the graph of the equation. The plural of locus is loci (lō′sī). A locus (graph) is a geometric interpretation of a set of conditions.

For a geometric figure to be a graph of an equation, two conditions must be fulfilled.

(1) The coordinates of every point on the assumed graph must satisfy the equation. (Necessary condition)

(2) Every point whose coordinates satisfy the equation lies on the assumed graph. (Sufficient condition)

DE—2. The sum of the squares of two numbers is 25. Describe the locus represented by these conditions.

Solution

Let x represent one number and y represent the second number. The relationship may be expressed $x^2+y^2=25$.

Thus, $y^2=25-x^2$ or $y=\pm\sqrt{25-x^2}$.

If $x=$	-5	-4	-3	-2	-1	0	1	2	3	4	5
Then $y=$	0	± 3	± 4	$\pm\sqrt{21}$	$\pm 2\sqrt{6}$	± 5	$\pm 2\sqrt{6}$	$\pm\sqrt{21}$	± 4	± 3	0

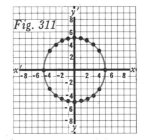

Fig. 311

Notice that as values of x change from -5 to 5 there are corresponding changes of y from 0 to 5 to 0 and 0 to -5 to 0. If these values are plotted, the points suggest a circle. As more values are computed and plotted, a circle is formed with its center at the origin and a radius of 5.

Examine the circle in Figure 311. The coordinates of each point on the circle satisfy the equation $x^2+y^2=25$. Each pair of x and y values that satisfies the equation is represented by a point on the circle. Thus, this circle is the locus of points that satisfies the equation.

DE—3. Describe the geometric figure that fulfills the conditions expressed in $y=2x$ and $x_2+y_2=25$.

Solution

In Developmental Exercise **1** the graph of $y=2x$ was represented. In Developmental Exercise **2** the graph of $x^2+y^2=25$ was represented. Only the points that lie on each of the graphs satisfy each of the conditions. The points that lie on both of these graphs (the intersections of the loci) satisfy both sets of conditions. The points $(\sqrt{5}, 2\sqrt{5})$ and $(-\sqrt{5}, -2\sqrt{5})$ fulfill both conditions. These points may be approximately located at $(2.2, 4.4)$ and $(-2.2, -4.4)$.

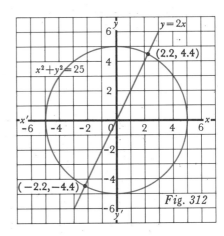

Fig. 312

Exercises

In Exercises **1-16** *represent the locus of each of the equations or pairs of equations.*

1. $y = 2x.$ **2.** $y = -x.$ **3.** $y = 4x.$

4. $y = -4x.$ **5.** $y = \frac{1}{2}x.$ **6.** $y = \frac{1}{4}x.$

7. $y = x^2.$ **8.** $x^2 + y^2 = 9.$ **9.** $x^2 + y^2 = 4.$

10. $y = ax$ (if a is a positive number).

11. $y = ax$ (if a is a negative number).

12. $y = x$, $14 \geq y \geq 1.$

13. $y = 1$, $14 \geq x \geq 1.$

14. $x = 14$, $14 \geq y \geq 1.$

15. $x = \pm 10$, $10 \geq y \geq -10.$

16. $y = \pm 10$, $10 \geq x \geq -10.$

17. Determine if the graph of $3x + y = 2$ is parallel to the graph of $9x + 3y = 6.$

18. Determine if the graph of $4x - 3y = 5$ intersects the graph of $2x + 3y = 1.$

19. Determine if the graph of $x + y = 5$ intersects the graph of $x^2 + y^2 = 16.$

20. Represent the graphs of $x^2 + y^2 = 25$ and $x + 2y = 8$ on the same axes. Read from the graph the corresponding values of x and y which satisfy both equations.

21. Draw the loci of the following equations on the same axes. Determine what points they have in common.

    a. $x^2 + y^2 = 9.$

    b. $x^2 - y^2 = 9.$

    c. $x^2 - 9 = y.$

22. Draw the loci of the following equations on the same axes. Determine what points they have in common.

    a. $x = -y + 4.$

    b. $y = x + 4.$

    c. $x + y^2 = 16.$

    d. $x^2 + y^2 = 16.$

THE PATH OF A POINT IN MOTION

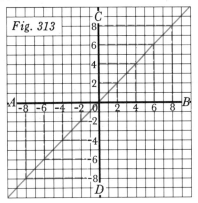

Fig. 313

A locus may also be thought of as the path of a point in motion fulfilling stated conditions. For example, if a point moves so that it is always equally distant (perpendicularly) from two perpendicular line segments, its path (locus) is a straight line that bisects the right angle between the perpendiculars.

If you cannot discover a locus intuitively, make a free-hand sketch of one point that satisfies the conditions given. Next, locate a second point, close to the first, that also satisfies the conditions. Then locate a third and fourth point and, if necessary, more points to roughly trace a geometric figure. When you know the locus, draw a new, neat sketch with a straightedge and compass. Before concluding that the interpretation is correct, consider any special positions the point, or points, may have. If necessary alter your sketch to include the special positions.

In describing a locus it would be incorrect to merely identify the geometric figure. For example, it is not enough to say "a circle." This is vague, since circles have varying radii and position. If the locus is a circle, the position is described by noting the location of its center and stating its radius.

Exercises

1. Determine the locus of the center of an automobile wheel as it moves in a straight line along a horizontal surface.

2. Sketch the locus of the center of a baseball when a home run is hit.

3. A quarter is rolled around a dime with the coins always in contact. Sketch the locus of the center of the quarter.

4. What is the locus of points 5 units from the *x*-axis of a coordinate plane?

5. On graph paper determine the locus of points equidistant from $x = 2$, $y = 0$, and $x = 4$, $y = 0$.

6. Find the locus of points equidistant from the sides of an angle.

7. Find the locus of points one inch from the sides of an obtuse angle.

8. Determine the path of a runner in the middle lane of a circular race track.

9. State in words the locus of all points $\frac{1}{2}$ inch from a circle of radius 2 inches.

10. What is the locus of a point equally distant from two parallel lines?

11. A pair of parallel lines are $1\frac{1}{2}$ inches apart. What is the locus of of points $\frac{3}{4}$ inch from each line?

12. A contractor, believing that he had completed an addition to a school building, received a telephone call informing him that no switch could be located to turn on lights in the third floor corridor. From his blueprints the contractor found that the switch was to be placed five feet above the hall floor and eighteen inches from the vertical edge of a right-angled turn in the hall. No switch could be found, so believing the workmen had carelessly covered it with plaster, the contractor decided to drive a punch into the plaster where the switch should be. How did he know where to punch the hole? Explain, using a diagram.

13. Determine the locus of the vertex of triangles having the same base and a constant altitude.

14. A pair of chords intersect in a circle. Determine the locus of points equidistant from the chords.

15. Determine the locus of a point a given distance from a given line segment.

16. Determine the locus of a point a given distance from a given ray. How does this differ from Exercise **15**?

17. Sketch the locus of points that satisfies the statement $x + y \geq 6$.

18. Sketch the locus that satisfies the statement $y \leq |x|$.

If a car may be considered a point, each light line is the locus of a car moving
on the Los Angeles Freeway.

VALID CONCLUSIONS CONCERNING LOCI

So far in this chapter you have been discovering and describing loci. No attention have been given to. proving theorems concerning loci. To prove that a geometric figure is the locus that fulfills the given conditions, two statements must be proved: a statement of the necessary conditions and a statement of the sufficient conditions.

(1) *The necessary condition*

If a point is on the supposed locus, it satisfies the given conditions.

(2) *The sufficient condition*

If a point satisfies the given conditions, it lies on the supposed locus.

The developmental exercises will illustrate such a proof.

Developmental Exercises

DE—1. Prove the following theorem:

THEOREM 89

In a plane the locus of points equidistant from two given points is the perpendicular bisector of the line segment joining the points.

Solution

The proof consists of two parts, the proof of the necessary condition and the proof of the sufficient condition.

(1) The necessary condition

Any point on the perpendicular bisector of a line is equidistant from the ends of the line segment.

Given: CD is the perpendicular bisector of AB.
E is any point on CD.
Prove: $AE = EB$.

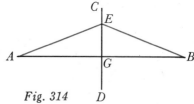

Fig. 314

Proof:

Since CD is the perpendicular bisector of AB, $CD \perp AB$ and $AG = GB$.
$\triangle BGE \cong \triangle AGE$ by **s.a.s. = s.a.s.**
Hence, $AE = BE$ as corresponding sides of congruent triangles.

(2) The sufficient condition

Any point equidistant from two given points lies on the perpendicular bisector of the line segment joining the given points.

Given: $EA = EB$.
Prove: E is on the perpendicular bisector of AB.

Fig. 315

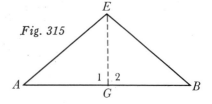

Construction: Join E to G, the midpoint of AB.
Proof:

Since G is the midpoint of AB, $AG = GB$. That $AE = EB$ is given.
Therefore, $\triangle AGE \cong \triangle BGE$ by **s.s.s. = s.s.s.**
$\angle 1 = \angle 2$ as corresponding angles of congruent triangles.
Why are $\angle 1$ and $\angle 2$ right angles?
Hence, $EG \perp AB$. EG is therefore the perpendicular bisector of AB.
Since both conditions have been proved, the theorem is established.

DE—2. Prove the following theorem:

> **THEOREM 90**
>
> **The locus of points equidistant from the sides of an angle is the bisector of the angle.**

Solution

Again the proof of the theorem depends on the proof of two statements.

(1) The necessary condition

Any point on the bisector of an angle is equally distant from the sides of the angle.

Given: $\angle ABC$ bisected by BD. $\quad$ *Fig. 316*
$\quad\quad\quad\quad$ P is any point on BD.

Prove: P is equidistant from AB and BC.

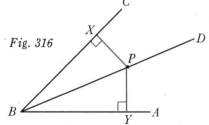

Construction: From P construct a perpendicular to AB and BC. (The distance from P to AB is measured along PY. The distance from P to BC is measured along, PX.)

Analysis:

$\triangle PBX \cong \triangle YBP$. Why?

Therefore, $PX = PY$ and P is equidistant from BC and AB.

(2) The sufficient condition

Any point equidistant from the sides of an angle is on the bisector of the angle.

Given: P is any point equidistant from AB and BC.
$\quad\quad\quad\quad$ $(PY = PX.)$ $\quad\quad\quad\quad$ *Fig. 317*

Prove: BP is the bisector of $\angle ABC$. $(\angle 1 = \angle 2.)$

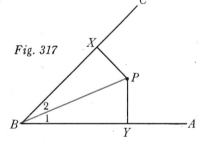

Analysis:

$\triangle PBX \cong \triangle PBY$. Why?

$\angle 1 = \angle 2$ as corresponding angles of congruent triangles. Therefore, BP bisects $\angle ABC$.

Since both conditions have been proved the theorem is established.

Be sure that in proving all locus theorems you prove both the necessary and sufficient conditions. Other theorems concerning loci which your teacher may have you prove are the following:

THEOREM 91

In a plane the locus of all points a given distance from a given point is a circle with the given point as its center and the given distance as its radius.

THEOREM 92

In a plane the locus of points a given distance from a given line is a pair of parallel lines, one on each side of the given line at the given distance from the given line.

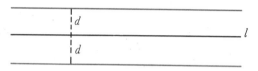

Fig. 318

THEOREM 93

In a plane the locus of points equidistant from two parallel lines is a line parallel to the given lines and halfway between them.

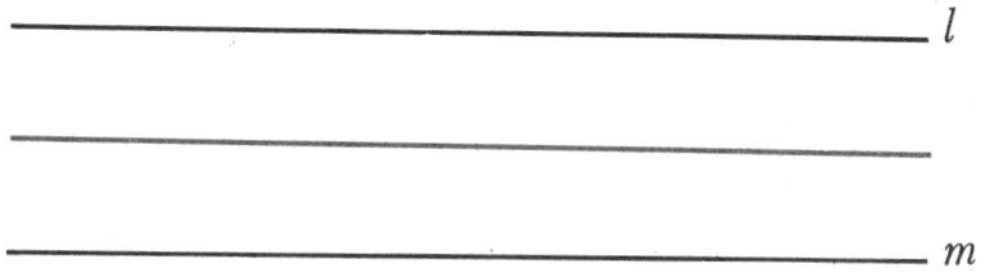

Fig. 319

THEOREM 94

The locus of points equidistant from two intersecting lines is a pair of lines bisecting the four angles.

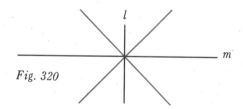

Fig. 320

Exercises

1. Write a formal proof for Theorem 90.

2. Prove Theorem 91.

3. Prove Theorem 92.

4. Prove Theorem 93.

5. Prove Theorem 94.

6. a. What is the locus of the center of a circle of radius r tangent to a given line?

    b. What two statements must be proved to establish this locus?

    c. Prove this locus proposition.

7. a. What is the locus of the midpoints of all chords through a given point, not the center, in a circle.

    b. What two statements must be proved to establish this locus?

    c. Prove this locus proposition.

8. Given a point on a circle, determine the locus of the midpoints of all chords of a circle drawn to the given point. Prove this locus proposition.

9. Given two tangent circles, determine the locus of points from which equal tangents can be drawn to the circles. Prove this locus proposition.

10. Determine the locus of the midpoints of line segments parallel to the base of a given trapezoid and terminating in the nonparallel sides of the trapezoid. Prove this proposition.

11. Determine the locus of the intersection of the diagonals of all rhombuses having a given line as their common base. Prove this proposition.

12. Determine the locus of the center of a circle tangent to two intersecting lines. Discuss the change in the length of the radius of the circle as the circle assumes various positions. As a result of this discussion, would you be willing to define a point as a circle having a radius of 0 units measure. Recall that *point* in our discussion is an undefined term.

INTERSECTING LOCI

Previously you determined the locus of points that satisfied two conditions by sketching the locus of each condition and identifying their intersection. Since the point, or points, of intersection satisfied both conditions, the intersection was the required locus. Here again you are to determine the locus of points satisfying multiple conditions.

Developmental Exercises

DE—1. Find the locus of points equidistant from three given points.

Solution

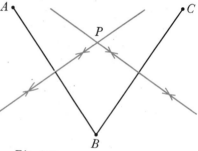

Connect the three given points *A* (*A*, *B*, and *C*) in order. Perpendicularly bisect the line segment *AB*. All points on this perpendicular bisector are an equal distance from *A* and *B*. Why? Perpendicularly bisect the line segment *BC*. All points on this perpendicular bisector are an equal distance from *B* and *C*. Why? The point *P* is an equal distance from *A*, *B*, and *C*. Why?

Fig. 321

Discuss the solution if *A*, *B*, and *C* are located on the same straight line.

Exercises

1. Locate the points equidistant from the vertices

   a. of an acute triangle.

   b. of an obtuse triangle.

   c. of a right triangle.

2. Locate the points equidistant from the vertices of a triangle and a given distance from one of the sides. Discuss the possibility of solutions for this problem.

3. *X*, *Y*, and *Z* are points on arc *XZ*. Determine the center of the circle and its radius.

4. Locate points equidistant from two given points and from the intersection of two given lines. When is no solution possible?

5. Experiment to learn the kind of triangle which must be drawn to have the locus of points equidistant from its vertices lie upon one side of the triangle.

6. Summarize the conditions which must be controlled to have the locus of points equidistant from the vertices lie inside the triangle, outside the triangle. Support your summary with neat sketches.

DE—2. Locate a point equidistant from the sides of an angle and one inch from the vertex of the angle.

Solution

The locus of points equidistant from the sides of an angle is the bisector of the angle (*BP*).

The locus of points equidistant from a given point is the circle with the given point as center and the given distance as radius ($\odot B$).

Point *T* satisfies both conditions.

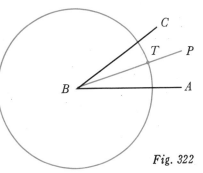

Fig. 322

Exercises

1. Locate the points equidistant from the sides

    a. Of an acute triangle.

    b. of an obtuse triangle.

    c. of a right triangle.

2. Locate the points equidistant from the sides of an obtuse angle and $\frac{1}{2}$ inch from the vertex.

3. Locate the points equidistant from the sides of an acute angle and one inch from one side. Discuss the possible solutions.

4. Locate the points equidistant from two sides of a triangle and a given distance from the third side.

5. Locate the points equidistant from two sides of a triangle and a given distance from one of the noncommon vertices.

6. Locate points equidistant from the sides of each angle of a quadrilateral. Under what conditions will there be a solution of one point?

DE—3. Where would points be located that are at a distance, a, from a given point, O, and also at a distance, b, from a given point, P.

Solution

The locus of points at distance a from point O is a circle with its center at O and a as radius.

The locus of points at distance b from point P is a circle with its center at P and b as radius.

If the line OP is drawn and $OP \leq (a+b)$, the locus of points is the intersection of the two circles.

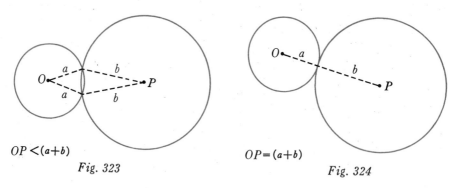

$OP < (a+b)$

Fig. 323

$OP = (a+b)$

Fig. 324

What is the situation if $OP > (a+b)$.

Exercises

In the following exercises draw a sketch of the required points and give a reason that justifies your sketch.

1. Locate all points which are one inch from each of two intersecting lines.

2. Find the locus of all points equidistant from two fixed points, X and Y, and equidistant from two intersecting lines, AB and AD.

3. Find all the points equidistant from two given intersecting lines and at a distance of one inch from the point of intersection of the two lines.

4. Find all the points at a given distance from a given point and at a given distance from a given line. Discuss the possibilities.

5. If X and Y are $2\frac{1}{2}$ inches apart, what is the locus of points $1\frac{1}{2}$ inches from X and 2 inches from Y.

6. A circle lies between two parallel lines. Locate all points on the circle equidistant from the parallels.

7. Two lines are perpendicular to each other. What is the locus of the midpoint of a third line whose endpoints lie on the perpendicular lines?

8. In a triangle, ABC, locate a point equidistant from A, B, and C.

9. Find all the points at a given distance from a given circle and equidistant from two given points.

10. Find the locus of all points equidistant from two parallel lines, a and b, and equidistant from two points, A and B.

11. Locate all points at a given distance from a fixed line, XY, and equidistant from two given points.

12. Locate all points on a line, XY, which are equidistant from two intersecting lines, AB and CD.

13. What is the locus of points two inches from a given point and one inch from a given line? Show that there may be no solutions, one, two, three, or four solutions.

14. Construct a circle that will be tangent to a given line and to a given circle. How many such circles are there?

15. Sides of a triangle are 4, 5, and 6 inches in length. Locate all points two inches from one vertex and equally distant from the other two vertices.

16. With a point and a line fixed in position, locate all points a given distance from the point and line.

17. Knowing the length or base of a triangle, and also the median to that base, can you locate the third vertex of the triangle? Include a sketch with your answer.

18. Construct a tangent to a given circle which will form an angle of $30°$ with a given line.

19. Show by a sketch the centers of all circles which have a given radius, are tangent to a given line, and pass through a given point.

20. Determine the locus of all points equidistant from two concentric circles and equidistant from two given points.

CONCURRENT LINES

Lines which have a point in common are said to be *concurrent*. Some examples of concurrent lines are the perpendicular bisectors of the sides of a triangle, the bisectors of the angles of a triangle, and the medians of a triangle. The proofs that these lines are concurrent are given in the following developmental exercises.

Developmental Exercises

DE—1. Prove the following theorem:

> **THEOREM 95**
> **The perpendicular bisectors of the sides of a triangle are concurrent at a point equally distant from the vertices.**

Solution

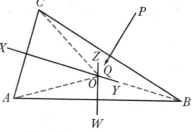

Fig. 325

Given: In $\triangle ABC$, XY, ZW, and PQ are perpendicular bisectors of AC, AB, and BC, respectively.

Prove: XY, ZW, and PQ meet at one point equidistant from A, B, and C.

Proof:

STATEMENTS	REASONS
1. XY and ZW meet at a point, O.	1. If two lines are respectively perpendicular to two nonparallel lines, they intersect.
2. $OA = OC$, $OA = OB$.	2. Any point on the perpendicular bisector of a line segment is equally distant from its ends.
3. $OC = OB$.	3. Quantities equal to the same quantity are equal.
4. PQ passes through O.	4. The locus of a point equidistant from two given points is the perpendicular bisector of the line segment joining them.
5. XY, ZW, and PQ are concurrent.	5. Definition of concurrent lines.

This point of intersection is called the *circumcenter* of the triangle.

Exercises

1. Circumscribe a circle about an acute triangle.

2. Circumscribe a circle about an obtuse triangle.

3. Circumscribe a circle about a right triangle.

4. Circumscribe a circle about a square.

5. Given an arc of a circle, locate the center of the circle.

6. Is it possible to circumscribe a circle about any type of quadrilateral other than a square?

DE—2. Prove the following theorem:

> ## THEOREM 96
> **The bisectors of the angles of a triangle are concurrent at a point equally distant from the sides.**

Solution

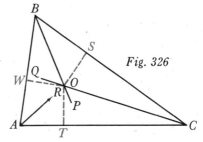

Fig. 326

    Given: In $\triangle ABC$, AR bisects $\angle BAC$,
             BP bisects $\angle CBA$,
             CQ bisects $\angle ACB$.
    Prove: AR, BP, and CQ are concurrent at a point equidistant from AB, AC, and BC.

Proof:

STATEMENTS	REASONS
1. BP bisects $\angle CBA$, CQ bisects $\angle ACB$.	1. Given.
2. BP meets CQ at O.	2. The bisectors of two angles of a triangle intersect.
3. $OS = OW$, $OS = OT$.	3. The bisector of an angle is the locus of points equidistant from the sides of the angle.
4. $OW = OT$.	4. Quantities equal to the same quantity are equal.
5. AR will pass through O.	5. Same as Reason 3.
6. AR, BP, and CQ are concurrent.	6. Definition of concurrent.

This point of intersection is called the *incenter* of the triangle.

DE—3. Prove the following theorem:

║ **THEOREM 97**
║ **The altitudes of a triangle are concurrent.**

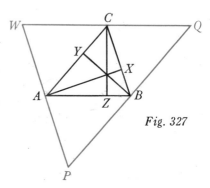

Fig. 327

Solution

Given: AX, BY, and CZ are altitudes of $\triangle ABC$.

Prove: AX, BY, and CZ are concurrent.

Proof:

STATEMENTS	REASONS
1. Through A, B, and C; WP, PQ, and WQ are constructed respectively parallel to BC, AC, and AB.	1. Through a point, not on a given line, one and only one line can be constructed parallel to the given line.
2. $AX \perp BC$, $BY \perp AC$, $CZ \perp AB$.	2. Given.
3. $WABC$ is a $\square$, $ABQC$ is a $\square$, $APBC$ is a $\square$.	3. A quadrilateral having opposite sides parallel is a parallelogram.
4. $AB = WC$, $AC = BQ$, $BC = WA$, $AB = CQ$, $AC = BP$, $BC = AP$.	4. The opposite sides of a parallelogram are equal.
5. $WC = CQ$, $BQ = BP$, $WA = AP$.	5. Quantities equal to the same quantity are equal.
6. CZ, BY, and AX are perpendicular bisectors of WQ, PQ, and WP, respectively in $\triangle WPQ$.	6. Definition of perpendicular bisector.
7. AX, BY, and CZ are concurrent.	7. The perpendicular bisectors of the sides of a triangle are concurrent.

This point of intersection is called the *orthocenter* of the triangle.

Exercises

1. Inscribe a circle in an obtuse triangle.

2. Inscribe a circle in a right triangle.

3. Construct an equilateral triangle. Inscribe a circle in the triangle. Circumscribe a circle about the triangle.

4. Construct an isosceles triangle. Inscribe a circle in the triangle. Circumscribe a circle about the triangle.

5. Do the altitudes, angle bisectors, and perpendicular bisectors of the sides of a triangle ever intersect in the same point? Give evidence to support your answer.

6. Inscribe a circle in a given square.

7. Is it possible to inscribe a circle in any type of quadrilateral other than a square? Be prepared to give evidence to support your answer.

8. Can a circle be inscribed in any type of polygon? Explain.

9. Construct a circle that is tangent to a pair of intersecting lines and has a given radius.

10. Construct a circle tangent to two given parallel lines that also passes through a given point between the two parallels.

DE—4. Prove the following theorem:

> ||**THEOREM 98**
> ||The medians of a triangle meet in a point which is two-thirds the distance on each median from a vertex of the triangle to the midpoint of the opposite side.

Solution

Given: AX, BY, and CZ are medians in $\triangle ABC$ with AX and BY intersecting at O.

Prove: AX, BY, and CZ are concurrent.

$AO = \frac{2}{3}AX$,

$BO = \frac{2}{3}BY$,   *Fig. 328*

$CO = \frac{2}{3}CZ$.

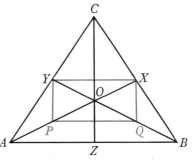

Proof:

STATEMENTS	REASONS
1. AX, BY, and CZ are medians in $\triangle ABC$ with AX and BY intersecting at O.	1. Given.
2. Join Q, the midpoint of BO, to X. Join P, the midpoint of AO, to Y. Join P to Q.	2. Two points determine a straight line.
3. $XY \parallel AB$, $XY = \frac{1}{2}AB$, $PQ \parallel AB$, $PQ = \frac{1}{2}AB$.	3. A line joining the midpoints of two sides of a triangle is parallel to the third side and equal to one-half of it.
4. $XY = PQ$.	4. Why?
5. $XY \parallel PQ$.	5. Two lines parallel to a third line are parallel.
6. $PQXY$ is a $\square$.	6. A quadrilateral with two sides equal and parallel is a parallelogram.
7. $OX = OP$, $YO = OQ$.	7. The diagonals of a parallelogram bisect each other.
8. $OP = PA$, $OQ = BQ$.	8. Definition of midpoint.
9. $OX = PA$, $YO = BQ$.	9. Same as Reason 4.
10. $AP + PO + OX = AX$, $BQ + QO + OY = BY$.	10. The whole is equal to the sum of its parts.
11. $3OP = AX$, $3OQ = BY$.	11. A quantity may be substituted for its equal.
12. $OP = \frac{1}{3}AX$, $OQ = \frac{1}{3}BY$.	12. If equals are divided by equals the quotients are equal.
13. $2OP = \frac{2}{3}AX$, $2OQ = \frac{2}{3}BY$.	13. Why?
14. $AO = \frac{2}{3}AX$, $BO = \frac{2}{3}BY$.	14. Why?

The medians have not yet been established as concurrent. If CZ intersects BY at some point other than O, such as O', then $BO' = \frac{2}{3}BY$, and $BO = BO'$ which makes O coincide with O'. Hence, the medians are concurrent.

This point of intersection is called the *centroid* of the triangle.

Exercises

1. Prove that in a trapezoid if one leg is perpendicular to a base, its endpoints are equidistant from the midpoint of the other leg.

2. Draw a straight line so that segments of it, intercepted between three concurrent lines, are equal.

3. If the medians of a triangle are five, six, and seven cm. respectively, determine the length of each segment into which their common point divides them.

4. If the medians of a triangle are 3, 6, and 9 inches respectively, determine the length of each segment into which their common point divides them.

5. Is a triangle determined by the data in Exercise **4**? If not, state what is needed.

6. Prove that if a triangle is equilateral, six congruent triangles are formed when its medians are drawn.

7. Construct a right triangle given an acute angle and the hypotenuse.

8. Given one leg of an isosceles right triangle, construct the triangle.

9. Given the base and altitude to the base of an isosceles triangle, construct the triangle.

10. Construct an isosceles triangle given its base and a base angle.

11. Draw an obtuse triangle. Show that the altitudes, when extended, are concurrent.

12. Construct a rhombus when an angle and one diagonal are given.

13. Given one side and the altitude of a rhombus, construct the rhombus.

14. Construct an isosceles trapezoid, given a diagonal and the base.

15. Given the diagonals of a parallelogram and the angle between them, construct the parallelogram.

16. If line segments join the ends of a diagonal of a parallelogram to the midpoints of two opposite sides, prove that the other diagonal is divided into three equal parts.

SOLID GEOMETRY

Many conclusions about locus in space (three-dimensional) will be similar in some ways to those presented earlier in this chapter.

You may accept the following assumption:

Assumption 6$_s$

A straight line connecting two points in a plane lies entirely in the plane.

Developmental Exercises

DE—1. Prove the following theorem:

> **THEOREM 5$_s$**
>
> **The locus of a point in space that is equidistant from the endpoints of a line segment is the plane that is the perpendicular bisector of the line segment.**

Solution

There are, of course, two statements to be proved, a statement of the necessary condition and a statement of the sufficient condition.

(1) The necessary condition

Any point in the plane which is perpendicular to a line segment at its midpoint is equally distant from the ends of the line segment.

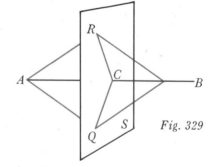

Given: Q lies in plane S,
$S \perp AB$ at C,
$AC = CB$.
Prove: $AQ = QB$.

Fig. 329

Proof:

Line QC lies in plane S by Assumption 6$_s$. A straight line connecting two points in a plane lies entirely in the plane.

$AB \perp QC$ because if a line is perpendicular to a plane, it is perpendiculat to every line in the plane passing through its foot.

$AQ = QB$ since any point on the perpendicular bisector of a line segment is equally distant from its endpoints.

(2) The sufficient condition

If a point is equidistant from the endpoints of a line segment, it lies in the plane perpendicular to the line segment at its midpoint.

Given: $AR = BR$, plane $S \perp AB$ at C, $AC = CB$.

Prove: R lies in plane S.

Proof:

C and R determine the perpendicular bisector of AB (CR).

Since all the lines perpendicular to a given line at a given point lie in a plane perpendicular to the line at the given point (Assumption 5_s), R lies in plane S.

DE—2. Prove the following theorem:

> **THEOREM 6_s**
>
> **The locus of a point within a dihedral angle and equally distant from its faces is the plane that bisects the dihedral angle.**

Solution

(1) The necessary condition

Any point in the plane which bisects a dihedral angle is equidistant from its faces.

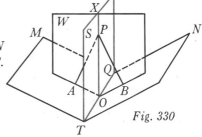

Given: Dihedral angle M-TQ-N is bisected by plane S. P is on plane S.

Prove: $PA = PB$.

Fig. 330

Analysis:

Construct the plane W containing PA and PB perpendicular to line QT. Right triangles AOP and BOP are congruent. Therefore, $PA = PB$ as corresponding sides of congruent triangles.

(2) The sufficient condition

If a point is equidistant from the faces of a dihedral angle, it lies in the plane that bisects the dihedral angle.

Given: $PA = PB$, plane S contains P and QT.

Prove: Plane S bisects angle M-TQ-N.

Analysis:

Construct plane W containing PA and PB perpendicular to QT. Plane S bisects M-TQ-N if $\angle POA = \angle POB$. Prove $\triangle PAO \cong \triangle PBO$. Write a complete proof for this theorem.

Exercises

1. Describe the locus of points upon the floor of your classroom which are equally distant from two points in each of two opposite walls.

2. State the locus of a point at a given distance from a given point.

3. Show the locus of points equally distant from the sides of an angle.

4. Locate all points at a given distance from a given plane.

5. State the locus of points equally distant from two parallel planes.

6. Describe the locus of points equidistant from two intersecting planes.

7. Show the locus of a point equally distant from the vertices of a triangle.

8. Illustrate the locus of a point upon the floor of your classroom at a given distance from a point upon a wall of the room.

9. Describe the locus of points equidistant from two given points and also equidistant from two parallel planes. Explain the positions which will yield no locus.

10. State the locus of a point equidistant from two parallel planes and a given distance from a third plane. When is there no locus?

11. Illustrate the locus of a point at a given distance from P and a different fixed distance from Q. Explain how there can be no locus.

12. Given a line perpendicular to a plane, describe the locus of all points equally distant from the plane and the line.

13. Explain how you would locate a point equidistant from four points which do not all lie in one plane.

14. Draw a right triangle. With the hypotenuse in a fixed position, what is the locus of the vertex of the opposite angle when the triangle rotates around the hypotenuse?

15. Show the locus of a point at a given distance from a given line.

16. Describe the locus of points equally distant from a circle. How is the locus affected if the distance is equal to the radius of the circle? Is greater than the radius?

EXTEND YOUR HORIZON

Geometric figures in space are frequently represented by *projections* on a plane. Lines are drawn through the geometric figure and the plane in much the same way that a viewer shows the image contained on a camera slide film upon the screen.

The projection of a line upon a plane is the locus of the projections of all the points of the line. The line can be curved, dotted, dashed, straight, or broken, and the plane may or may not be parallel to the line.

Central projection is used when a pinhole camera takes a picture. Rays of light project outlines of objects to the retina of the human eye. Projecting lines pass from or through a central point. Note that in central projection, the projection upon a plane may not have exactly the same size and shape as the object projected. You can use a small flashlight to show that the central projection of a circle can be an ellipse.

Projective geometry is a branch of mathematics concerned with a study of properties of geometric figures which are unchanged when the figures are centrally projected.

The lights from the ships in the Hudson River show that as light diffuses, the projection in the sky is not the same size or shape as the source.

CHAPTER SUMMARY

A geometric figure is the locus of points satisfying given conditions if

1. every point on the supposed locus satisfies the given conditions. (page 338)

2. every point that satisfies the given conditions is on the supposed locus.   (page 338)

In a plane the locus of points equidistant from

1. two given points is the perpendicular bisector of the line segment joining the points.   (page 344)

2. the sides of an angle is the bisector of the angle.   (page 345)

3. two parallel lines is a line parallel to the given lines and half-way between them.   (page 346)

4. two intersecting lines is a pair of lines bisecting the four angles. (page 346.)

In a plane the locus of points a given distance from

1. a given point is a circle with the given point as its center and the given distance as radius.   (page 346)

2. a given line is a pair of parallel lines, one on each side of the given line, at the given distance from the given line.   (page 346)

Lines are concurrent if

1. they are the perpendicular bisectors of the sides of a triangle. (page 352)

2. they are the bisectors of the angles of a triangle.   (page 353)

3. they are the altitudes of a triangle.   (page 354)

4. they are the medians of a triangle.   (page 355)

CHAPTER REVIEW

Vocabulary

Match the word in the left hand column with its correct definition in the right hand column.

1. Origin

    a. The point of intersection of the altitudes of a triangle.

    b. The path of a point in motion fulfilling given conditions.

2. Abscissa

    c. The point of intersection of a pair of axes.

3. Ordinate

    d. Having a point in common.

    e. The point of intersection of the vertices of a triangle.

4. Coordinates

    f. The point of intersection of the medians of a triangle.

5. Concurrent

    g. The distance measured along the vertical axis.

6. Locus

    h. The abscissa value and the ordinate value of a point.

7. Circumcenter

    i. The point of intersection of the angle bisectors of a triangle.

8. Orthocenter

    j. The distance measured from the origin to a point.

    k. The distance measured along the horizontal axis.

9. Incenter

    l. The point of intersection of the perpendicular bisectors of a triangle.

10. Centroid

Exercises

1. Sketch the course of a ship as it passes between two reefs and remains equally distant from them.

2. Sketch the locus of a point at a given distance from a given circle.

3. Sketch the locus of the midpoints of line segments parallel to one side of a triangle and ending in the other two sides of the triangle.

4. Sketch the locus of the center of a circle having a radius of three inches and which also passes through a given point.

5. Describe the locus of points equidistant from two given points and also equally distant from two parallel lines. Describe the conditions when no such locus is possible.

6. Describe the locus of points equally distant from two parallel lines and also at a given distance from a given straight line. When is no locus possible?

7. Given a circle and two parallel lines which have no points in common with the circle, describe the locus of all points on the circle equally distant from the parallel lines.

8. Given a circle and two intersecting straight lines, describe the locus of all points on the circle equally distant from the given lines.

9. Draw a general rectangle. Inside it, construct circles tangent to two sides. Describe the locus of the centers of the circles.

10. Sketch the locus of points for which $(x-2)^2 = y$.

11. Sketch the locus of points for which $x + y = 3$ and $2x + 2y = 6$.

12. Sketch the locus of points for which $x^2 + y^2 = 10$ and $y = 2x + 5$.

13. Is a locus of points possible for which $x + y = 5$ and $y = 6 - x$?

14. Determine the position of a point which is always the same distance from point X as from line PQ.

15. Construct an equilateral triangle given the radius of the circumscribed circle.

16. Construct an isosceles triangle given the base and the radius of the inscribed circle.

CHAPTER TEST

1. Describe the locus of points $\frac{1}{4}$ inch from a given line.

2. Describe the locus of a satellite in orbit about the earth.

3. Construct the locus of the midpoints of all line segments that have their endpoints on a pair of parallel lines.

4. Construct the locus of all points which satisfy the following:

    a. $3x - y = 7$ **b.** $x + 2y = 7$

5. Construct the locus of points at a distance of $\frac{1}{2}$ inch from a circle whose radius is three inches.

6. Two circles have equal radii, their centers are in fixed positions, and they are tangent externally. Describe the locus of the centers of all circles tangent to both of them.

7. Determine the locus which satisfies the following equations:

    a. $x^2 + y^2 = 4$ **b.** $x + y = 2$

8. Three lines intersect at X, Y, and Z. Determine the locus of points equidistant from X and Y and equidistant from XY and YZ.

9. Complete the following proposition and state what must be proved to establish it. *The locus of points at a given distance from a circle is two circles with the same center as the given circle and radii. . . .*

10. Circumscribe a circle about an isosceles triangle.

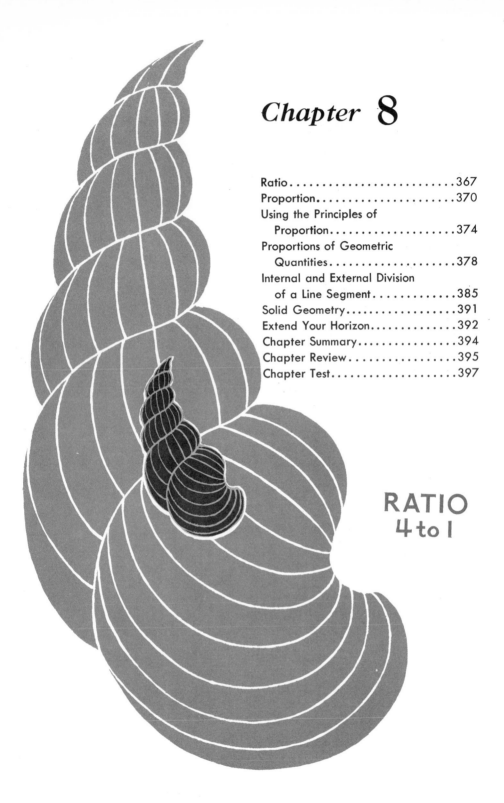

Chapter 8

RATIO
4 to 1

RATIO AND PROPORTION

RATIO

Quantities are frequently compared by means of **ratios.** *The ratio of one quantity to another quantity may be defined as the* **quotient** *obtained when the first quantity is divided by the second quantity.*

The ratio of two geometric quantities of the same kind, such as line segments, arcs, and angles, is the quotient of their numerical measures expressed in the same units of measure. Remember that only like quantities may be compared.

> **The ratio of two like quantities is the ratio of their measures in terms of the same unit.**

The two numbers used in a ratio are called the *terms of the ratio.* A ratio is a fraction and all the rules for performing the fundamental operations of addition, subtraction, multiplication, and division of fractions will apply to ratios. Both terms of a ratio may be divided or multiplied by the same number without changing the value of the ratio.

Developmental Exercises

DE—1. Express the ratio $6x$ to $12x^2$ in its simplest form.

Solution

$6x$ to $12x^2$ may be written as the fraction $\dfrac{6x}{12x^2}$. Dividing numerator and denominator of this fraction by the common factor $6x$, simplifies the fraction to $\dfrac{1}{2x}$.

DE—2. Find the ratio of 1 yard to 2 feet.

Solution

Since the units are unlike, change 1 yard to 3 feet and then proceed to divide. The result would be $\frac{3}{2}$. Another way of denoting this ratio is 3:2.

Exercises

1. Express the following ratios in simplest form.

    a. 3 to 6   **b.** 2 feet to 3 inches

    c. $\frac{4}{5}$ to $\frac{7}{12}$ **d.** 14 to 168

    e. 16 to 4   **f.** $\frac{3}{11}$ to $\frac{1}{2}$

    g. a right angle to $60°$

    h. the sum of all the angles of a triangle to $360°$

2. The perimeter of a rectangle is 24 feet and the length is 7 feet. Find the ratio of the length to the width.

3. Find the ratio of the perimeter of a rectangle 6 inches by 8 inches to the perimeter of a rectangle 3 inches by 12 inches.

4. Express the following ratios in simplest form.

    a. $3c$ to $4c$ **b.** $8x^2$ to $12x^3$

    c. $x+y$ to $x+y$ **d.** c^2-d^2 to $c-d$

    e. $a+b$ to a^2-b^2

    f. $\dfrac{5xy}{15xy^2}$, where x and $y \neq 0$.

    g. $34abc:17a^2$, where $a \neq 0$.

    h. $\dfrac{a^2+4a-21}{5a^2+35a}$, where $a \neq 0$ and $a \neq -7$.

5. Express the ratio of the measure of a right angle to the sum of all of the angles of the triangle.

6. Express the ratio of one angle of a square to the sum of the angles of the square.

7. Express the ratio of one angle of a regular hexagon to the sum of the angles of the hexagon.

8. In the diagram, $AC=12x$, $AB=3x$. What is the ratio of the following:

    a. AB to AC.

    b. AB to BC.

    c. AC to AB.

    d. BC to AC.

    e. AC to BC.

    f. BC to AB.

XXXXXXXXXXXXXX

A   B   C

Ex. 8

9. The ratio of two numbers is 4:5. If $4x$ represents the smaller number, how can you represent the larger?

10. Express the ratio of an exterior angle of a triangle to the sum of the two nonadjacent interior angles.

11. What is the ratio of the sum of the interior angles of a triangle to the sum of the exterior angles of a triangle?

12. How is the ratio $\frac{12}{8}$ affected by
   a. multiplying each term by 4?
   b. dividing each term by 4?
   c. increasing each term by 4?
   d. diminishing each term by 4?

13. Find the ratio of one angle of an equilateral triangle to the sum of the interior angles of the triangle.

14. The sides of two squares are in the ratio of 1:4. What is the ratio of their perimeters?

15. Express the ratio of an interior angle of the following regular polygons to the sum of the interior angles of that polygon.
   a. a regular pentagon   **b.** a regular hexagon
   c. a regular heptagon   **d.** a regular octagon
   e. a regular nonagon   **f.** a regular decagon
   g. a regular n-gon

16. Using the answers in Exercise **15** as a basis, form a generalization concerning the ratio of an interior angle of a regular polygon to the sum of the interior angles of the polygon.

17. Prove the generalization in Exercise **16.**

18. Express the ratio of $(1 - \frac{4}{x})$ to $(1 - \frac{16}{x^2})$ in simplest terms.

19. Express the ratio of $(\frac{x^2}{4} - 1)$ to $(1 + \frac{x}{2})$ in simplest terms.

20. An inscribed angle and a central angle intercept the same arc of a circle. What is the ratio of the inscribed angle to the central angle?

PROPORTION

A *proportion* is a statement that two ratios are equal. For example, $\frac{2}{3} = \frac{4}{6}$ is a proportion. The general form of a proportion may be written $\frac{a}{b} = \frac{c}{d}$ or $a:b = c:d$. This proportion would be read as "a divided by b equals c divided by d" or "a is to b as c is to d."

In the proportion $\frac{a}{b} = \frac{c}{d}$, the quantities a, b, c, and d are the first, second, third, and fourth terms, respectively, of the proportion. The *extremes* of a proportion are the first and fourth terms (a and d). The *means* of a proportion are the second and third terms (b and c). The *fourth proportional* in a proportion is the fourth term of the proportion (d).

In the special case where the means are equal, as in $\frac{a}{b} = \frac{b}{d}$, b is the mean proportional between a and d. The fourth term is then called a *third proportional*.

Since a proportion is an equation, all the assumptions concerning equations may be applied to proportions. For example, if both members of the proportion are multiplied by the same nonzero number, the equality will be retained. Proportions have special properties also, that may not apply to all equations.

Through measurement determine the ratio of these two dahlias. Do their measurements form a proportion?

Developmental Exercises

DE—1. Prove the following principle:

> **Principle 1**
>
> **In a proportion the product of the means is equal to the product of the extremes.**

Solution

In order to prove a principle for any proposition, start with a general proposition, such as, $\dfrac{a}{b} = \dfrac{c}{d}$, where a, b, c, and d are any real numbers.

It is to be proved that $ad = bc$.

If $\dfrac{a}{b} = \dfrac{c}{d}$ and $bd = bd$, (bd is the lowest common denominator.)

then $bd \cdot \dfrac{a}{b} = \dfrac{c}{d} \cdot bd$, (If equals are multiplied by equals the products

or $ad = bc$.   are equal.)

Example

If $\frac{2}{3} = \frac{4}{6}$, then $2 \times 6 = 3 \times 4$ or $12 = 12$.

DE—2. Prove the following principle:

> **Principle 2**
>
> **If the product of two quantities is equal to the product of two other quantities, either pair may be made the means and the other pair made the extremes of a proposition.**

Solution

This means that if $ad = cb$, then $\dfrac{a}{c} = \dfrac{b}{d}$, $\dfrac{d}{c} = \dfrac{b}{a}$, $\dfrac{c}{a} = \dfrac{d}{b}$, and

$\dfrac{a}{b} = \dfrac{c}{d}$.

If $ad = cb$ and $cd = cd$,

then $\dfrac{ad}{cd} = \dfrac{cb}{cd}$, (If equals are divided by equals the quotients are equal.)

or $\dfrac{a}{c} = \dfrac{b}{d}$.

Example:

If $3 \times 4 = 2 \times 6$, then $\frac{3}{2} = \frac{6}{4}$.

Likewise, if $ad = cb$ and $ca = ca$,

then $\dfrac{ad}{ca} = \dfrac{cb}{ca}$ (Why?) or $\dfrac{d}{c} = \dfrac{b}{a}$.

Example:

If $3\times4=2\times6$, then $\frac{4}{2}=\frac{6}{3}$.

Likewise, if $ad=cb$

and $ab=ab$,

then $\dfrac{ad}{ab}=\dfrac{cb}{ab}$ (Why?)

or $\dfrac{d}{b}=\dfrac{c}{a}$.

Example:

If $3\times4=2\times6$, then $\frac{4}{6}=\frac{2}{3}$.

If $ad=cb$, what would you divide both members by to arrive at $\dfrac{a}{b}=\dfrac{c}{d}$?

Can you give an example of this situation?

DE—3. Prove the following principle:

> **Principle 3**
>
> **If any three terms of a proportion are equal to the three corresponding terms of another proportion, the fourth terms are equal.**

Solution

Given the general proportions $\dfrac{a}{b}=\dfrac{c}{d}$ and $\dfrac{a}{b}=\dfrac{c}{e}$. It is to be proved

that $d=e$.

If $\dfrac{a}{b}=\dfrac{c}{d}$, then $ad=bc$. (Principle 1.)

Likewise, if $\dfrac{a}{b}=\dfrac{c}{e}$, then $ae=bc$.

therefore $ae=ad$ and $e=d$. (Why?)

Exercises

1. In the proportion $\frac{3}{5}=\frac{6}{10}$ what is the first term? The second term? The third term? The fourth term? Name the extremes and the means. What number is the fourth proportional?

2. Use the following set of numbers to form a proportion: 52, 12, 48, 13.

3. Write a proportion in which x is the mean proportional between 16 and 4.

4. Write a proportion in which 8 is the fourth proportional to 3, 4, and 6.

5. Prove the following principle:

> **Principle 4**
>
> **If four quantities are in proportion, they are also in proportion by inversion; that is, the second term is to the first term as the fourth term is to the third term.**

6. Prove the following principle:

> **Principle 5**
>
> **If four quantities are in proportion, they are also in proportion by alternation; that is, the first term is to the third term as the second term is to the fourth term.**

7. Prove the following principle:

> **Principle 6**
>
> **If four quantities are in proportion, they are also in proportion by addition; that is, the sum of the first and second terms is to the second term as the sum of the third and fourth terms is to the fourth term.**

(Hint: If $\dfrac{a}{b}=\dfrac{c}{d}$, then $\dfrac{a+b}{b}=\dfrac{c+d}{d}$. Adding 1 to each member $\dfrac{a}{b}+1=$ $\dfrac{c}{d}+1$ or $\dfrac{a}{b}+\dfrac{b}{b}=\dfrac{c}{d}+\dfrac{d}{d}$.)

8. Prove the following principle:

> **Principle 7**
>
> **If four quantities are in proportion, they are also in proportion by subtraction; that is, the first term minus the second term is to the second term as the third term minus the fourth term is to the fourth**
>
> **term.** (Hint: If $\dfrac{a}{b}=\dfrac{c}{d}$ prove $\dfrac{a-b}{b}=\dfrac{c-d}{d}$ by subtracting 1 from each

member.

9. Given the proportion $\frac{2}{5}=\frac{10}{25}$, form another proportion by applying Principles 4 and 6, respectively.

10. Given the proportion, $\frac{2}{5}=\frac{10}{25}$, form another proportion by applying Principles 6 and 4, respectively.

11. Given the proportion $\frac{8}{4}=\frac{2}{1}$, form another proportion by applying Principles 5 and 7, respectively.

12. Given the proportion $\frac{8}{4}=\frac{2}{1}$, form another proportion by applying Principles 7 and 5, respectively.

USING THE PRINCIPLES OF PROPORTION

The seven principles of proportion may now be used as theorems. Since each has been proved, it can be used to establish future proofs.

Developmental Exercises

DE—1. Determine if the ratios $\frac{8}{13}$ and $\frac{4}{7}$ are equal.

Solution

If $\frac{8}{13} = \frac{4}{7}$, a proportion is formed and, using Principle 1, the product of means should equal the product of the extremes.

Is $8 \times 7 = 4 \times 13$? Since $56 \neq 52$, the ratios are not equal.

DE—2. Solve for x in the proportion $12:8 = x:6$.

Solution

$$\frac{12}{8} = \frac{x}{6},$$
$8x = 72$, (Principle 1.)
$x = 9$.

DE—3. Find the fourth proportional to 2, 3, and 4.

Solution

$$2:3 = 4:x \text{ or } \frac{2}{3} = \frac{4}{x},$$
$2x = 12$, (Principle 1.)
$x = 6$.

DE—4. Find the mean proportional between 8 and 2.

Solution

$$8:x = x:2 \text{ or } \frac{8}{x} = \frac{x}{2},$$
$x^2 = 16$, (Principle 1.)
$x = \pm \sqrt{16}$, or ± 4.

DE—5. Find the ratio $\dfrac{x}{y}$ in the proportion $\dfrac{3}{x} = \dfrac{9}{y}$.

Solution

If $\dfrac{3}{x} = \dfrac{9}{y}$, then $\dfrac{3}{9} = \dfrac{x}{y}$. (Principle 5.)

$\dfrac{x}{y} = \dfrac{3}{9}$ or $\dfrac{x}{y} = \dfrac{1}{3}$. (In simplest form.)

DE—6. If $\dfrac{x}{3} = \dfrac{1}{8}$, find $\dfrac{x+3}{3}$.

Solution

$$\frac{x}{3} = \frac{1}{8},$$

$$\frac{x+3}{3} = \frac{1+8}{8} \text{ or } \frac{9}{8}. \text{ (Principle 6.)}$$

DE—7. Two supplementary angles are in the ratio 2:7. Find the number of degrees in each angle.

Solution

This problem may be solved in two ways. Using the definition of supplementary angles, two angles whose sum is 180°, an equation may be formed which also expresses the 2 to 7 relationship between the angles. In Method 1, the equation is a proportion. In Method 2, the equation expresses the sum of the angles. Notice how the manner of denoting the angles differs in the methods.

Method 1

Let $x =$ the number of degrees in one angle.

$180 - x =$ the number of degrees in its supplement.

$$\frac{x}{180-x} = \frac{2}{7},$$
$$7x = 2(180 - x),$$
$$7x = 360 - 2x,$$
$$7x + 2x = 360,$$
$$9x = 360,$$
$$x = 40.$$
$$180 - x = 140.$$

Method 2

Let $2x =$ the number of degrees in one angle.

$7x =$ the number of degrees in its supplement.

$$2x + 7x = 180,$$
$$9x = 180,$$
$$x = 20.$$
$$2x = 40.$$
$$7x = 140.$$

Exercises

1. Form proportions from the following pairs of equal products:

   a. $3 \times 8 = 12 \times 2$.　　　　　**b.** $ab = cd$.

   c. $4 \times 2\frac{1}{2} = 5 \times 2$.　　　　**d.** $xy = zw$.

2. Solve for the value of x in each of the following proportions:

   a. $\dfrac{5}{6} = \dfrac{10}{x}$.　　　　　**b.** $\dfrac{8}{14} = \dfrac{x}{9}$.

   c. $x:13 = 15:1$.　　　　　**d.** $a:x = b:c$.

   e. $\dfrac{x+14}{x} = \dfrac{9}{2}$.　　　　**f.** $\dfrac{x}{16-x} = \dfrac{10}{22}$.

3. Find the fourth proportional to the following:

   a. $1, 3, 9$　　　　　　　**b.** $3, 4, 12$

   c. x, y, z　　　　　　　**d.** $3a, 4b, c$

4. Find the mean proportional between the following:

   a. 16 and 4　　　　　　**b.** 3 and 27

   c. $\frac{1}{2}$ and $\frac{1}{18}$　　　　　　**d.** 1.5 and 12.5

   e. x and y

5. Form another proportion by inversion from each of the following proportions:

   a. $\frac{4}{3} = \frac{8}{6}$.　　　　　　　**b.** $x:y = b:a$.

   c. $\frac{2}{3} = \frac{24}{36}$.　　　　　　**d.** $\dfrac{x-y}{y} = \dfrac{c-d}{d}$.

   e. $a:2 = b:5$.

6. Form another proportion by addition from each of the proportions in Exercise **5**.

7. Form another proportion by alternation from each of the proportions in Exercise **5**.

8. Form another proportion by subtraction from each of the proportions in Exercise **5**.

9. If $\dfrac{d}{e} = \dfrac{f}{x}$ and $\dfrac{d}{e} = \dfrac{f}{y}$, why does $x = y$?

10. A map is drawn to a scale on which 1 inch represents 16 miles. How long a line must be drawn to indicate a distance of 40 miles?

11. Divide a line 24 inches long into two parts which are in the ratio 1:3.

12. Two supplementary angles are in the ratio 2:3. Find the number of degrees in the angle and in the supplement of the angle.

13. A line is 90 inches in length. Divide it into two parts which are in the ratio 7:2.

14. If $cd = ef$, what is the ratio of $c:e$? $d:f$? $e:d$?

15. An angle and its supplement are in the ratio 1:8. Find the number of degrees in the supplement.

16. Use a principle of proportions to find the ratio of $\dfrac{x}{y}$ in each of the following:

a. $\dfrac{x}{3} = \dfrac{y}{4}$.

b. $2x = 3y$.

c. $\dfrac{y}{x} = \dfrac{8}{7}$.

d. $6x = 12y$.

e. $y:x = 10:40$.

f. $x = 5y$.

g. $y:8 = x:6$.

h. $9x = y$.

17. An angle and its complement are in the ratio 1:5. Find the number of degrees in the angle.

18. Solve for x in the following:

a. $a:b = c:x$.

b. $d:3e = f:x$.

19. Two complementary angles are in the ratio 4:5. Find the number of degrees in each angle.

20. Write a proportion in which x is the fourth proportional and which when solved for x, will give the following:

a. $x = \dfrac{cd}{e}$.

b. $x = \dfrac{a^2}{b}$.

c. $x = \dfrac{rs}{s}$.

PROPORTIONS OF GEOMETRIC QUANTITIES

A line segment, AB, whose length is 5 units and a line segment, CD, whose length is 2 units, may be expressed in the ratio of $5:2$. This may be written $AB:CD = 5:2$. AB in this case means the length of AB and not the line segment. When there can be no misunderstanding, you may say line segments or angles are proportional when you mean the measures of these figures.

Two line segments are divided proportionally when the ratio of the lengths of the segments of one is equal to the ratio of the lengths of the corresponding segments of the other. The line segments are also divided proportionally when the length of one line segment is to the length of one of its segments as the length of the other line segment is to the length of its corresponding segment.

‖ *Developmental Exercises*

DE—1. In triangle ABC, DE is parallel to BC. Select a unit which can be contained in AD and DB an integral number of times. At each of these points of subdivision, construct a line parallel to DE. Compare the ratio

$$\textbf{a.} \quad \frac{AD}{DB} \text{ to } \frac{AE}{EC}, \qquad\qquad \textbf{b.} \quad \frac{AB}{AD} \text{ to } \frac{AC}{AE}.$$

Solution

The unit d is contained 5 times in AD and 2 times in DB. If three or more parallel lines intercept equal segments on one transversal, they cut off equal segments on any transversal. Thus, AE is divided into 5 equal parts, and EC is divided into 2 equal parts.

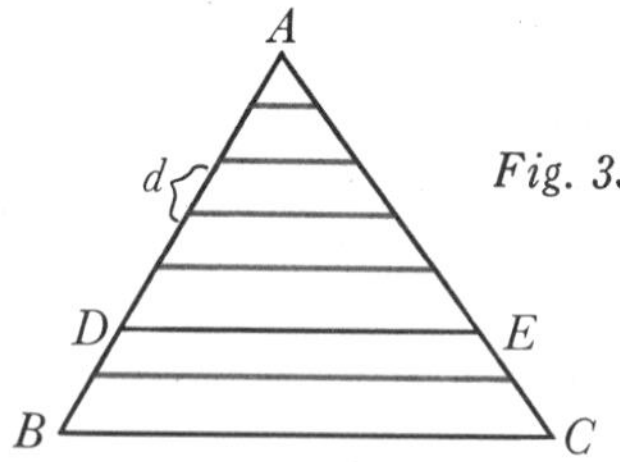

Fig. 331

$$\textbf{a.} \quad \frac{AD}{DB} = \frac{5}{2}, \frac{AE}{EC} = \frac{5}{2}, \text{ thus, } \frac{AD}{DB} = \frac{AE}{EC}.$$

$$\textbf{b.} \quad \frac{AB}{AD} = \frac{7}{5}, \frac{AC}{AE} = \frac{7}{5}, \text{ thus, } \frac{AB}{AD} = \frac{AC}{AE}.$$

‖ THEOREM 99

‖ **A line parallel to one side of a triangle and intersecting the other two sides divides these sides proportionally.**

Exercises

1. In $\triangle XYZ$, $MN \parallel YZ$. Complete the following:

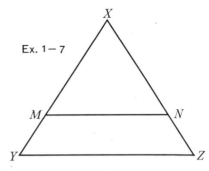

Ex. 1−7

a. $\dfrac{YM}{XM} = \dfrac{ZN}{?}$.

b. $\dfrac{XY}{MX} = \dfrac{XZ}{?}$.

c. $\dfrac{YM}{?} = \dfrac{XY}{XZ}$.

d. $MX \cdot XZ = MX \cdot ?$.

Using the diagram in Exercise **1**, *find the length of the indicated line segment.*

2. $MY = 2$ units, $NZ = 3$ units, $XM = 4$ units, $XN = ?$.

3. $MY = 3$ units, $NZ = 4$ units, $NX = 5$ units, $XY = ?$.

4. $XY = 7$ units, $XZ = 8$ units, $MX = 4\frac{1}{2}$ units, $NZ = ?$.

5. YM is twice as long as XM and NZ is 3 units longer than XN, $XZ = ?$.

6. $MY = XN$, $XM = 9$ units, $NZ = 4$ units, $MY = ?$.

7. $XM = NZ$, $XY = 12$ units, $XN = 2$ units, $XM = ?$.

8. In the diagram, $MN \parallel OP \parallel XY$, $PY = 3$ units, $ZN = 3\frac{1}{2}$ units, $ZM = 2$ units, $NP = 5$ units. Find OM and OX.

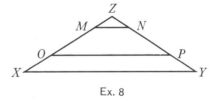

Ex. 8

9. Determine the locus of the midpoints of line segments drawn to a given line from a given point not on the line.

10. In $\triangle ACE$, $FD \parallel AC$. Write three proportions.

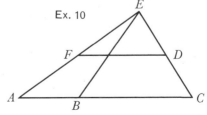

Ex. 10

DE—2. Prove the following theorem:

┃THEOREM 100
┃Parallel lines intercept proportional segments on any two transversals.

Solution

Given: $AB \parallel CD \parallel EF$.

Prove: $\dfrac{AC}{CE} = \dfrac{BD}{DF}$.

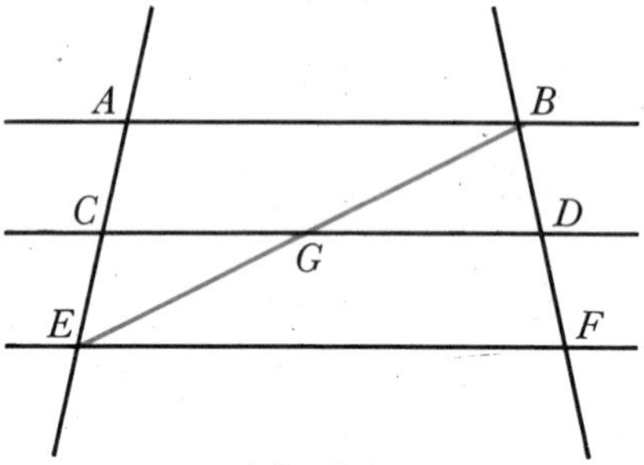

Fig. 332

Analysis:

If BE is constructed forming two triangles, then $\dfrac{AC}{CE} = \dfrac{BG}{GE}$ and $\dfrac{BG}{GE} = \dfrac{BD}{DF}$.

Why? Therefore, $\dfrac{AC}{CE} = \dfrac{BD}{DF}$. Why?

This theorem may be used as a basis for dividing line segments into parts having a given ratio.

DE—3. Divide a given line segment into parts proportional to two given line segments.

a

Solution

Given: b

C ———————————————————— D

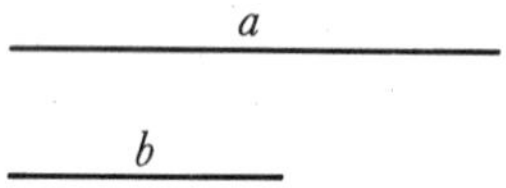

You are to divide CD into two parts with the ratio $\dfrac{a}{b}$.

● Duplicate line CD.

● At C draw any line, CG, making a convenient angle, DCG.

● On CG, using C as center, construct a line segment, CE, equal in length to a, and EF equal in length to b.

● Draw DF.

● Using equal corresponding angles, construct EH parallel to DF intersecting CD at H.

Therefore, $\dfrac{CH}{HD} = \dfrac{a}{b}$.

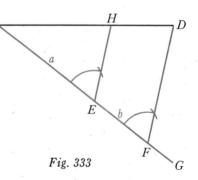

Fig. 333

DE—4. Construct the fourth proportional to three given line segments.

Solution

Given:

r

s

t

- On a line lay off AD equal to r.
- On any other line through A, lay off AF equal to t.
- Connect points F and D.
- At D lay off DE equal to s.
- By forming equal corresponding angles, construct $EG \parallel DF$.

The length of FG is the fourth proportional to r, s, and t.

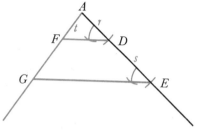

Fig. 334

Exercises

1. By construction divide a line segment, XY, into parts proportional to three given line segments, a, b, and c.

2. Construct the fourth proportional to line segments which are 1 inch, $\frac{1}{2}$ inch, and $1\frac{1}{2}$ inches long. Measure the result.

3. Draw a line segment of convenient length and by construction, divide it into segments having the ratio $1:2:3$.

4. In trapezoid $ABCD$, EF is parallel to the bases and intersects the nonparallel sides. Prove that DE: $EA = CF:FB$.

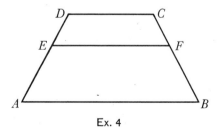

Ex. 4

5. Construct the fourth proportional to the given line segments, 2 inches, 1 inch, and 3 inches. Measure the result and also solve for the fourth proportional algebraically.

6. *a*, *b*, and *c* are given line segments. Construct *x* so that

a. $x = \dfrac{ab}{c}$. **b.** $x = \dfrac{2ab}{c}$. **c.** $x = \dfrac{a^2}{b}$.

7. Divide a given line segment into two parts, *x* and *y*, so that $x : y = 2:3$.

8. The nonparallel sides of a trapezoid are 10 inches and 15 inches, respectively. A line parallel to the bases divides the longer diagonal in the ratio of 2 to 3. Find the segments of the nonparallel sides.

9. The nonparallel sides of a trapezoid are 8 inches and 12 inches, respectively. A line parallel to the bases divides the 8 inch side in the ratio of 1 to 3. Find the segments of the 12 inch side.

10. In the $\triangle DEF$, $GH \parallel EF$ and $DG = 2DH$. What is the ratio of HF to GE?

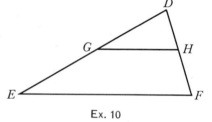

Ex. 10

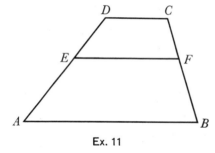

Ex. 11

11. *ABCD* is a trapezoid with $EF \parallel$ base AB. If $DE = 5$ units, $AE = 9$ units, and $CF = 4$ units, find the length of BF.

12. Given: $\odot O$ and $\odot O'$ are tangent to AB at P. PR and PS are chords.

Prove: $\dfrac{PM}{MR} = \dfrac{PN}{NS}$.

Ex. 12

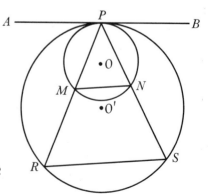

DE—5. Prove the following theorem:

THEOREM 101

If a line divides two sides of a triangle proportionally, it is parallel to the third side.

Solution

Given: In $\triangle ABC$, DE intersects
AB and AC.
$$\frac{AD}{DB} = \frac{AE}{EC}.$$

Prove: $DE \parallel BC$.

Fig. 335

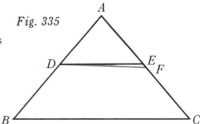

Construction: Through D construct $DF \parallel BC$.

Proof:

STATEMENTS	REASONS
1. $DF \parallel BC$.	1. Why?
2. $\dfrac{AB}{DB} = \dfrac{AC}{FC}$.	2. A line parallel to one side of a triangle and intersecting the other two sides divides these sides proportionally.
3. $\dfrac{AD}{DB} = \dfrac{AE}{EC}$.	3. Given.
4. $\dfrac{AD+DB}{DB} = \dfrac{AE+EC}{EC}$.	4. If four quantities are in proportion, they are also in proportion by addition.
5. $AB = AD+DB$, $AC = AE+EC$.	5. The whole is equal to the sum of its parts.
6. $\dfrac{AB}{DB} = \dfrac{AC}{EC}$.	6. A quantity may be substituted for its equal without changing the value of the expression.
7. $FC = EC$.	7. If any three terms of a proportion are equal respectively to the three corresponding terms of another proportion, the fourth terms are equal.
8. F and E coincide.	8. Why?
9. DE and DF coincide.	9. Why?
10. $DE \parallel BC$.	10. Why?

Exercises

For Exercises **1** *and* **2** *refer to the diagram below.*

1. If $CD = 2''$, $DA = 3\frac{1}{2}''$, $BE = 7''$, and $CE = 4\frac{1}{4}''$, is $DE \parallel AB$? Explain.

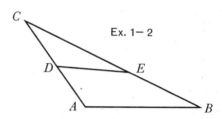

Ex. 1–2

2. If $CA = 8''$, $BE = 12''$, $CE = 7\frac{1}{5}''$, and CE is $2''$ shorter than DA, is $DE \parallel AB$? Explain.

3. State if $XZ \parallel AC$ when given each of these conditions:

    a. $DX:AX = DZ:ZC$.

    Ex. 3

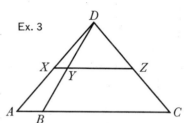

    b. $DY:DB = DX:DA$.

    c. $DX:DY = DA:DB$.

4. In the diagram equal distances were marked off as shown. How long is the segment AB? Is $BC \parallel XY$? Explain your answer.

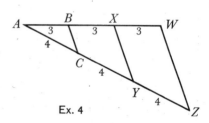

Ex. 4

5. Prove that if a line divides two sides of a triangle so that either side is to one of its segments as the second side is to its corresponding segment, then the line is parallel to the remaining side of the triangle.

6. Given: $\dfrac{BZ}{CZ} = \dfrac{AY}{CY}$, $\dfrac{DX}{CX} = \dfrac{AY}{CY}$.

    Prove: $XZ \parallel DB$.

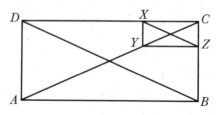

Ex. 6

INTERNAL AND EXTERNAL DIVISION OF A LINE SEGMENT

A line segment is divided *internally* into two segments if the point of division lies on the line segment. In Figure 336, P divides XY internally into the two segments XP and PY. $XP+PY=XY$.

Fig. 336

$X\text{———————————}Y$
P

A line segment is divided *externally* into two segments if the point of division lies on the extension of the line segment. In Figure 336, X divides PY externally into the two segments PX and XY. $XY-PX=PY$.

Developmental Exercises

DE—1. Prove the following theorem:

THEOREM 102

The bisector of an interior angle of a triangle divides the opposite side internally into segments which are proportional to the two adjacent sides.

Solution

Given: In $\triangle ABC$, AD bisects $\angle BAC$.

Prove: $\dfrac{BD}{DC}=\dfrac{AB}{AC}$.

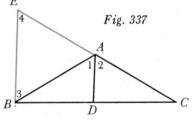

Fig. 337

Construction: Through B construct $BE \parallel AD$ intersecting the extension of AC at E.

Proof:

STATEMENTS	REASONS
1. $BE \parallel AD$.	1. Why?
2. In $\triangle EBC$, $\dfrac{BD}{DC}=\dfrac{EA}{AC}$.	2. Why?
3. $\angle 1 = \angle 2$.	3. Why?
4. $\angle 1 = \angle 3$.	4. Why?
5. $\angle 2 = \angle 4$.	5. Why?
6. $\angle 3 = \angle 4$.	6. Why?
7. $AB = EA$.	7. Why?
8. $\dfrac{BD}{DC}=\dfrac{AB}{AC}$.	8. Why?

DE—2. The sides of a triangle measure 6 units, 9 units, and 12 units. Find the length of the segments formed by the bisector of the largest angle when it intersects the opposite side.

Solution

The 12 unit side, AC, is the longest side and is opposite the largest angle of the triangle. Bisect $\angle ABC$. Denote the number of units in the length of the segments made by the bisector as x and $12-x$.

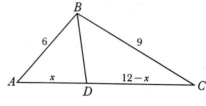

$$\frac{x}{12-x} = \frac{6}{9},$$

$$9x = 6(12-x),$$

$$9x = 72 - 6x,$$

$$15x = 72,$$

$$x = 4\tfrac{4}{5}.$$

$$12 - x = 7\tfrac{1}{5}.$$

Fig. 338

DE—3. A line segment, RS, is divided externally at point T into two segments, RT and TS. If $\dfrac{RT}{ST} = \dfrac{8}{3}$, what is the ratio of $\dfrac{RS}{RT}$?

Solution

T is on the extension of RS.

$$RT - ST = RS.$$

$$\frac{RS}{RT} = \frac{5}{8}.$$

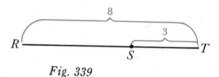

Fig. 339

Exercises

1. A line segment is divided internally into two segments, x and y. If $x:y = 3:5$, what is the ratio of x to the entire segment?

2. A line segment 12 inches long is divided internally into two segments which have the ratio 2:3. What is the length of each segment?

3. A line segment, XY, is divided externally at point W into two segments, XW and WY. If $\dfrac{XW}{WY} = \dfrac{7}{4}$, what is the ratio of XY to XW?

4. A 20 inch line segment is divided externally into two segments which have the ratio 5:7. What is the length of each segment?

5. In the figure for Theorem 102, if $BD = 2$ units, $DC = 6$ units, and $AC = 15$ units, find the length of AB.

6. In the figure for Theorem 102, if $BC = 9$ units, $DC = 3$ units, and $AB = 6$ units, find the length of AC.

7. The sides of a triangle are 3 inches, 5 inches, and 7 inches. Find the length of the segments formed by the bisector of the smallest angle when it intersects the opposite side.

8. One side of a triangle is twice as long as a second side. The third side is 14 inches. Find the length of the segments formed when an angle bisector intersects the third side.

DE—4. Prove the following theorem:

> **THEOREM 103**
>
> **The bisector of an exterior angle of a triangle divides the opposite side externally into segments which are proportional to the adjacent sides.**

Solution

Given: AD bisects exterior $\angle BAF$ of $\triangle ABC$ and intersects BC extended at D.

Prove: $\dfrac{DB}{DC} = \dfrac{AB}{AC}$.

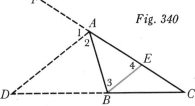

Fig. 340

Construction: Through B draw $BE \parallel AD$ meeting AC at E.

Proof:

STATEMENTS	REASONS
1. $EB \parallel AD$.	1. Why?
2. $\dfrac{CE}{EA} = \dfrac{CB}{BD}$.	2. A line parallel to one side of a triangle and intersecting the other two sides divides these sides proportionally.
3. $\dfrac{AC}{EA} = \dfrac{DC}{DB}$.	3. Why? Fill in the missing steps.
4. $\dfrac{EA}{AC} = \dfrac{DB}{DC}$.	4. If four terms are in proportion, they are in proportion by inversion. (Principle 4.)
5. $\angle 1 = \angle 2$.	5. Why?
6. $\angle 2 = \angle 3$.	6. Why?
7. $\angle 1 = \angle 4$.	7. Why?
8. $\angle 3 = \angle 4$.	8. Why?
9. $AB = AE$.	9. Why?
10. $\dfrac{AB}{AC} = \dfrac{DB}{DC}$.	10. Why?

DE—5. The sides of a triangle measure 7 units, 11 units, and 14 units. Find the segments into which the bisector of the largest exterior angle divides the opposite side.

Solution

The largest exterior angle would be adjacent to the smallest interior angle of the triangle, the angle opposite the smallest side (7 units).

The bisector of $\angle BCE$, DC, divides AB externally. Denote the number of units in the length of the segments by x and $x+7$.

By Theorem 103 $\dfrac{x}{x+7}=\dfrac{11}{14}$,

$$14x=11(x+7),$$
$$14x=11x+77,$$
$$3x=77,$$
$$x=25\tfrac{2}{3}.$$
$$x+7=32\tfrac{2}{3}.$$

Exercises

1. In $\triangle DEF$, $DG=3$ units, $DE=12$ units, $DH=2$ units, $HF=8$ units. Is $GH \parallel EF$?

Ex. 1

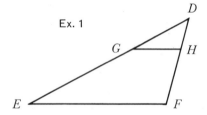

2. AD bisects $\angle BAC$ in $\triangle ABC$ and intersects side BC at D. If $AB=4$ units, $AC=8$ units, and $DC=6$ units, find the length of BD.

Ex. 2–3

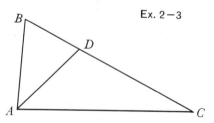

3. AD bisects $\angle BAC$, $AB=3$ units, $BD=2$ units, and $DC=5$ units. Find the length of AC.

4. The sides of a triangle measure 6, 9, and 12 inches, respectively. Find the lengths of the segments into which the longest side of the triangle is divided by the bisector of the opposite angle.

5. In what kind of a triangle is the bisector of an exterior angle parallel to one side of the triangle?

6. The sides of a triangle measure 10 inches, 12 inches, and 14 inches. Find the length of the segments into which the bisector of the smallest exterior angle divided the opposite side.

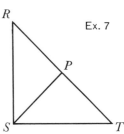

Ex. 7

7. In $\triangle RST$ the bisector of $\angle S$ intersects RT at P. If $RP = PT$, what is the ratio of SR to ST and what kind of triangle is RST?

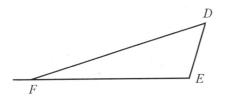

Ex. 8

8. In $\triangle DEF$, $DF = 15$ units, $DE = 5$ units, and $EF = 13$ units. If the exterior angle at F is bisected, will the bisector meet the opposite side extended through D or through E? Find the length of the segments of DE.

9. BD bisects $\angle ABC$. If $\dfrac{AB}{BC} = \dfrac{2}{5}$ and $DC = 1.50$ units, find the length of AD.

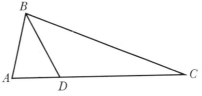

Ex. 9

10. Construct a triangle with angles that measure $90°$, $60°$, and $30°$. Show that the bisector of the $60°$ angle divides the opposite side into segments having the ratio $2:1$.

Ex. 11

11. Through point P construct a line which will divide the sides YX and YZ proportionally.

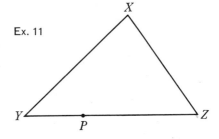

12. The sides of a triangle measure 6 units, 8 units, and 10 units. Find the length of the segments into which the longest side is divided externally by the bisector of the opposite exterior angle.

13. In the diagram if $DH \parallel EG$, then what kind of a line is EG? Complete the proportion $\dfrac{DG}{GF} = \dfrac{?}{EF}$.

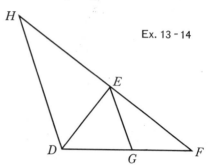

Ex. 13 - 14

14. In the diagram if $DE = 9$ units, $EF = 12$ units, and $DF = 3x$ units, find the length of GF and DF.

Ex. 15

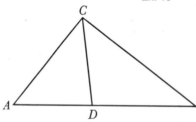

15. CD bisects $\angle ACB$, $AC = 3$ units, $BC = 4$ units, and $AB = 5$ units. Find the lengths of AD and DB.

Ex. 16

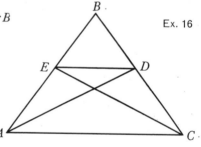

16. Given: $AB = BC$,
           AD bisects $\angle CAB$,
           CE bisects $\angle BCA$.
    Prove: $ED \parallel AC$.

Ex. 17

17. EG bisects $\angle DEF$ in $\triangle DEF$. $DE = 5$ units, $EF = 10$ units, and $GF = 4$ units. Find the length of DG.

18. In rectangle $ABCD$, BD is a diagonal and CF bisects $\angle DCB$. $AB = 20$ units, $AD = 15$ units, and $DB = 25$ units. Find the lengths of DE and EB.

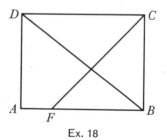

Ex. 18

SOLID GEOMETRY

In this chapter you learned that parallel lines intercept proportional segments of any two transversals. The following applies to solid geometry.

> **THEOREM 7₈**
>
> **If two straight lines are cut by three parallel planes, their corresponding segments are proportional.**

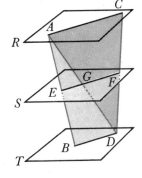

Given: The lines AB and CD intersected by the parallel planes R, S, and T in the points A, E, B, and C, F, D, respectively.

Prove: $\dfrac{AE}{EB} = \dfrac{CF}{FD}$.

Fig. 341

Proof:

STATEMENTS	REASONS
1. The lines AB and CD intersected by the parallel planes R, S, and T at the points A, E, B, and C, F, D, respectively.	1. Given.
2. Draw AD and let it intersect plane S at G. Let the plane determined by AB and CD intersect S at GF and R at AC. Let the plane determined by AB and AD intersect S at EG and T at BD.	2. Two points determine a line. Two intersecting lines determine a plane. The intersection of two planes is a straight line.
3. $EG \parallel BD$, $AC \parallel GF$.	3. The intersections of two parallel planes with any third plane are parallel.
4. $\dfrac{AE}{EB} = \dfrac{AG}{GD}$, $\dfrac{AG}{GD} = \dfrac{CF}{FD}$.	4. A line parallel to one side of a triangle and intersecting the other two sides divides these sides proportionally.
5. $\therefore \dfrac{AE}{EB} = \dfrac{CF}{FD}$.	5. Quantities equal to the same quantity are equal.

Exercises

1. If the statement $\dfrac{AB}{AE} = \dfrac{CD}{CF}$ is added to the proof, what reason would be given?

2. Using Figure 341 in the preceding proof, find the length of CD if $AE = 3$ units, $EB = 2$ units, and $CF = 9$ units.

3. Again using Figure 341, find the length of EB if $CF = a$ units, $FD = 3a$ units, and $AB = 8a$ units.

4. An escalator from the first to the second floor in a building has a length of 18 feet. The floor of the second story of the building is 14 feet above the level of the first floor. Each succeeding floor is 12 feet higher than the one directly below. What should be the length of the escalator between the higher floors if they have the same slope.

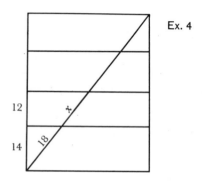

Ex. 4

EXTEND YOUR HORIZON

Harmonic division—*A line segment is divided harmonically if it is divided internally and externally into line segments which have the same ratio.*

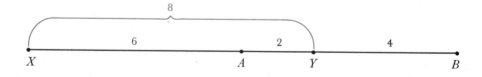

Fig. 342

In the above diagram $XY = 8$ units, $XA = 6$ units, and $YB = 4$ units.
$$\frac{XA}{AY} = \frac{6}{2} = \frac{3}{1}, \qquad \frac{XB}{YB} = \frac{12}{4} = \frac{3}{1}.$$
Therefore, points A and B divide XY harmonically.

(*1*) Supply the reasons for the statements in the following proof. The bisector of the interior angle of a triangle at any vertex and the bisector of the exterior angle at the same vertex divide the opposite side harmonically.

Given: *AE* bisects $\angle BAC$ in $\triangle ABC$, *AD* bisects exterior $\angle BAF$ of $\triangle ABC$ meeting *CB* extended at *D*.

Prove: $\dfrac{DB}{BE} = \dfrac{DC}{EC}$.

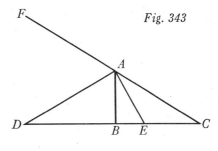

Fig. 343

STATEMENTS	REASONS
1. *AE* bisects $\angle BAC$ in $\triangle ABC$, *AD* bisects exterior $\angle BAF$ of $\triangle ABC$ meeting *CB* extended at *D*.	1. Given
2. $\dfrac{BE}{EC} = \dfrac{AB}{AC}$.	2. Why?
3. $\dfrac{DB}{DC} = \dfrac{AB}{AC}$.	3. Why?
4. $\dfrac{DB}{DC} = \dfrac{BE}{EC}$.	4. Why?
5. $\therefore \dfrac{DB}{BE} = \dfrac{DC}{EC}$.	5. Why?

(*2*) Circles *O* and *O'* are tangent externally at point *P*. Their common external tangent, *AB*, meets *O O'* extended at *C*. Prove that *C* and *P* divide *O O'* harmonically.

Students who are interested in music will find a practical application of harmonic division in the study of harmony. Simple experiments with the string of a monachord will produce different tones depending upon the position where the string is touched. The Greeks used a stringed instrument with a bridge that divided the strings at two-thirds of their length. The shorter section of the strings sounded an octave higher than the longer section.

CHAPTER SUMMARY

The special properties concerning proportions are

1. in a proportion the product of the means is equal to the product of the extremes.   (page 371)

2. if the product of two quantities is equal to the product of two other quantities, either pair may be made the means and the other pair made the extremes of a proportion.   (page 371)

3. if any three terms of a proportion are equal to the three corresponding terms of another proportion, the fourth terms are equal. (page 372)

4. if four quantities are in proportion, they are also in proportion by inversion.   (page 373)

5. if four quantities are in proportion, they are also in proportion by alternation.   (page 373)

6. if four quantities are in proportion, they are also in proportion by addition.   (page 373)

7. if four quantities are in proportion, they are also in proportion by subtraction.   (page 373)

Line segments are divided proportionally if

1. they are sides of a triangle intersected by a line parallel to the third side.   (page 378)

2. they are intercepted by three or more parallel lines.   (page 380)

The bisector of an angle of a triangle divides the opposite side

1. internally into segments which are proportional to the adjacent sides if the angle is an interior angle.   (page 385)

2. externally into segments which are proportional to the adjacent sides if the angle is an exterior angle.   (page 387)

CHAPTER REVIEW

Vocabulary

Match the word in the left hand column with its correct definition in the right hand column.

1. Ratio of one quantity to another

2. Proportion

3. Extremes of a Proportion

4. Means of a Proportion

5. Fourth Proportional

6. Mean Proportional

7. Proportion by Inversion

8. Proportion by Alternation

9. Internal Division of a Line Segment

10. External Division of a Line Segment

a. One of two equal means of a proportion.

b. The point of division lies on the extension of the line segment.

c. The first term is to the fourth term as the second term is to the third term.

d. The first term is to the third term as the second term is to the fourth term.

e. The fourth term of the proportion.

f. The quotient obtained when the first quantity is divided by the second.

g. The first and fourth terms of a proportion.

h. The first and third terms of a proportion.

i. The second and third terms of a proportion.

j. An equation which states that two ratios are equal.

k. The point of division lies on the line segment.

l. The second term is to the first term as the fourth term is to the third term.

Exercises

1. Find the ratio of 1 hour 36 minutes to 2 hours 24 minutes.

2. Find the ratio of the perimeter of a regular hexagon to one of its sides.

3. How is the ratio $\dfrac{4x}{3x^2}$ affected by

    a. multiplying each term by 2?   **b.** dividing each term by x?
    c. increasing each term by 3?   **d.** diminishing each term by 3?

4. Determine if $\frac{8}{11}$ and $\frac{4}{5}$ are equal.

*Solve for the value of **x** in the following proportions:*

5. $\dfrac{x}{6} = \dfrac{7}{8}.$ **6.** $\dfrac{x}{12-x} = \dfrac{14}{28}.$

7. Find the fourth proportional to 1, 3, and 5.

8. Find the fourth proportional to $2x$, $3y$, and z.

9. Find the mean proportional between 5 and 8.

10. Find the mean proportional between a and b.

11. From the proportion $\dfrac{a-b}{b} = \dfrac{c-d}{d}$ form another proportion by

    a. inversion.   **b.** alternation.
    c. addition.   **d.** subtraction.

12. Two complementary angles are in the ratio $2:3$. Find the number of degrees in the angle and in the complement of the angle.

13. A line is 70 inches in length. Divide it into two parts which are in the ratio $5:2$.

14. If $ab:cd$, what is the ratio of $a:c$? $b:d$? $c:b$?

15. A line parallel to side AC of triangle ABC intersects AB at D and BC at E. If $BD = 3x$ units, $DA = 4y$ units, and $BE = z$ units, express the length of EC in terms of x, y, and z.

16. In triangle DEF, EG is the bisector of $\angle DEF$. If $DE = 10$ units and $EF = 12$ units, find the ratio of $DG:GF$.

CHAPTER TEST

In Exercises **1-9** *complete the statement and give a reason why the completion is valid.*

1. If $a:x = b:y$, then $ay = $? .

2. If $a:x = b:y$, then $x:a = $? .

3. If $a:x = b:y$, then $a+x:x = $? .

4. If $a:x = b:y$, then $a:b = $? .

5. Two supplementary angles are in the ratio 3:5. The measure of the larger angle is ? .

6. A line parallel to side AC of triangle ABC intersects AB at D and BC at E.

7. In triangle DEF, EG bisects angle DEF. $DG:GF = $? .

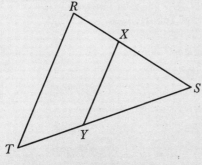

8. In $\triangle RST$, $YT:ST = XR:SR$, XY ? RT.

Ex. 8

9. In $\triangle GHJ$, GV bisects exterior angle UGH. $GH:GJ = $? .

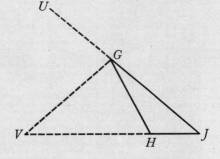

Ex. 9

10. Construct the fourth proportional to line segments of $\frac{1}{2}$ inch, $1\frac{1}{2}$ inches, and 1 inch. Measure the result and check it algebraically.

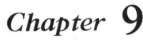

Chapter 9

SIMILAR POLYGONS

OBJECTS HAVING THE SAME SHAPE

When you look at an object through a telescope or a pair of binoculars, you see an enlarged image of the object. The object and the image have the same shape; they differ only in size. Two figures that have the same shape are said to be *similar*.

Similarity is apparent in the clothing you buy, the homes you live in, and the cars you drive. Which of the following polygons are similar?

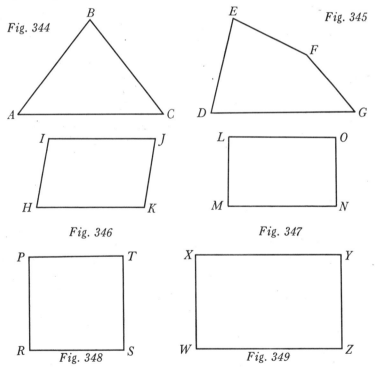

Fig. 344

Fig. 345

Fig. 346

Fig. 347

Fig. 348

Fig. 349

The polygons in Figures 347 and 349 are similar. The symbol for "similar to" is $\sim$. Thus, $\square LMNO \sim \square WXYZ$ is read "parallelogram *LMNO* is similar to parallelogram *WXYZ*."

Developmental Exercises

DE—1. Develop a criterion for determining whether two or more polygons are similar.

Solution

Obviously the triangle is not similar to any of the quadrilaterals. Similarity though, is not determined by the number of sides alone, for if it were, all quadrilaterals would be similar. Are they?

Measure the angles of the parallelograms. The angles in Figures 347, 348, and 349 are all right angles and are therefore equal. If the shape of a polygon were determined entirely by the angles, these parallelograms would all be similar. Do these parallelograms have the same shape?

Compare the lengths of the sides of the parallelograms. In Figures 346 and 347, $\dfrac{HI}{LM} = \dfrac{IJ}{LO} = \dfrac{HK}{MN} = \dfrac{JK}{NO}$. In Figures 347 and 349, $\dfrac{LM}{XW} = \dfrac{XY}{LO} = \dfrac{WZ}{MN} = \dfrac{YZ}{ON}$.

Notice that $\square LMNO$ and $\square WXYZ$ have equal angles and their corresponding sides in proportion. If you constructed several similar polygons and measured their sides and angles you might conclude

  (*1*) Corresponding angles of similar polygons are equal.

  (*2*) Corresponding sides of similar polygons are in proportion.

The converse of this may be used for determining similar polygons.

Polygons which have their corresponding angles equal and their corresponding sides in proportion are similar.

DE—2. Are any two rectangles similar?

Solution

Draw any two rectangles.

Their corresponding angles are right angles and, therefore, are equal. Compare the lengths of their sides.

$$\frac{AD}{EH} = \frac{3}{3} = \frac{1}{1}. \qquad \frac{AB}{EF} = \frac{6}{4} = \frac{3}{2}.$$

Their corresponding sides do not have the same ratio and, therefore, are not in proportion. Since both requirements for similar polygons are not satisfied, any two rectangles are not necessarily similar.

Exercises

1. Name two properties or conditions which must be satisfied before two or more polygons may be classified as similar.

2. Write the inverse and contrapositive of the definition of similar polygons. Are they both valid?

3. Name the corresponding angles and the corresponding sides in the following similar triangles.

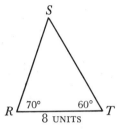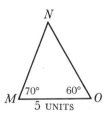

Ex. 3

4. If two polygons are similar do they have the same shape? Do they have the same size?

5. Congruent triangles are similar. True or false? Why?

6. All squares are similar. True or false? Why?

7. Determine the common ratio of the triangles in Exercise **3.**

8. Given: In $\triangle ABC$, D and E are midpoints of AB and BC respectively.
    Prove: $\triangle DBE \sim \triangle ABC$.

Ex. 8

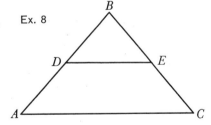

9. Why are any two equilateral triangles similar?

10. Prove that any two equiangular triangles are similar.

11. Are similar figures necessarily congruent? Why?

12. Are any two regular polygons similar? Why?

13. The legs of a right triangle are 7 inches and 9 inches. If the shorter leg of a similar triangle is $31\frac{1}{2}$ inches, determine the length of the other leg.

14. Given: $\Box ABCD \sim \Box EFGH$. The corresponding vertices are as shown in the diagram.

Then: $\dfrac{AB}{?} = \dfrac{?}{?} = \dfrac{?}{?} = \dfrac{?}{?}$.

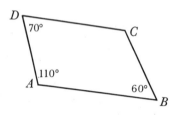 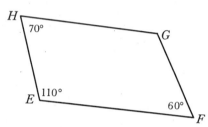

Ex. 14

15. Using the data in Exercise **14,** if $AB = 7$ units, $AD = 5$ units, $DC = 5\frac{1}{2}$ units, $BC = 4$ units, and $EF = 3$ units, find the lengths of GF, GH, and HE.

16. A regular pentagon has a side which is one foot in length. Another regular pentagon has a side which is $3\frac{1}{2}$ inches in length. Are the two pentagons similar? If so, what is the common ratio of the lengths of the larger side to that of the smaller side?

17. The sides of a triangle are 4, 7, and 9 inches, respectively. If the shortest side of a similar triangle is 6 inches long, find the lengths of the other two sides.

18. Two isosceles triangles are similar if a base angle of one equals a base angle of the other. True or false? Why?

19. If the angles of one polygon are equal respectively to the angles of another polygon, are the polygons necessarily similar? Why?

20. Tell whether the following statements are sometimes true, always true, or never true.

    a. Two equilateral polygons having the same number of sides are similar.

    b. If the vertex angles of two isosceles triangles are equal, the triangles are similar.

**Are all of the above sockets similar? Do they have exactly the same shape?
To be similar must they be the same size?**

SIMILAR TRIANGLES

In the previous section you learned that two quadrilaterals having equal angles are not necessarily similar. Two triangles though, that have equal angles are similar. Study the proof of this theorem in the developmental exercises.

Developmental Exercises

DE—1. Prove the following theorem:

THEOREM 104

If three angles of one triangle are equal respectively to three angles of another triangle, the two triangles are similar.

Solution

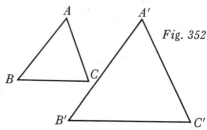

Fig. 352

Given: $\triangle ABC$,
$\quad\quad\quad \triangle A'B'C'$,
$\quad\quad\quad \angle A = \angle A'$,
$\quad\quad\quad \angle B = \angle B'$,
$\quad\quad\quad \angle C = \angle C'$.

Prove: $\triangle ABC \sim \triangle A'B'C'$.

Proof:

Either $AB < A'B'$, or $AB = A'B'$, or $AB > A'B'$.

(*1*) If $AB = A'B'$, the two triangles are congruent by **a.s.a.** and are therefore similar.

(*2*) If $AB < A'B'$ the following proof will apply.

Construction: On $A'B'$ lay off $A'B'' = AB$. Through B'' construct a line, $B''D$, parallel to $B'C'$.

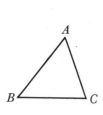

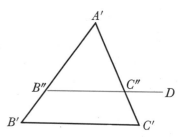

Fig. 353

STATEMENTS	REASONS
1. $\angle A = \angle A'$, $\quad \angle B = \angle B'$, $\quad \angle C = \angle C'$.	1. Given.
2. $A'B'' = AB$.	2. A line may be constructed equal to another line.
3. $B''D \parallel B'C'$.	3. Through a point not on a given line one, and only one, line can be constructed parallel to the given line.

4. $B''D$ intersects $A'C'$, call this point C''.

    4. Why?

5. $\angle A'B''C'' = \angle A'B'C'$.

    5. A transversal intersecting two parallel lines forms equal corresponding angles.

6. $\angle B = \angle A'B''C''$.

    6. Two quantities equal to the same quantity are equal.

7. $\triangle ABC \cong \triangle A'B''C''$.

    7. Why?

8. $A'B'' = AB$,
    $A'C'' = AC$,
    $B''C'' = BC$.

    8. Corresponding sides of congruent triangles are equal.

9. $\dfrac{A'B''}{A'B'} = \dfrac{A'C''}{A'C'}$.

    9. A line parallel to one side of a triangle and intersecting the other two sides divides these sides proportionally.

10. $\dfrac{AB}{A'B'} = \dfrac{AC}{A'C'}$.

    10. A quantity may be substituted for its equal.

11. In like manner, by constructing $B'C'' = BC$ and $C''A'' \parallel C'A'$, it can be shown that
$$\frac{AB}{A'B'} = \frac{AC}{B'C'}.$$

    11. Reasons 1-9.

12. $\dfrac{AB}{A'B'} = \dfrac{BC}{B'C'} = \dfrac{AC}{A'C'}$.

    12. Quantities equal to the same or to equal quantities are equal.

13. $\triangle ABC \sim \triangle A'B'C'$.

    13. Polygons which have their corresponding angles equal and their corresponding sides in proportion are similar.

(3) If $AB > A'B'$ then $A'B'$ would be laid off on AB and a proof similar to that in (2) will apply.

Corollary 1

If two angles of one triangle are equal respectively to two angles of another triangle, the triangles are similar.

Corollary 2

If an acute angle of one right triangle is equal to an acute angle of another right triangle, the right triangles are similar.

Corollary 3

If triangles are similar to the same triangle they are similar to each other.

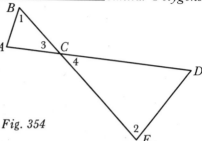

DE—2. Given: *AB* ∥ *DE*,
         AD and *BE* intersect at *C*.
     Prove: △*ABC* ∼ △*CDE*.

Fig. 354

Solution

STATEMENTS	REASONS
1. *AB* ∥ *DE*.	1. Given.
2. ∠1 = ∠2.	2. If two parallel lines are cut by a transversal, the alternate-interior angles are equal.
3. ∠3 = ∠4.	3. Vertical angles are equal.
4. △*ABC* ∼ △*CDE*.	4. If two angles of one triangle are equal respectively to two angles of another triangle, the triangles are similar.

Exercises

1. Given: In △*ABC*, *DE* ∥ *AC*.
     Prove: △*DBE* ∼ △*ABC*.

Ex. 1

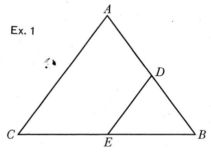

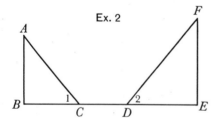

Ex. 2

2. Given: *AB* ⊥ *BE*,
         FE ⊥ *BE*,
         ∠1 = ∠2.
     Prove: △*ABC* ∼ △*DEF*.

3. Given: *MN* ⊥ *NP*,
         RP ⊥ *NP*.
     Prove: △*MNO* ∼ △*ROP*.

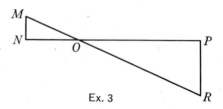

Ex. 3

4. Given: $\triangle ABC \sim \triangle FGH,$
$DE \parallel AB.$
Prove: $\triangle CDE \sim \triangle FGH.$

Ex. 4

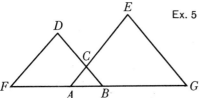

5. Given: $AC = BC,$
$\angle D = \angle E.$
Prove: $\triangle FBD \sim \triangle GAE.$

Ex. 5

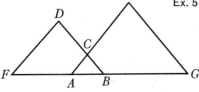

6. Given: Chords XV and YW intersect at Z within $\odot O.$
XY and WV are chords.
Prove: $\triangle XYZ \sim \triangle ZWV.$

Ex. 6

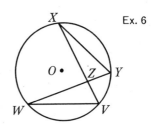

7. Prove that the line segment joining the midpoints of two sides of a triangle cuts off a triangle similar to the original triangle.

Ex. 8

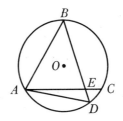

8. Given: In $\odot O,$ $\overset{\frown}{AB} = \overset{\frown}{BC}.$
Prove: $\triangle ABE \sim \triangle ABD.$

Ex. 9

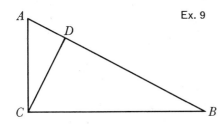

9. Given: In $\triangle ACB,$ ACB is a right angle,
$CD \perp AB.$
Prove: $\triangle ACD \sim \triangle ABC,$
$\triangle BCD \sim \triangle ABC,$
$\triangle ACD \sim \triangle BCD.$

10. Given: MN is a diameter of $\odot O,$
PR is tangent to $\odot O$ at $N.$
Prove: $\triangle MSN \sim \triangle MNP.$

Ex. 10

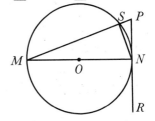

11. Given: In $\triangle DEF$, $DE = DF$,
$\qquad$ $PM \perp DE$,
$\qquad$ $PN \perp DF$.
$\quad$ **Prove:** $\triangle PME \sim \triangle PNF$.

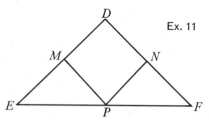

Ex. 11

12. Prove that two isosceles triangles are similar if the vertex angle of one is equal to the vertex angle of the other.

13. Construct a triangle similar to a given triangle. Be ready to explain the steps in your construction.

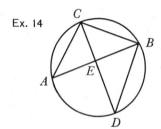

Ex. 14

14. Given: CD bisects $\angle ACB$ of
$\qquad$ inscribed $\triangle ABC$.
$\quad$ **Prove:** $\triangle ACE \sim \triangle CBD$.

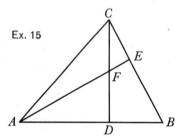

Ex. 15

15. Given: In $\triangle ABC$, CD and
$\qquad$ AE are altitudes to AB
$\qquad$ and CB.
$\quad$ **Prove:** $\triangle AEB \sim \triangle ADF$,
$\qquad\qquad$ $\triangle ADF \sim \triangle CFE$.

16. Given: Circles O and O' inter-
$\qquad$ sect at S and T. ST is
$\qquad$ the common chord.
$\qquad$ SU is tangent to $\odot O$
$\qquad$ at S and RS is tangent
$\qquad$ to $\odot O'$ at S.
$\quad$ **Prove:** $\triangle SRT \sim \triangle STU$.

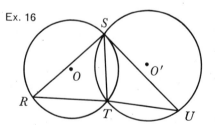

Ex. 16

17. Prove that if the sides of two triangles are respectively parallel, the triangles are similar.

18. Prove that if the sides of one triangle are perpendicular respectively to the sides of another triangle, the triangles are similar.

CORRESPONDING SIDES OF SIMILAR TRIANGLES

Corresponding sides of similar triangles are sides of the triangles located opposite pairs of equal angles. From the definition of similar triangles, you know that the lengths of these sides are proportional. In the following developmental exercises, identify the pairs of corresponding sides.

Developmental Exercises

DE—1. $\triangle ABC$ is similar to $\triangle DEF$, $\angle A = \angle D$, $\angle B = \angle E$, and $\angle C = \angle F$. Identify the pairs of corresponding sides.

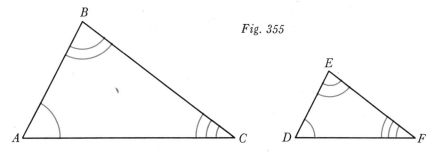

Fig. 355

Solution

The pairs of equal angles in the two similar triangles have been marked in the above diagram. You can now locate the corresponding sides opposite these angles.

BC (opposite $\angle A$) corresponds to EF (opposite $\angle D$) since $\angle A = \angle D$.
AC (opposite $\angle B$) corresponds to DF (opposite $\angle E$) since $\angle B = \angle E$.
AB (opposite $\angle C$) corresponds to DE (opposite $\angle F$) since $\angle C = \angle F$.

DE—2. Using the data in Developmental Exercise **1** express the relationship between the lengths of the sides of the triangles.

Solution

Since the triangles are similar, the lengths of the corresponding sides are in proportion.

$$\frac{BC \text{ (opposite } \angle A)}{EF \text{ (opposite } \angle D)} = \frac{AC \text{ (opposite } \angle B)}{DF \text{ (opposite } \angle E)} = \frac{AB \text{ (opposite } \angle C)}{DE \text{ (opposite } \angle F)}.$$

Notice that the sides represented by the numerator and denominator of each fraction or ratio are opposite equal angles. The numerators correspond to the sides of one triangle and the denominators correspond to the sides of the second triangle.

Exercises

In the following exercises, prove similar triangles are formed. Name the corresponding sides and express the proportion between the lengths of these sides.

1. In $\triangle XYZ$ and $\triangle MNO$, $\angle X = \angle M$ and $\angle Y = \angle N$.

2. In $\triangle RST$ and $\triangle ABS$, $\angle RST = \angle ASB$, and $\angle T$ and $\angle A$ are right angles.

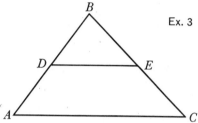

Ex. 3

3. Given: In $\triangle ABC$, $DE \parallel AC$.

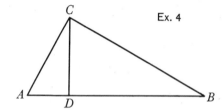

Ex. 4

4. Given: $\angle ACB$ is a right angle, CD is the altitude to AB.

5. Line segments KN and JM intersect at L and KJ is parallel to MN.

6. Isosceles triangles ABC and DEF have equal vertex angles.

MORE ABOUT SIMILAR TRIANGLES

Frequently, when attempting to prove that two triangles are similar it is not always possible to easily prove the necessary angles are equal. It is therefore important to develop other methods for establishing similar triangles.

It will now be shown in the developmental exercises that two triangles can be proved similar if

(1) two sides of one triangle are in proportion to two sides of the other triangle and the included angles are equal.

(2) the sides of one triangle are in proportion to the sides of the other triangle.

Developmental Exercises

DE—1. Prove the following theorem:

THEOREM 105

If two triangles have an angle of one equal to an angle of the other and the sides including these angles in proportion, the triangles are similar.

Solution

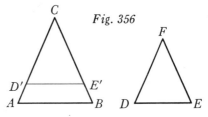

Fig. 356

> **Given:** $\triangle ABC$ and $\triangle DEF$,
> $\angle C = \angle F$,
> $\dfrac{AC}{DF} = \dfrac{CB}{FE}$.

Prove: $\triangle ABC \sim \triangle DEF$.

Proof:

Either $DF < AC$, or $DF = AC$, or $DF > AC$.

(*1*) If $DF = AC$, then the triangles are congruent by **s.a.s.** and the triangles are similar.

(*2*) If $DF < AC$, the following proof will apply.

Construction: Lay off $CD' = FD$ and $CE' = FE$. Draw $D'E'$.

STATEMENTS	REASONS
1. $\dfrac{AC}{DF} = \dfrac{CB}{FE}$.	1. Given.
2. $CD' = FD$, $\quad CE' = FE$.	2. A line may be constructed equal to another line.
3. $\dfrac{AC}{CD'} = \dfrac{CB}{CE'}$.	3. A quantity may be substituted for its equal.
4. $D'E' \parallel AB$.	4. If a line divides two sides of a triangle proportionally, it is parallel to the third side.
5. $\angle E'D'C = \angle BAC$.	5. Why?
6. $\angle ACB = \angle D'CE'$.	6. Identity.
7. $\triangle D'CE' \sim \triangle ABC$.	7. Why?
8. $\triangle D'CE' \cong \triangle DFE$.	8. Why?
9. $\triangle D'CE' \sim \triangle DFE$.	9. Why?
10. $\triangle DFE \sim \triangle ABC$.	10. Why?

(*3*) If $DF > AC$, then DF may be laid off on AC and a proof similar to that in (*2*) will apply.

Corollary

If the lengths of the legs of two right triangles are in proportion, the triangles are similar.

DE—2. Prove the following theorem:

> **THEOREM 106**
>
> **If the corresponding sides of two triangles are in proportion, the triangles are similar.**

Solution

 Given: $\triangle ABC$ and $\triangle DEF$,

$$\frac{AB}{DE} = \frac{BC}{EF} = \frac{AC}{DF}.$$

 Prove: $\triangle ABC \sim \triangle DEF$.

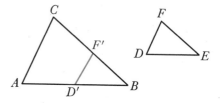

Fig. 357

Proof:

Either $DE = AB$, or $DE > AB$, or $DE < AB$.

(1) If $DE = AB$, then the triangles are similar.

(2) If $DE < AB$ the following proof will apply.

Construction: On AB lay of $BD' = DE$. On BC lay off $BF' = EF$. Draw $D'F'$.

STATEMENTS	REASONS
1. $\dfrac{AB}{DE} = \dfrac{BC}{EF} = \dfrac{AC}{DF}$.	1. Given.
2. $D'B = DE$, $BF' = EF$.	2. A line may be constructed equal to another line.
3. $\dfrac{AB}{D'B} = \dfrac{BC}{BF'}$.	3. A quantity must be substituted for its equal.
4. $\angle ABC = \angle D'BF'$.	4. Identity.
5. $\triangle D'BF' \sim \triangle ABC$.	5. If two triangles have an angle of one equal to an angle of the other and the sides including these angles in proportion, the triangles are similar.
6. $\dfrac{AC}{D'F'} = \dfrac{AB}{D'B}$.	6. Why?
7. $\dfrac{AC}{DF} = \dfrac{AB}{DE}$.	7. Given.
8. $AC = AC$, $AB = AB$.	8. Identity.
9. $D'F' = DF$.	9. Why?
10. $\triangle DEF \cong \triangle D'BF'$.	10. **s.s.s. = s.s.s.**

11. $\angle D = \angle BD'F$, $\angle F = \angle BF'D'$.	11. Corresponding angles of congruent triangles are equal.
12. $\triangle D'BF' \sim \triangle DEF$.	12. Why?
13. $\triangle ABC \sim \triangle DEF$.	13. Why?

(3) If $DE > AB$, then AB may be laid off on DE and a proof similar to that in (2) will apply.

Exercises

1. In $\triangle ABC$, $AB = 8''$, $BC = 10''$, and $AC = 13''$. In $\triangle DEF$, $DE = 4''$, $EF = 5''$, and $DF = 6.5''$. Are the triangles similar?

2. Given: OA and MB are altitudes to the equal sides of isosceles triangle MNO.

Prove: $\dfrac{OA}{MB} = \dfrac{MA}{OB}$.

Ex. 2

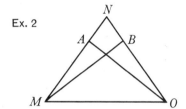

3. The nonparallel sides, AB and CD, of trapezoid $ABCD$ are extended until they meet at point P. Find AP and BP if $AB = 3$ units, and the bases are 6 units, and 8 units respectively.

4. Given: In $\triangle RST$, $XZ \parallel ST$, $YZ \parallel RS$.

Prove: $\dfrac{RX}{YZ} = \dfrac{RZ}{ZT}$.

Ex. 4

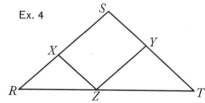

5. A tree casts a shadow 28 feet long at the same time that a 5 foot boy casts a shadow 4 feet long. How high is the tree?

6. Given: Secants PC and PD intersect $\odot O$ at A and B.

Prove: $\dfrac{PC}{PD} = \dfrac{PB}{PA}$.

Ex. 6

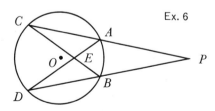

Ex. 7

7. Given: $AB \parallel CD$, $AB = 30'$, $AE = 20'$, $DE = 120'$. Find the length of CD.

8. Given: AS bisects $\angle RSB$,
$RT \perp AS$,
$AS \perp AB$.

Prove: $\dfrac{RT}{AB} = \dfrac{RS}{BS}$.

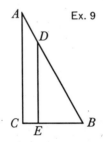

Ex. 8

Ex. 9

9. Given: $DE \perp BC$, $AC = 60$ units,
$AC \perp BC$, $DE = 40$ units,
$CE = 10$ units.
Find the length of BE.

10. Given: $\triangle ABC$ with line segment DE connecting point D on AB with point E on AC. $AD = \frac{3}{4}AB$ and $AE = \frac{3}{4}AC$.

Prove: $\triangle ADE \sim \triangle ABC$.

11. Two triangles are similar if two sides of one are proportional to two sides of the other. True or false?

Ex. 12

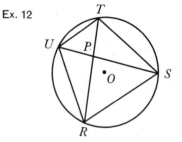

12. Given: Quadrilateral $RSTU$ is inscribed in $\odot O$,
RT bisects $\angle UTS$.

Prove: $\triangle PST \sim \triangle RTU$,
$\triangle PTU \sim \triangle RST$.

13. Prove that the diagonals of a trapezoid divide each other proportionally.

Ex. 14

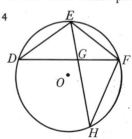

14. Given: In $\odot O$, DE, EF, FH, and DF are chords.

Prove: $\dfrac{DE}{FH} = \dfrac{DG}{GH}$.

15. Given: *EG* and *FH* are altitudes of △*DEF*.

Prove: $\dfrac{GK}{HK} = \dfrac{GF}{HE}$.

Ex. 15

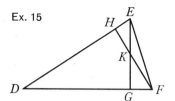

16. Given: Polygon *MNOPQ* ∼ polygon *M'N'O'P'Q'*, *PM* and *P'M'* are diagonals.

Prove: △*PQM* ∼ △*P'Q'M'*.

Ex. 16

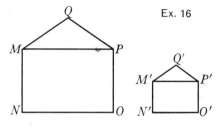

17. Given: *D*, *E*, and *F* are midpoints of *AB*, *BC*, and *AC* respectively in △*ABC*.

Prove: △*DEF* ∼ △*ABC*.

Ex. 17

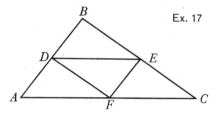

18. Given: ⊙*O* and ⊙*O'* are internally tangent. *AB* and *AC* are diameters of ⊙*O* and ⊙*O'* respectively.

Prove: △*ADB* ∼ △*AEC*.

Ex. 18

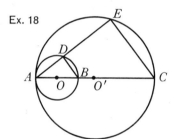

19. Given: *AB* ∥ *CD*, *CF* ∥ *BE*.

Prove: $\dfrac{CG}{BG} = \dfrac{FG}{GE}$,

$\dfrac{CG}{BG} = \dfrac{DG}{AG}$,

△*FGD* ∼ △*AGE*.

Ex. 19

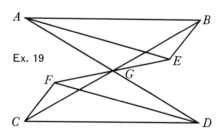

20. Given that *DE* ⊥ *EF*, *GF* ⊥ *EF*, *DF* ⊥ *EG*, prove five pairs of triangles similar.

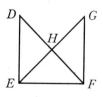

Ex. 20

DE—3. Prove the following theorem:

║**THEOREM 107**

║**If two triangles are similar, the corresponding altitudes have the**
║**same ratio as any two corresponding sides.**

Solution

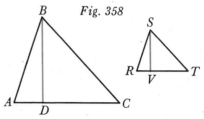

Fig. 358

Given: BD and SV are altitudes to corresponding sides AC and RT of similar triangles ABC and RST.

Prove: $\dfrac{BD}{SV} = \dfrac{AB}{RS} = \dfrac{BC}{ST} = \dfrac{AC}{RT}$.

Proof:

STATEMENTS	REASONS
1. $\triangle ABC \sim \triangle RST$, AC corresponds to RT.	1. Given.
2. $\angle A = \angle R$.	2. Why?
3. $BD \perp AC$, $SV \perp RT$.	3. An altitude of a triangle is a line from a vertex perpendicular to the opposite side.
4. $\angle BDA$ and $\angle SVR$ are right angles.	4. Why?
5. $\triangle BDA$ and $\triangle SVR$ are right triangles.	5. Why?
6. $\triangle BDA \sim \triangle SVR$.	6. If an acute angle of one right triangle is equal to an acute angle of another right triangle, the right triangles are similar.
7. $\dfrac{BD}{SV} = \dfrac{AB}{RS}$.	7. Corresponding sides of similar triangles are in proportion.
8. $\dfrac{AB}{RS} = \dfrac{BC}{ST} = \dfrac{AC}{RT}$.	8. Reason 7.
9. $\dfrac{BD}{SV} = \dfrac{AB}{RS} = \dfrac{BC}{ST} = \dfrac{AC}{RT}$.	9. Why?

Again notice that "$\dfrac{AB}{RS}$" is really comparing the length of AB to the length of RS. Also the statement "the corresponding altitudes have the same ratio as any two corresponding sides" really means "the lengths of the corresponding altitudes have the same ratio as the lengths of the corresponding sides."

DE—4. Two corresponding sides of two similar triangles are 6 units and 9 units, respectively. If the altitude of the smaller triangle is 8 units, find the length of the corresponding altitude of the larger triangle.

Solution

$$\frac{\text{Altitude of smaller triangle}}{\text{Altitude of larger triangle}} = \frac{\text{Side of smaller triangle}}{\text{Side of larger triangle}}.$$

Let x represent the number of units in the measure of the altitude of the larger triangle.

$$\frac{8}{x} = \frac{6}{9}.$$
$$6x = 72.$$
$$x = 12.$$

Exercises

1. The altitude of a triangle is 16 inches. At a point on the altitude 4 inches from the base, a line segment 18 inches long is drawn parallel to the base. Find the length of the base.

2. The base of a triangle is 20 inches and its altitude to the base is 15 inches. Find the length of a line segment, drawn parallel to the base which is 3 inches from the vertex of the triangle.

3. Prove that in any triangle the product of an altitude and the side to which it is drawn is equal to the product of any other altitude and the side to which it is drawn.

Ex. 4

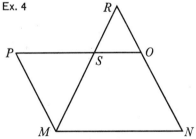

4. Given: $MNOP$ is a $\square$.
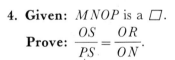
   Prove: $\dfrac{OS}{PS} = \dfrac{OR}{ON}.$

5. Prove that the bisectors of corresponding angles of similar triangles have the same ratio as any two corresponding sides.

6. Prove that two corresponding medians of two similar triangles have the same ratio as the bisectors of the angles drawn from the same vertices as the medians.

7. Given: $MN \parallel ST,$
$\qquad MP \parallel RS.$

Prove: $\dfrac{NO}{PO} = \dfrac{OR}{OT}.$

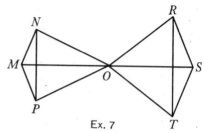

Ex. 7

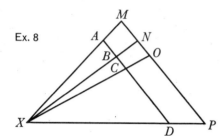

Ex. 8

8. Given: $AD \parallel MP.$

Prove: $\dfrac{AB}{MN} = \dfrac{BC}{NO} = \dfrac{CD}{OP}.$

DE—5. Prove the following theorem:

> **THEOREM 108**
>
> **The perimeters of two similar triangles have the same ratio as any pair of corresponding sides.**

Solution

Given: $\triangle ABC \backsim \triangle DEF,$
$\qquad \dfrac{a}{d} = \dfrac{b}{e} = \dfrac{c}{f}.$

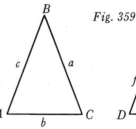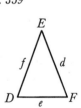

Fig. 359

Prove: $\dfrac{a+b+c}{d+e+f} = \dfrac{a}{d} = \dfrac{b}{e} = \dfrac{c}{f}.$

Analysis:

Let each of the given ratios equal r.

Then $\dfrac{a}{d} = r, \dfrac{b}{e} = r,$ and $\dfrac{c}{f} = r.$

$\qquad a = dr, \ b = er,$ and $c = fr.$

Therefore $a+b+c = dr+er+fr = r(d+e+f).$

$\qquad \dfrac{a+b+c}{d+e+f} = r.$

But r is defined to equal each of the given ratios, therefore

$\qquad \dfrac{a+b+c}{d+e+f} = \dfrac{a}{d} = \dfrac{b}{e} = \dfrac{c}{f}.$

Now you complete the proof by supplying the reasons for each step.

Exercises

1. The corresponding sides of two similar triangles are 5″ and 8″. What is the ratio of their perimeters?

2. The corresponding sides of two similar triangles are 2″ and 5″. Find the ratio of their perimeters.

3. An isosceles triangle has sides of 5″, 4″, and 4″. The base of a similar triangle is 13″. Find the perimeter of the larger triangle.

4. The longest side of a triangle is $6\frac{3}{4}$″. What is the longest side of a similar triangle whose perimeter is $2\frac{1}{2}$ times as large as that of the first triangle?

Ex. 5

5. Find the ratio of the perimeter of $\triangle ADO$ to the perimeter of $\triangle ABC$.

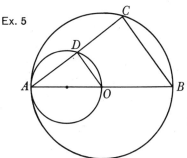

6. The perimeters of two similar triangles are 14″ and 35″, respectively. Find the ratio of the altitudes to the longest sides.

7. An isosceles triangle with a base 1″ longer than the legs has a perimeter of 16″ and an altitude (to the base) of 4″. Find the lengths of the altitude to the base of a similar triangle having a base of 9″.

8. The perimeter of one equilateral triangle is twice the perimeter of a second equilateral triangle. If the side of one of the triangles is $3\frac{1}{2}$″ longer than the side of the other, find their perimeters.

9. The perimeters of two similar triangles are 40″ and 32″ respectively, and a side of the larger triangle is 5″. Determine the length of the corresponding side of the other triangle.

10. A regular polygon with a side 8″ long is circumscribed about a circle whose radius is 3″. How long is each side of a similar polygon circumscribed about a circle with a radius of 10″?

GENERALIZATIONS ABOUT SIMILAR POLYGONS

The next group of theorems applies to all similar polygons. Before using these theorems remember that they apply only to figures whose corresponding angles are equal and whose corresponding sides are in proportion.

At the request of your teacher, be able to prove the following theorems.

THEOREM 109

If two polygons are similar, the ratio of two corresponding diagonals is equal to the ratio of any two corresponding sides.

> **Given:** $ABCDE \sim A'B'C'D'E'$, the corresponding vertices are A and A', B and B', etc.
>
> **Prove:** $\dfrac{AC}{A'C'} = \dfrac{AB}{A'B'}.$

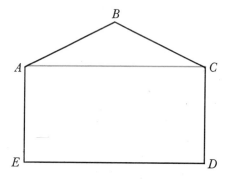

Fig. 360

THEOREM 110

The perimeters of two similar polygons are to each other as the lengths of any pair of corresponding sides.

THEOREM 111

Regular polygons of the same number of sides are similar.

THEOREM 112

Similar polygons may be divided into triangles so that the corresponding triangles are similar.

THEOREM 113

If two polygons are composed of the same number of similar triangles similarly placed, they are similar.

Exercises

1. The ratio of the corresponding sides of two similar pentagons is 3 : 2. What is the ratio of the corresponding diagonals?

2. Divide two similar hexagons into triangles. How many pairs of similar triangles are formed?

3. Prove that the triangles formed in Exercise **2** are similar.

4. Construct a polygon composed of triangles similar to those in Exercise **2** and similarly placed. Is this polygon similar to the polygons in Exercise **2**? Why?

5. Corresponding sides of two similar polygons are 6 units and 9 units. Find the ratio of their perimeters.

6. The perimeters of two similar triangles are 30 units and 10 units. If a side in the smaller triangle is 2 units, find the length of the corresponding side in the larger triangle.

7. The sides of a triangle are 12″, 18″, and 24″. Find the perimeter of a similar triangle whose shortest side is 8″.

8. Corresponding sides of two similar polygons are 4″ and 6″. If the perimeter of the larger polygon exceeds the perimeter of the smaller polygon by 9″, find the perimeter of the smaller polygon.

9. Corresponding diagonals of two similar polygons are in the ratio 4 to 3. If the perimeter of the larger polygon exceeds the perimeter of the smaller polygon by 6″, find the perimeter of the smaller polygon.

10. Two sections of land are to be enclosed with fencing. Both sections are in the shape of similar rectangles. The length of one section is 100′ and the length of the other rectangular section is 150′. If 300′ of fencing is needed to enclose the smaller section, how much is needed to enclose the larger section?

11. The perimeter of a rectangle is 22″ and its length is 8″. Find the perimeter of a similar rectangle whose length is 12″.

12. The perimeter of the smaller of two similar polygons is $\frac{1}{4}$ the perimeter of the larger. If a side in the smaller polygon is 6″ less than the corresponding side of the larger, find the length of the side of the smaller polygon.

PROPORTIONS IN CIRCLES

Previously you learned that if two triangles are similar, the corresponding sides are in proportion. For example, if $\triangle ABC \sim \triangle DEF$ it follows that $\dfrac{AB}{DE} = \dfrac{AC}{DF}$. Since, in a proportion, the product of the means is equal to the product of the extremes, this proportion may be expressed as $AC \times DE = AB \times DF$. All proportions may be written in this form. Remember that the symbol AC in this case refers to the length of the line segment AC and not to the line segment itself. The following theorems might be stated as proportions. However, they are easier to remember if they are expressed in the form of equal products.

Developmental Exercises

DE—1. Prove the following theorem:

THEOREM 114

If two chords intersect within a circle, the product of the lengths of the segments of one chord is equal to the product of the lengths of the segments of the other chord.

Solution

Fig. 361

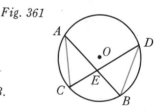

Given: Chords AB and CD intersect at E within $\odot O$.

Prove: $AE \times EB = CE \times ED$.

Construction: Draw chords AC and DB.

Proof:

STATEMENTS	REASONS
1. Chords AB and CD intersect at E within $\odot O$.	1. Given.
2. Chords AC and DB are drawn.	2. Two points determine a straight line.
3. $\angle AEC = \angle BED$.	3. Vertical angles are equal.
4. $\angle A = \angle D$.	4. Why?
5. $\triangle AEC \sim \triangle BED$.	5. Why?
6. $\dfrac{AE}{ED} = \dfrac{CE}{EB}$.	6. Corresponding sides of similar triangles are in proportion.
7. $AE \times EB = CE \times ED$.	7. Why?

DE—2. Chords AB and CD intersect at E within $\odot O$. If AE is 6 units, EB is 4 units, and CE is 3 units, find the length of ED.

Solution

Using Figure 361 in Theorem 114, $AE \times EB = CE \times ED$. Let x represent the length of ED in units.

$$\text{Then } 6(4) = 3(x),$$
$$3x = 24,$$
$$x = 8.$$

Exercises

1. Two chords intersect in a circle. The segments of one chord are $8''$ and $3''$. If one segment of the second chord is $4''$, find the length of the other segment.

2. Two chords intersect in a circle with one chord having segments of $9''$ and $4''$. If the length of the other chord is $12''$, find the length of its segments.

3. The height of an arc is the line segment which joins the midpoint of the arc with the midpoint of its chord. The chord of an arc is $14''$ and the height of the arc is $5''$. Find the length of the diameter of the chord.

4. Two chords intersect in a circle with one chord having segments of $7''$ and $12''$. If one of the segments of the second chord is $8''$ less than the other segment, find the length of the segments of the second chord.

5. A chord is $6''$ from the center of a circle. If the chord is $16''$ long, find the length of the radius of the circle.

6. A chord is drawn through a point $6''$ from the center of a circle. If the radius of the circle is $16''$, what is the product of the lengths of the segments into which the chord is divided?

7. Two chords intersect in a circle with one chord having segments of $12''$ and $4''$. If the length of the other chord is $14''$, find the length of its segments. Is there more than one solution to this problem? Explain.

8. The length of the chord of an arc is four times the length of the height of the arc. If the radius is $6'$, find the length of the height of the arc. See Exercise **3**.

DE—3. Prove the following theorem:

‖**THEOREM 115**

‖**If, from a point outside a circle, a tangent and a secant are drawn to the circle, the length of the tangent is the mean proportional between the length of the whole secant and its external segment.**

Solution

Given: PA is tangent to $\odot O$ at A,
Secant PC intersects the circle at B.

Prove: $PA^2 = PC \times PB$.
(PA^2 means $PA \times PA$.)

Construction: Draw AC and CB.

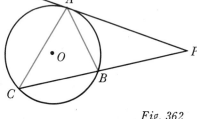

Fig. 362

Proof:

STATEMENTS	REASONS
1. PA is tangent to $\odot O$ at A, secant PC intersects the circle at B.	1. Given.
2. AB and AC are drawn.	2. Two points determine a straight line.
3. $\angle P = \angle P$.	3. Identity.
4. $\angle ACB \overset{\circ}{=} \frac{1}{2} \overset{\frown}{AB}$.	4. An inscribed angle is measured by one-half its intercepted arc.
5. $\angle BAP \overset{\circ}{=} \frac{1}{2} \overset{\frown}{AB}$.	5. An angle formed by a tangent and a chord drawn to the point of contact is measured by one-half its intercepted arc.
6. $\angle ACB = \angle BAP$.	6. Quantities equal to the same quantity are equal to each other.
7. $\triangle BAP \sim \triangle PAC$.	7. If two angles of one triangle are equal to two angles of another triangle, the triangles are similar.
8. $\dfrac{PC}{PA} = \dfrac{PA}{PB}$.	8. Corresponding sides of similar triangles are equal.
9. $PA^2 = PC = PB$.	9. In a proportion, the product of the means is equal to the product of the extremes.

DE—4. A tangent and a secant are drawn to a circle from an external point. If the external segment of the secant measures 4 units and the whole secant is 9 units, find the length of the tangent.

Solution

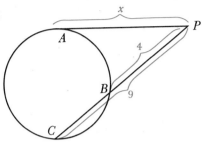

Let x represent the length of the tangent in units.

$$PA^2 = PC \times PB,$$
$$x^2 = 9(4),$$
$$x^2 = 36,$$
$$x = 6.$$
$$PA = 6 \text{ units.}$$

DE—5. Prove the following theorem:

THEOREM 116   *Fig. 363*

If from a point outside a circle two secants are drawn, the product of the length of one secant and the length of its external segment is equal to the product of the length of the other secant and the length of its external segment.

Solution

Given: Secants PAB and PCD are drawn to circle O from P.

Prove: $PB \times AP = PD \times CP$.

Construction: Draw AD and BC.

Analysis:

Fig. 364

$PB \times AP = PD \times CP$ if $\dfrac{PB}{PD} = \dfrac{CP}{AP}$. These line segments are in proportion if $\triangle PCB \sim \triangle PAD$. Notice that $\angle P = \angle P$ and $\angle CBP = \angle PDA$. Why? Now write a formal proof for this theorem.

DE—6. Two secants meet outside a circle. One secant measures 12 inches long and its external segment measures 8 inches. The other secant measures 16 inches long. Find the length of its external segment.

Solution

Let x represent the length of the external segment of the secant in inches.

$$PB \times AP = PD \times CP,$$
$$12(8) = 16(x),$$
$$16x = 96,$$
$$x = 6.$$
$$CP = 6 \text{ inches.}$$

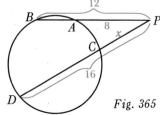

Fig. 365

Exercises

1. Two chords intersect with a circle and the segments of one chord are 16″ and 9″. If one segment of the second chord is 6″, find the length of the other segment.

2. Two chords intersect within a circle. The segments of one chord are 21″ and 8″. The segments of the second chord are represented by x and $x+2$. Solve for the lengths of the segments of the second chord.

3. Two secants meet at a point outside a circle. One secant is divided into two equal parts by the circle. The other secant is 18″ and has an external segment of 8″. Find the length of the unknown secant.

4. A tangent and a secant are drawn to a circle from the same external point. The secant is 27″ and the tangent is 9″. Find the length of the external segment of the secant.

5. Two secants meet at a point outside a circle. The internal segment of one secant is 21″ and its external segment is 4″. The length of the other secant is 20″. Find the length of its external segment.

6. A tangent and a secant are drawn to a circle from the same external point. The internal segment of the secant is denoted by a and the external segment by b. Find the length of the tangent in terms of a and b.

7. A tangent and a secant are drawn to a circle from the same external point. The tangent is $a″$ long and the secant is $b″$ long. Find the length of the external segment of the secant.

8. Two concentric circles have radii of 12″ and 20″, respectively. Find the length of the chord of the larger circle which is tangent to the smaller circle.

9. A tangent and a secant are drawn to a circle from an outside point. The tangent is 8′ long and the secant is 16 times its external segment. Find the length of the secant.

10. A tangent and a secant are drawn to a circle from the same external point. The external segment of the secant is denoted by $x+2$ and the internal segment by $23x-1$. The tangent is denoted by $7x$. Find the length of the tangent and the length of the secant.

PROPORTIONS IN RIGHT TRIANGLES

All the theorems previously proved for triangles in general, of course, apply to the right triangle. Still the right triangle has additional properties not applicable to other triangles.

Developmental Exercises

DE—1. Prove the following theorem:

THEOREM 117

If the altitude is drawn to the hypotenuse of a right triangle, the two triangles thus formed are similar to the given triangle and similar to each other.

Solution

Given: $\angle ACB$ is a right angle in $\triangle ABC$,
CD is an altitude to the hypotenuse AB.

Prove: $\triangle ADC \sim \triangle ABC$,
$\triangle BDC \sim \triangle ABC$,
$\triangle ADC \sim \triangle BDC$.

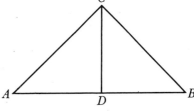

Fig. 366

Proof:

STATEMENTS	REASONS
1. CD is an altitude to the hypotenuse AB.	1. Given.
2. $CD \perp AB$.	2. Why?
3. $\angle CDA$ is a right angle, $\angle BDC$ is a right angle.	3. Perpendicular lines form right angles.
4. $\triangle CDA$ is a right triangle, $\triangle BDC$ is a right triangle.	4. A triangle that contains a right angle is a right triangle.
5. $\angle A = \angle A$, $\angle B = \angle B$.	5. Identity.
6. $\triangle CDA \sim \triangle ABC$, $\triangle BDC \sim \triangle ABC$.	6. If an acute angle of one right triangle is equal to an acute angle of another right triangle, the right triangles are similar.
7. $\triangle CDA \sim \triangle BDC$.	7. If triangles are similar to the same triangle, they are similar to each other.

||Corollary 1

||The length of the altitude drawn to the hypotenuse of a right triangle is the mean proportional between the lengths of the segments of the hypotenuse.

||Corollary 2

||If the altitude is drawn to the hypotenuse of a right triangle, each leg of the given triangle is the mean proportional between the whole hypotenuse and the segment of the hypotenuse adjacent to that leg.

DE—2. $\angle ACB$ is a right angle in $\triangle ABC$,
$CD \perp AB$,
$AD = 4$ units,
$DB = 16$ units.
Find the length of CD, AC, and BC.

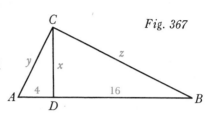

Fig. 367

Solution

Let x represent the length of CD in units.
Let y represent the length of AC in units.
Let z represent the length of BC in units.

$\dfrac{AD}{CD} = \dfrac{CD}{DB},$	$\dfrac{AD}{AC} = \dfrac{AC}{AB},$	$\dfrac{DB}{BC} = \dfrac{BC}{AB},$
$\dfrac{4}{x} = \dfrac{x}{16},$	$\dfrac{4}{y} = \dfrac{y}{20},$	$\dfrac{16}{z} = \dfrac{z}{20},$
$x^2 = 64,$	$y^2 = 80,$	$z^2 = 320,$
$x = 8.$	$y = \sqrt{80},$	$z = \sqrt{320},$
$CD = 8$ units.	$y = \sqrt{16} \cdot \sqrt{5}.$	$z = \sqrt{64} \cdot \sqrt{5},$
	$y = 4\sqrt{5}.$	$z = 8\sqrt{5}.$
	$AC = 4\sqrt{5}$ units.	$BC = 8\sqrt{5}$ units.

Notice that only the positive roots are used. The length of a line segment can only have meaning if it is an absolute value. If the positive root is irrational, the final result should be left in its simplest form.

DE—3. $\angle ACB$ is a right angle in $\triangle ABC$,
$DC \perp AB$,
$CD = 6$ units.
If the length of AD is 16 less than the length of DB, find the length of AD and DB.

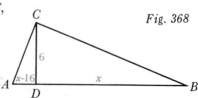

Fig. 368

Solution

Let x represent the length of BD in units, then $x-16$ represents the length of AC in units.

$$\frac{AD}{CD}=\frac{CD}{DB},$$
$$\frac{x-16}{6}=\frac{6}{x},$$
$$x^2-16x=36,$$
$$x^2-16x-36=0,$$
$$(x-18)(x+2)=0,$$
$$x-18=0$$
$$x=18.$$
$$BD=18 \text{ units.}$$
$$x-16=18-16=2.$$
$$AD= \ 2 \text{ units.}$$

The factor $x+2$ yields $x=-2$, which satisfies the derived equation but has no meaning for the problem being solved.

Exercises

In the diagram $AC \perp BC$, $CD \perp AB$.

1. Find the lengths of CD, AC, and BC if
    a. $AB=13$ units and $DB=$ 4 units.
    b. $AD=7$ units and $DB=28$ units.
    c. $AD=15$ units and $AB=40$ units.

Ex. 1-2

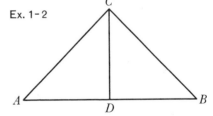

2. Find AD if
    a. $CD=6$ units and $DB=9$ units.
    b. $CD=5$ units and $DB=7\frac{1}{2}$ units.
    c. $CD=4$ units and $AB=8$ units.
    d. $CD=12$ units and DB is 7 units longer than AD.

3. Given that the segments of the hypotenuse made by the altitude are 8 inches and 12 inches. Determine the length of the altitude.

4. If the base of an isosceles right triangle is 10 inches long, compute the length of the altitude.

5. Given that the altitude to the hypotenuse of a right triangle is 4 inches and one segment of the hypotenuse is 3 inches longer than the other, compute the length of the hypotenuse.

6. Given that the sides of a right triangle are 5 units, 12 units, and 13 units. Find the length of the altitude to the hypotenuse.

7. Given that the sides of a right triangle are 12 units, 16 units, and 20 units, how long is each segment of the hypotenuse made by the altitude?

8. Given: Diameter *AOB* and tangent *AC*.
   Prove: $CD : AD = AD : DB$.

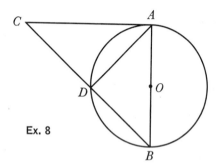

Ex. 8

9. If an altitude drawn to the hypotenuse of a right triangle divides it into segments of $36''$ and $64''$, find the lengths of the legs of the triangle.

Ex. 10

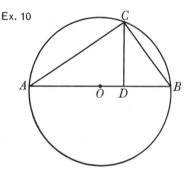

10. Given: $\triangle AOB$ inscribed in $\odot O$, *AOB* is a diameter, *CD* is an altitude.
   Prove: $AD : DC = DC : DB$.

CONSTRUCTING THE MEAN PROPORTIONAL

Using the concept stated in Corollary 1 of Theorem 117 that the altitude upon the hypotenuse of a right triangle is the mean proportional between the segments of the hypotenuse, it is possible to construct the mean proportional between two given line segments.

Developmental Exercises

DE—1. Given two line segments, a and b, construct the mean proportional between a and b.

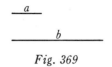

Fig. 369

Solution
- Draw a working line, l.
- At any point, A, on l construct $AB = a$.
- Construct $BC = b$.

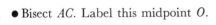

Fig. 370

- Bisect AC. Label this midpoint O.

- With O as center and radius AO construct a semicircle having AC as the diameter.

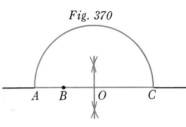

Fig. 371

- At B construct $BE \perp AC$. D is the intersection of BE and the semicircle.

- BD is the required mean proportional between a and b.

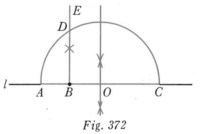

Fig. 372

DE—2. Show that the above construction is valid.

Solution

x is the mean proportional between a and b if it is an altitude drawn to the hypotenuse of a right triangle having a and b as segments of the hypotenuse.

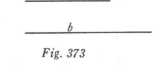

Fig. 373

Draw $\triangle ADC$. If $\overset{\frown}{ADC}$ is a semicircle, why is $\triangle ADC$ a right triangle? How do you know that $\overset{\frown}{ADC}$ is a semicircle? Is $a+b$ the hypotenuse of the right triangle ADC? Is x the altitude of $\triangle ADC$?

Now write the proof for this construction.

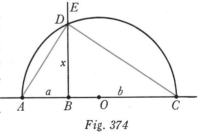

Fig. 374

Exercises

1. In $\triangle ABC$, $\angle ACB$ is a right angle and $CD \perp AB$. Find the lengths of AD, DB, and CD if the length of AC is $4''$ and the length of AB is $8''$.

2. In rectangle $ABCD$, AC is a diagonal, and DE is an altitude to side AC in $\triangle ADC$, prove that DE is the mean proportional between AE and EC.

3. Construct the mean proportional between two line segments which are $\frac{1}{2}''$ and $2''$ long. Measure the mean proportional with a ruler. Then check the accuracy of your work by computing the mean proportional between $\frac{1}{2}''$ and $2''$.

4. Construct a right triangle when a leg and the altitude upon the hypotenuse are given.

5. The sides of a right triangle are 9 units, 12 units, and 15 units. Find the length of the shorter segment of the hypotenuse made by the altitude to the hypotenuse.

6. In $\triangle ABC$, $\angle ACB$ is a right angle and $CD \perp AB$. Find the length of AD and DB if AB is $14''$ and CD is $2\sqrt{6}''$.

7. Either leg of a right triangle is the mean proportional between the hypotenuse and the other leg. True or false?

8. Construct the mean proportional between two line segments x and $2x$. Express the length of the mean proportional algebraically.

9. From point P on circle O, PR is drawn perpendicular to diameter AB meeting it at R. Prove that PB is the mean proportional between AB and BR.

10. Given: AB is a diameter of $\odot O$,
A is the midpoint of minor arc CD.

Prove: AC is the mean proportional between AE and AB.
DE is the mean proportional between AE and EB.

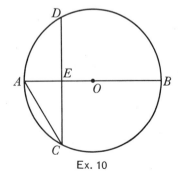

Ex. 10

PYTHAGOREAN THEOREM

Between 550 and 500 B.C., the philosopher Pythagoras and his followers made several important discoveries in mathematics that were concerned with number relationships. Although the Egyptian surveyors probably made use of a right triangle relationship where the sides were in the ratio of $3 : 4 : 5$. Pythagoras is credited with the discovery of the generalized statement about the sides of any right triangle. This statement, "in a right triangle the square of the hypotenuse is equal to the sum of the squares of the legs," is called the *Pythagorean Theorem.*

Developmental Exercises

DE—1. Prove the Pythagorean theorem:

THEOREM 118

In a right triangle the square of the length of the hypotenuse is equal to the sum of the squares of the length of the legs.

Solution

Given: $\angle ACB$ is a right angle in $\triangle ABC$,
AB is denoted by c,
BC is denoted by a,
AC is denoted by b.

Prove: $c^2 = a^2 + b^2$.

Construction: $CD \perp AB$.

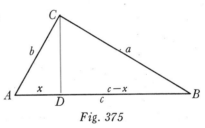

Fig. 375

Proof:

STATEMENTS	REASONS
1. $\angle ACB$ is a right angle.	1. Given.
2. $CD \perp AB$, (denote AD as x and BD as $c-x$).	2. Through a point not on a line one, and only one, perpendicular can be constructed to the line.
3. $\dfrac{c}{b} = \dfrac{b}{x}$, $\dfrac{c}{a} = \dfrac{a}{c-x}$.	3. Why?
4. $b^2 = cx$, $a^2 = c^2 \neq cx$.	4. In a proportion the product of the means is equal to the product of the extremes.
5. $a^2 + b^2 = c^2$.	5. If equals are added to equals, the sums are equal.

‖ **Corollary**
‖ **In a right triangle, the square of either leg is equal to the square of**
‖ **the hypotenuse minus the square of the other leg.**

Since $c^2 = a^2 + b^2$ it follows that $a^2 = c^2 - b^2$ and $b^2 = c^2 - a^2$. Why?

DE—2. In right triangle ABC, $\angle C$ is the right angle and AB is the hypotenuse. If side a is $5''$ and side b is $12''$, find the length of the hypotenuse.

Solution

$$c^2 = a^2 + b^2,$$
$$c^2 = 5^2 + 12^2,$$
$$c^2 = 25 + 144,$$
$$c^2 = 169,$$
$$c = \sqrt{169},$$
$$c = 13''.$$

DE—3. The hypotenuse of a right triangle is $25''$ and one leg is $20''$. How long is the other leg?

Solution

$$b^2 = c^2 - a^2,$$
$$b^2 = (25)^2 - (20)^2,$$
$$b^2 = 625 - 400,$$
$$b^2 = 225,$$
$$b = \sqrt{225},$$
$$b = 15''.$$

Exercises

1. The sides of a triangle are $10''$, $12''$, and $16''$. Is this a right triangle? Show work to support your answer.

2. The side of an equilateral triangle is $10''$. Find the length of its altitude. Leave your answer in simplest radical form.

3. Find the length of the hypotenuse of a right triangle whose legs are $8'$ and $15'$.

4. The leg of an isosceles right triangle is $6''$. Find the length of the hypotenuse. Leave your answer in simplest radical form.

5. A point is $15''$ from the center of a circle that has a $9''$ radius. How long is the tangent to the circle from this point?

6. Represent the length of the altitude, h, of an equilateral triangle whose side is s. Leave your answer in simplest radical form.

7. Two parallel chords are each 48″ long. The distance between them is 14″. Find the length of the radius of the circle.

8. In the diagram $\angle ACB$ is a right angle in $\triangle ABC$, $CD \perp AB$, BC is 25″, CD is 7″. Find the length of DB and AD.

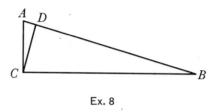

Ex. 8

9. The bases of an isosceles trapezoid are 10″ and 26″. Each non-parallel side is 17″. Find the length of the altitude of the trapezoid.

10. Write a formula for finding the length of the diagonal, d, of a rectangle whose base is b and whose altitude is h.

11. Find a side of a rhombus whose diagonals are 12″ and 16″.

12. A chord 16″ long is 6″ from the center of a circle. Find the length of a chord 8″ from the center of the circle.

13. The radii of two concentric circles are 8″ and 17″. Find the length of a chord in the larger circle which is tangent to the smaller circle.

14. Find the length of a chord 20″ from the center of a circle whose diameter is 58″.

15. Find the length of the altitude to the base of an isosceles triangle whose equal sides are 26″ and whose base is 48″.

16. Find the length of the common external tangent of two circles if the distance between the centers is 10″ and the radii are 3″ and 8″ respectively.

17. The common chord of two intersecting circles is 16″. Their radii are 17″ and 10″ respectively. Find the length of their line of centers.

18. The two legs of a right triangle are equal and the hypotenuse is 10″. Find the length of each leg. Leave your answer in simplest radical form.

PROPERTIES OF SPECIAL RIGHT TRIANGLES

The right triangles that contain angles of 30°, 60°, or 45° are used so frequently that special formulas have been derived for finding the lengths of their sides. You should become familiar with these formulas for they will simplify your work.

EGYPTIAN LAND MEASURERS –THEBES.

The ancient Egyptians developed a crude arithmetic and geometry to satisfy their everyday needs. They used special right triangle relationships in surveying the land and in building the pyramids.

Developmental Exercises

DE—1. Prove the following theorem:

THEOREM 119

The length of the side opposite the 30° angle in a 30°-60° right triangle is equal to one-half the length of the hypotenuse.

Solution

    Given: $\triangle ABC$ with $\angle C = 90°$,   *Fig. 376*
                 $\angle A = 30°$,
                 $\angle B = 60°$.
    Prove: $BC = \frac{1}{2}AB$.

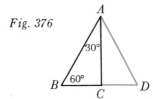

Construction: Extend BC to D so that $BC = CD$. Join A and D.

Analysis:

   $BC = \frac{1}{2}AB$ if $BC = \frac{1}{2}BD$ and $BD = AB$. This can be proved by showing that $\triangle ABD$ is equilateral since $\triangle ABC \cong \triangle ADC$. How do you know that $\triangle ABC \cong \triangle ADC$? Be able to write a formal proof for this theorem at the request of your teacher.

   Theorem 119 can be combined with the Pythagorean Theorem to derive the following corollaries.

Corollary 1

The length of the hypotenuse of a 30°-60° right triangle is equal to twice the length of the side opposite the 30° angle.

Corollary 2

The length of the leg opposite the 60° angle in a 30°-60° right triangle is equal to $\sqrt{3}$ times the length of the leg opposite the 30° angle.

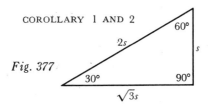

COROLLARY 1 AND 2

Fig. 377

Corollary 3

The length of the altitude of an equilateral triangle is equal to $\dfrac{s}{2}\sqrt{3}$, where s represents the length of a side.

DE—2. In right triangle ABC, $\angle A = 30°$, $\angle B = 60°$, and $\angle C = 90°$. Find the lengths of AB and BC if the length of AC is $10''$. Leave your answer in simplest radical form.

Solution

Notice that the side opposite the 60° angle is given. Using the relationships in Corollary 1 and 2, we have $\sqrt{3}\,BC = 10$

$$BC = \frac{10}{\sqrt{3}}$$

$$= \frac{10\sqrt{3}}{3}$$

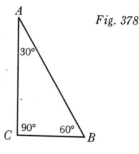

Fig. 378

$AB = 2BC$

$$AB = 2 \cdot \frac{10\sqrt{3}}{3}$$

$$= 20\frac{\sqrt{3}}{3}$$

Notice above that it was necessary to remove the radicals from the denominator in order to leave the answer in accepted simplest form. To accomplish this multiply the numerator and denominator of the fraction by the smallest number which makes the denominator rational. Remember that multiplying both numerator and denominator of a fraction by the same non-zero quantity does not alter the value of the fraction.

DE—3. Prove the following theorem:

|| **THEOREM 120**

|| **The length of the hypotenuse of an isosceles right triangle is equal to the length of a leg multiplied by $\sqrt{2}$.**

Solution

In an isosceles triangle the legs are of equal length. Therefore, in the Pythagorean Theorem, $c^2 = a^2 + b^2$, where c represents the length of the hypotenuse and a and b represent the lengths of the legs $a = b$.

Therefore $c^2 = a^2 + b^2$,

$$c^2 = b^2 + b^2,$$
$$c^2 = 2b^2,$$
$$c = b\sqrt{2} \text{ where } b \text{ is the length of either leg.}$$

|| **Corollary 1**

|| **The length of either leg of an isosceles right triangle is equal to one-half the length of the hypotenuse multiplied by $\sqrt{2}$.**

From the above theorem, $c = b\sqrt{2}$. Therefore b, the length of either leg, is equal to $\frac{c}{\sqrt{2}}$. Simplified this becomes $\frac{c\sqrt{2}}{2}$, which is one-half the length of the hypotenuse times $\sqrt{2}$.

Corollary 2
The length of the diagonal of a square is equal to the length of a side of the square multiplied by $\sqrt{2}$.

Corollary 3
The length of a side of a square is equal to one-half the length of the diagonal multiplied by $\sqrt{2}$.

DE—4. In right triangle ABC, $\angle A = 45°$, $\angle B = 45°$. Find the lengths of AB and AC if $BC = 4''$. Leave your answer in simplest radical form.

Solution

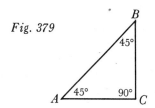

Fig. 379

Since $\angle A = \angle B$, $AC = BC$. Therefore $AC = 4''$. Using Theorem 120
$AB = 4\sqrt{2}$.

Exercises

1. Prove Corollary 2 of Theorem 119.

2. Prove Corollary 3 of Theorem 119.

3. Prove Corollary 2 of Theorem 120.

4. Prove Corollary 3 of Theorem 120.

In the following exercises leave your answers in simplest radical form.

5. In a right triangle the side opposite the 30° angle is 6″, find the length of the hypotenuse.

6. In isosceles $\triangle ABC$, $AC = BC$, $CD \perp AB$, $\angle ACB = 120°$, and $AC = 8''$. Find the lengths of CD and AD.

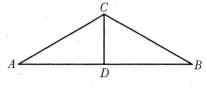

Ex. 6

7. Find the length of the diagonal of a square whose side is $7''$.

8. The length of a side of an equilateral triangle is $12''$. Find the length of the altitude of the triangle.

9. The side opposite a 45° angle in a right triangle is 10″. Find the length of the hypotenuse.

10. Two tangents to a circle from an external point form an angle of 60°. The radius of the circle is 5″. Find the length of each tangent.

11. In a right triangle one acute angle is double the other acute angle. What is the ratio of the hypotenuse to the shorter leg of the triangle?

12. Find the length of the radius of the circle inscribed in an equilateral triangle whose side is $4\sqrt{3}''$.

13. If the hypotenuse of an isosceles right triangle is $5\sqrt{2}''$, find the length of a leg of the triangle.

14. Find the length of the radius of a circle circumscribed about an equilateral triangle whose side is 12 units.

15. Two adjacent sides of a parallelogram are a and b. The angle included between these sides is 30°. Find the length of the segment of b adjacent to the 30° angle in terms of a.

16. A rhombus which contains an angle of 120° has a side of 6″. Find the length of each diagonal.

17. In rectangle $ABCD$, $\angle CAB =$ 30°, $DC = 10''$. Find the lengths of AC and BC.

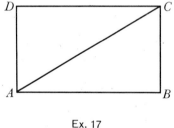

Ex. 17

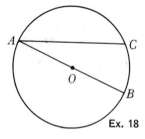

Ex. 18

18. In $\odot O$, AB is a diameter, $\angle A = 30°$, and $AO = 7''$. Find the length of chord AC.

19. The radius of a chord inscribed in an equilateral triangle is $\sqrt{3}''$. What is the length of the radius of the circumscribed circle?

20. The two adjacent sides of a parallelogram are 3″ and 8″. The angle included between these sides is 60°. Find the length of the shorter diagonal of the parallelogram.

SOLID GEOMETRY

The projection of a point on a line is the point of intersection of the perpendicular from the point to the line. In Figure 380 point *D* is the projection of point *C* on line *AB*.

The projection of a segment upon a line is the locus of the projection of all the points of the segment. In Figure 381, *CD* and the line segments parallel to *CD* are perpendicular to *AB*. The projection of *AC* on *AB* is *AD*. The projection of *CB* on *AB* is *DB*.

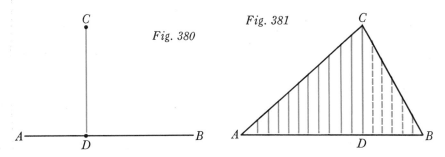

Fig. 380

Fig. 381

This concept of projection also applies in three-dimensional space. The projection of a point upon a plane is the foot of the perpendicular drawn from the point to the plane or the point of intersection of the perpendicular and the plane. In Figure 382, *A* is the projection of point *P* on plane *M*.

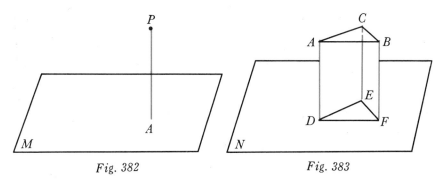

Fig. 382

Fig. 383

The projection of a geometric figure upon a plane is the locus of the projection of all the points of the figure on the plane. In Figure 383 △*DEF* is the projection of △*ABC* on plane *N*.

Developmental Exercises

DE—1. What is the projection of a straight line upon a plane not perpendicular to the line? Perpendicular to the line?

Solution

The projection of a straight line upon a plane not perpendicular to the line is another straight line. If the plane is perpendicular to the line, the projection is the point at the foot of the line.

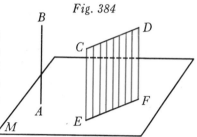

Fig. 384

DE—2. What is the projection of two intersecting lines on a plane?

Solution

The projection of two intersecting lines on a plane is two intersecting lines. See Figure 385. If the plane determined by the two given lines is perpendicular to the plane upon which the projection is made the projection is a straight line. See Figure 386.

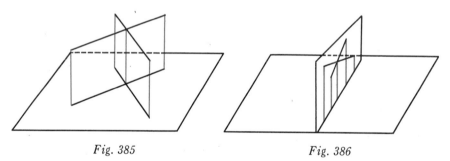

Fig. 385   *Fig. 386*

Exercises

For each of the following figures, tell what the projection upon a plane would be. Consider special locations of the figure with regard to the plane as well as the general case. There may be more than one possible answer for each figure.

1. Two points.   **2.** A triangle.

3. A straight line.   **4.** A plane quadrilateral.

5. Two parallel lines.   **6.** A circle.

7. A square.   **8.** Any solid figure.

EXTEND YOUR HORIZON

Vision is the ability of the eye to form an image of an object and to transmit this image to the brain. In order to do this, light rays must pass through the outer portion of the eye and fall on the retina. Notice in the diagram that these light rays form similar triangles, $\triangle ABC \sim \triangle DEC$.

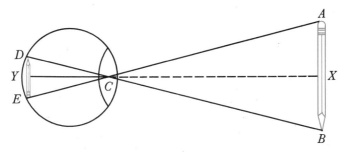

Fig. 387

The distance the object is from the eye is measured along the perpendicular XC. XC and YC are altitudes of the similar triangles. Therefore, $XC : AB = YC : DE$. YC is a constant length.

Compare the height of an image on the retina of an object 5 feet away to the height of an image on the retina of the same object 15 feet away.

In this case, YC and AB are constant while XC is being tripled. Similar triangles will still be formed.

$$\frac{XC}{AB} = \frac{YC}{DE} \quad \text{so} \quad \frac{3XC}{AB} = \frac{YC}{\frac{1}{3}DE}.$$

The image on the retina will be reduced one-third.

Can you understand why the farther you are from an object the smaller it seems to you?

Compare the height of an image on the retina of an object 1 foot away to the height of an image of the same object 2 feet away. Compare the height of the image of this same object if you are only 6 inches away.

Cameras operate on this same principle. In taking a picture do you move closer or further away to get a larger image? Can you explain why the term "close-ups" is used?

CHAPTER SUMMARY

Two polygons are similar if

1. their corresponding angles are equal and their corresponding sides are in proportion.   (page 400)

2. they have the same number of sides and are regular.   (page 420)

3. they are composed of the same number of similar triangles. (page 420)

If two polygons are similar

1. their corresponding angles are equal and their corresponding sides are in proportion.   (page 400)

2. the ratio of two corresponding diagonals is equal to the ratio of any two corresponding sides.   (page 420)

3. the perimeters are to each other as any pair of corresponding sides.   (page 420)

Two triangles are similar if

1. their corresponding angles are equal and their corresponding sides are in proportion.   (page 400)

2. three angles of one triangle are equal respectively to three angles of the other triangle.   (page 404)

3. they are right triangles and an acute angle of one is equal to an acute angle of the other.   (page 405)

4. they are similar to the same triangle.   (page 405)

5. an angle of one is equal to an angle of the other and the sides including these angles are equal.   (page 411)

6. they are right triangles and their legs are in proportion.   (page 411)

7. their corresponding sides are in proportion.   (page 412)

If two triangles are similar

1. their corresponding angles are equal and their corresponding sides are in proportion.   (page 400)

2. the corresponding altitudes have the same ratio as any the length of two corresponding sides.   (page 416)

3. the perimeters have the same ratio as the lengths of any two corresponding sides.   (page 418)

In a right triangle

1. having acute angles of 30° and 60°, the length of the side opposite the 30° angle is equal to one-half the length of the hypotenuse. (page 437)

2. having acute angles of 30° and 60°, the length of the hypotenuse is twice the length of the side opposite the 30° angle.   (page 437)

3. having acute angles of 30° and 60°, the length of the side opposite the 60° angle is equal to $\sqrt{3}$ times the length of the side opposite the 30° angle.   (page 437)

4. having equal sides, the length of the hypotenuse is equal to the length of either leg multiplied by $\sqrt{2}$.   (page 438)

5. having equal sides, the length of either leg is equal to one-half the length of the hypotenuse multiplied by $\sqrt{2}$.   (page 438)

6. if the altitude is drawn to the hypotenuse, the two triangles thus formed are similar to the given triangle and similar to each other. (page 427)

7. the altitude drawn to the hypotenuse is the mean proportional between the segments of the hypotenuse.   (page 428)

8. if the altitude is drawn to the hypotenuse, each leg of the given triangle is the mean proportional between the whole hypotenuse and the adjacent segment of the hypotenuse.   (page 428)

9. the square of the length of the hypotenuse is equal to the sum of the squares of the lengths of the legs.   (page 433)

10. the square of either leg is equal to the square of the hypotenuse minus the square of the other leg.   (page 434)

With a circle

1. if two chords intersect, the product of the lengths of the segments of one chord is equal to the product of the length of the segments of the other chord.   (page 422)

2. if, from a point outside a circle, a tangent and a secant are drawn, the tangent is the mean proportional between the whole secant and its external segment.   (page 424)

3. if, from a point outside a circle, two secants are drawn, the product of the length of one secant and the length of its external segment is equal to the product of the length of the other secant and the length of its external segment.   (page 425)

CHAPTER REVIEW

Vocabulary

Match the word in the left hand column with its correct definition in the right hand column.

1. Similar ($\sim$)

    a. A line that intersects a circle in two points.

    b. A rectangle with equal adjacent sides.

2. Congruent ($\cong$)

    c. A parallelogram with two equal adjacent sides.

3. Parallelogram ($\square$)

    d. A quadrilateral that has both pairs of opposite sides parallel.

4. Rhombus

    e. A line which joins two points of a circle.

5. Circle ($\odot$)

    f. In a right triangle, the side opposite the right angle.

    g. The quotient obtained when the first quantity is divided by the second.

6. Secant

    h. An equation which states that two ratios are equal.

7. Chord

    i. A line that has one, and only one, point in common with a circle.

8. Tangent

    j. Can be made to coincide.

    k. A closed curve in a plane all points of which are equidistant from a fixed point called the center.

9. Hypotenuse

10. Proportion

    l. Have the same shape.

Exercises

1. Is it true or false that two polygons are always similar if their corresponding sides are proportional.

2. Given: $\angle C = \angle B$.

Prove: $\dfrac{AD}{AB} = \dfrac{AE}{AC}$,

$\dfrac{CE}{AC} = \dfrac{BD}{AB}$,

$\dfrac{EF}{EB} = \dfrac{DF}{DC}$.

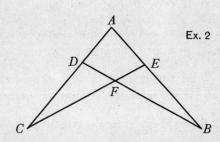

Ex. 2

3. The sides of a triangle are 20″, 25″, and 30″. The smallest side of a similar triangle is 8″. Find the length of the largest side in the same triangle.

4. Given: EG and DH intersect at F,

$DF = \frac{2}{3}FH$,

$EF = \frac{2}{3}FG$.

Prove: $\triangle DEF \sim \triangle FGH$.

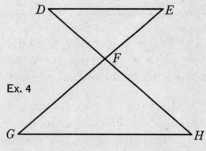

Ex. 4

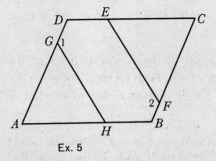

Ex. 5

5. Given: $ABCD$ is a $\square$,

$\angle 1 = \angle 2$.

Prove: $\dfrac{AH}{GH} = \dfrac{EC}{EF}$,

$FC \cdot GH = GA \cdot EF$.

6. Prove that the altitude to the hypotenuse of a right triangle is equal to the product of the legs divided by the hypotenuse.

7. Complete: The corresponding altitudes of two similar triangles have the same ratio as_____

8. The perimeter of a rectangle is $26''$ and the length is $8''$. Find the perimeter of a similar rectangle whose length is $12''$.

9. If the altitude is drawn to the hypotenuse of a right triangle three facts were proved. List these facts.

10. Similar polygons must have the same number of sides. True or false?

11. Find the lengths of the sides of a quadrilateral with a perimeter of $156''$ if the sides of a similar quadrilateral are $10''$, $12''$, $14''$, and $16''$.

12. Upon a given line segment as a side, construct a pentagon similar to a given pentagon.

13. Two corresponding sides in two similar polygons are $3''$ and $5''$. If the sum of the two perimeters is $60''$, find the perimeter of each given polygon.

14. Given the altitude, construct a triangle similar to a given triangle.

15. Two triangles are similar. If the sides of one triangle are $10''$, $16''$, $18''$ and the perimeter of the second triangle is $33''$, find the length of the sides of the second triangle.

16. In two similar triangles, the ratio of a pair of corresponding sides is $2:5$. If the perimeter of the larger triangle is 5 more than twice the perimeter of the smaller triangle, find the perimeter of each triangle.

17. In two regular hexagons, the radius of the larger is 5 times the radius of the smaller. If the perimeter of the larger exceeds the perimeter of the smaller by 48 units, find the length of a side of the larger hexagon.

18. A tangent and a secant are drawn to a circle from the same external point. If the tangent is $16''$ in length and the secant is $24''$ longer than its external segment, find the length of the segment.

19. One diagonal of a rhombus is $24''$ and one side is $13''$. Find the length of the other diagonal of the rhombus.

20. Find the length of a side of a square whose diagonal is $\sqrt{18}''$.

CHAPTER TEST

1. Given the perimeter, construct a triangle similar to a given triangle.

2. The distance between the centers of two circles is $18''$. If the radii are $4''$ and $5''$ respectively, find the length of the common internal tangent. Leave your answer in simplest radical form.

3. Given: $AB \perp CD$,
   E is the midpoint of $\overparen{BD}$.

   Prove: $\dfrac{AF}{CF} = \dfrac{FD}{FB}$,

   $\dfrac{AC}{CF} = \dfrac{OB}{BH}$,

   $\dfrac{OG}{GF} = \dfrac{AC}{FC}$.

Ex. 3

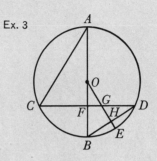

4. Using the diagram in Exercise **3**
   Given: $AB \perp CD$, E is the midpoint of $\overparen{BD}$.

   Prove: $FB \times GD = GH \times BD$, $\dfrac{OF}{FG} = \dfrac{DH}{GH}$, $CF \times FD = AF \times FB$.

5. Two triangles are isosceles. The vertex angle in one triangle is $30°$. An exterior angle at one end of the base of the other triangle is $100°$. Are the triangles similar?

6. Find the length of the diagonal of a square whose side measures $c\sqrt{2}$.

7. State and prove the Pythagorean Theorem.

8. From a point, A, outside a circle, tangent AB and secant ACD are drawn. If $AD = 36''$ and chord $DC = 32''$, find the length of AB.

9. The side of an equilateral triangle is $12''$. Find the radius of the inscribed circle and the radius of the circumscribed circle.

10. $ABCD$ is an isosceles trapezoid, $\angle A = 45°$, base $DC = 10$ units, and base $AB = 18$ units. Find the perimeter of $ABCD$. Leave your answer in simplest radical form.

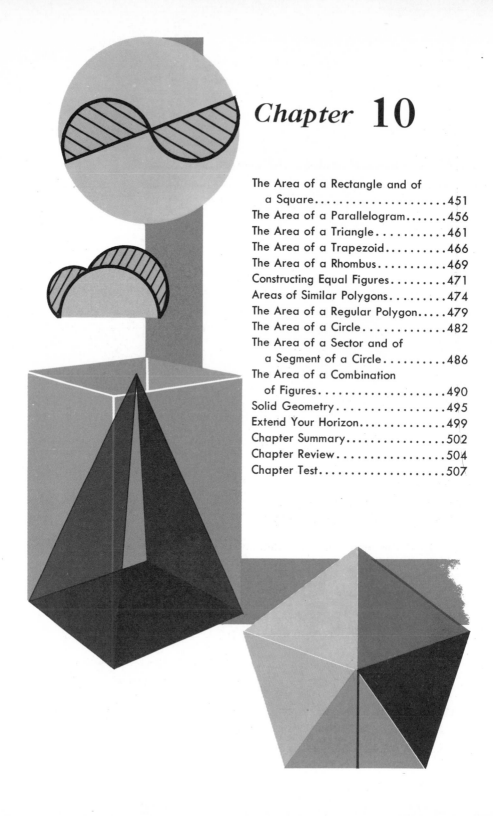

Chapter 10

AREAS

THE AREA OF A RECTANGLE AND OF A SQUARE

You will recall that a *polygon* is a *closed broken line which bounds a portion of a plane*. The measure of the portion of the plane bounded by the polygon is briefly referred to as the *area of the polygon*.

To determine the area of any figure, a unit of measure must first be determined. *A **unit of measure of area*** *is the surface bounded by a square whose side is a unit of length*. This unit for area, for example, may be a square inch, a square whose sides measure one inch, or a square foot, a square whose sides measure one foot.

> The area of a geometric figure is the number of square units in its interior.

Developmental Exercises

DE—1. Using the given unit, determine the area of the rectangle *ABCD*.

Solution

The area of the rectangle can be determined by counting the number of square units within the rectangle. There are 24 squares within the rectangle. Thus, the area of the rectangle is 24 square units. Also observe that there are 4 rows of 6 squares in each row. Thus, 4×6 squares $= 24$ squares. Similarly, the rectangle may be considered as having 6 rows of 4 squares in each row. Thus, 6×4 squares $= 24$ squares. From this you may assume

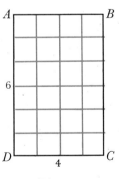

Fig. 388

ASSUMPTION 42

The area of a rectangle whose sides measure *b* units and *h* units is *bh* square units. $A = bh$.

DE—2. Compare the area of the given rectangles using the given units.

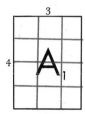
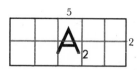

Fig. 389

Solution

The area of A_1 is 3×4 squares or 12 square units. The area of A_2 is 5×2 squares or 10 square units.

$$\frac{A_1}{A_2} = \frac{3 \times 4}{5 \times 2} = \frac{12}{10} \text{ or } \frac{6}{5} \text{ or } A_1 : A_2 = 6 : 5.$$

In general, if A_1, b_1, and h_1 represent the area, the length of the base, and the length of the altitude, respectively, of a rectangle and likewise A_2, b_2, and h_2 represent the area, the length of the base, and the length of the altitude, respectively, of another rectangle then

$$\frac{A_1}{A_2} = \frac{b_1 h_1}{b_2 h_2} \text{ or } \frac{A_1}{A_2} = \frac{b_1}{b_2} \times \frac{h_1}{h_2}.$$

This may be stated as follows:

‖ THEOREM 121

The ratio of the areas of two rectangles is equal to the ratio of the products of the length of their bases and altitudes.

DE—3. Determine the ratio of the areas of two rectangles that have bases of 6 units each and altitudes of 4 units and 2 units, respectively.

Solution

$$\frac{A_1}{A_2} = \frac{b_1}{b_2} \times \frac{h_1}{h_2}.$$

$$\frac{A_1}{A_2} = \frac{6}{6} \times \frac{4}{2}.$$

$$\frac{A_1}{A_2} = 1 \times \frac{4}{2}.$$

$$\frac{A_1}{A_2} = \frac{4}{2} = \frac{2}{1}.$$

From this exercise you might be led to prove

‖ COROLLARY 1

The ratio of the areas of two rectangles having equal bases is equal to the ratio of their altitudes.

DE—4. Determine the ratio of the areas of two rectangles that have bases of 3 units and 4 units, respectively, and altitudes of 5 units each.

Solution

$$\frac{A_1}{A_2} = \frac{b_1}{b_2} = \frac{h_1}{h_2}.$$

$$\frac{A_1}{A_2} = \frac{3}{4} \times \frac{5}{5}.$$

$$\frac{A_1}{A_2} = \frac{3}{4} \times 1.$$

$$\frac{A_1}{A_2} = \frac{3}{4}.$$

As a result of this exercise you might prove

COROLLARY 2

The ratio of the areas of two rectangles having equal altitudes is equal to the ratio of their bases.

DE—5. Determine the ratio of the areas of two rectangles that have equal bases and equal altitudes.

Solution

$$\frac{A_1}{A_2} = \frac{b_1}{b_2} \times \frac{h_1}{h_2}.$$

But, $b_1 = b_2$ and $h_1 = h_2$.

$$\frac{A_1}{A_2} = \frac{b_1}{b_1} \times \frac{h_1}{h_1}.$$

$$\frac{A_1}{A_2} = \frac{1}{1} \times \frac{1}{1} = \frac{1}{1}.$$

Therefore, the areas are equal.

Figures that have the same area will be called *equal figures*. Be sure to distinguish this term from *congruent* which is used to describe figures which are alike in both shape and size.

ASSUMPTION 43

All congruent figures have the same area.

Exercises

1. Prove Corollary 1 of Theorem 121.

2. Prove Corollary 2 of Theorem 121.

3. Prove the following theorem:

THEOREM 122

The area of a square whose sides measure *s* units is s^2 square units. $A = s^2$.

4. Find the area of a rectangle whose base is 8 inches and whose altitude is 6 inches.

5. Compare the areas of two rectangles having equal bases and equal altitudes.

6. Compare the areas of two squares whose sides are in the ratio of 2:1.

7. If the area of a square is 121 square inches, find its perimeter.

8. The diagonal of a rectangle is 17 inches and one side is 8 inches. Find the area of the rectangle.

9. Find the area of the shaded section in the diagram formed by two squares having sides of 30 inches and 17 inches, respectively.

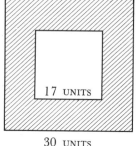

17 UNITS

Ex. 9

30 UNITS

10. Find the area of a square whose diagonal is 10 units.

11. If you double the base of a rectangle and leave the altitude the same, how is the area changed?

12. A diagonal of a rectangle is 14 inches and it makes an angle of $60°$ with one side. Find the area of the rectangle. Leave your answer in simplest radical form.

13. Find the area of a square if each side is $(x - 3)$ units.

14. Find the area of a rectangle inscribed in a circle with a radius of 10 inches if the base of the rectangle is 16 inches.

15. Express in terms of x the side of a square whose area is $81x^2$ square units.

16. How many square inches are there in the total surface of a cube that is 4 inches on an edge?

17. Find the area of a square circumscribed about a circle whose radius is 5 inches long.

18. Find the length of a side of a square whose area is equal to the area of a rectangle that has a base of $18x$ units and an altitude of $8x$ units.

Ex. 19

19. Show by areas in the diagram that $(a+b)^2 = a^2 + 2ab + b^2$.

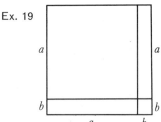

20. The base of a rectangle is denoted by b and its perimeter by p. Express its altitude in terms of p and b. Express its area in terms of p and b.

21. Write a formula to express the area of the shaded portion of this rectangle.

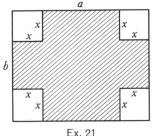

Ex. 21

22. If both the altitude and the base of a rectangle are doubled, how is the area changed? If they are tripled, how is the area changed?

23. The base of a rectangle measures $(x+y)$ units and the area of the rectangle is (x^2-y^2) square units. Express the length of the altitude of the rectangle in terms of x and y.

24. A square is inscribed in a circle whose radius is denoted by x. Express the area of the square in terms of x.

25. Find the area of a square inscribed in a circle whose diameter is 12 inches.

26. Derive the formula for the area of a square in terms of its diagonal.

THE AREA OF A PARALLELOGRAM

Before proving the theorem for finding the area of a parallelogram, it might be profitable to conduct a mathematical experiment. On a sheet of cardboard or stiff paper draw or construct a large parallelogram. Construct perpendiculars from two consecutive vertices of the parallelogram to the opposite side and the opposite side extended. (See the diagram.)

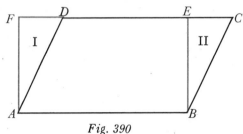

Fig. 390

Then cut out triangles I and II. They should coincide when placed together. They are congruent triangles and are, therefore, equal in area. By placing triangle II in the position occupied by triangle I, the resulting figure, *ABEF*, is a rectangle. The area of a rectangle is already known to be equal to the product of its base and altitude; therefore, the area of ☐*ABCD* is equal to the area of the rectangle.

‖Developmental Exercises

DE—1. Prove the following theorem:

‖**THEOREM 123**

The area of a parallelogram whose base measures *b* units and whose altitude to that base measures *h* units is *bh* square units. *A = bh*.

Solution

> **Given:** ☐*ABCD* with the length of base *AB* denoted by *b* and the length of altitude *DE* denoted by *h*.
>
> **Prove:** The area of ☐*ABCD = bh*.

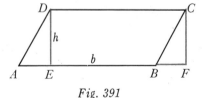

Fig. 391

> **Construction:** From *C* construct a perpendicular to *AB*, extended if necessary.

Proof:

STATEMENTS	REASONS
1. $\square ABCD$ with the length of base AB denoted by b and the length of altitude DE denoted by h.	1. Given.
2. Construct $CF \perp AB$. Extend AB if necessary.	2. Through a point outside a given line one, and only one, perpendicular can be constructed to the given line.
3. $DE \perp AB$.	3. Definition of altitude.
4. $CF \parallel DE$.	4. If two lines are perpendicular to the same line, they are parallel.
5. $DC \parallel AB$.	5. Why?
6. $DEFC$ is a $\square$.	6. If the opposite sides of a quadrilateral are parallel, the quadrilateral is a parallelogram.
7. $\angle F$ is a right angle.	7. Perpendicular lines form right angles.
8. $\square DEFC$ is a rectangle.	8. A parallelogram having a right angle is a rectangle.
9. Area of $DEFC = bh$.	9. Why?
10. $AD = BC$, $DE = CF$.	10. The opposite sides of a parallelogram are equal.
11. $\angle DEA$ is a right angle.	11. Reason 7.
12. $\triangle DEA \cong \triangle CFB$.	12. If two right triangles have the hypotenuse and leg of one equal respectively to the hypotenuse and leg of the other, the triangles are congruent.
13. $\square DECF = DEBC + \triangle CBF$, $\square ABCD = DEBC + \triangle DEA$.	13. The whole is equal to the sum of its parts.
14. $\triangle CBF = \triangle DEA$.	14. All congruent figures have the same area.
15. $\square DECF = \square ABCD$.	15. Why?
16. Area of $\square ABCD = bh$.	16. Why?

COROLLARY 1

The ratio of the areas of two parallelograms is equal to the ratio of the products of the lengths of their bases and altitudes. $\dfrac{A}{A'} = \dfrac{bh}{b'h'}$.

║**COROLLARY 2**

║**Parallelograms having equal bases and equal altitudes are equal.**

║**COROLLARY 3**

║**The ratio of the areas of two parallelograms having equal altitudes**

║**is equal to the ratio of the lengths of their bases.** $\dfrac{A}{A'}=\dfrac{b}{b'}.$

║**COROLLARY 4**

║**The ratio of the areas of two parallelograms having equal bases is**

║**equal to the ratio of the lengths of their altitudes.** $\dfrac{A}{A'}=\dfrac{h}{h'}.$

DE—2. $ABCD$ is a parallelogram, $AB=$ 12 units, $AD=8$ units, and $\angle A=$ 45°. Find the area of $ABCD$. Leave your answer in simplest radical form.

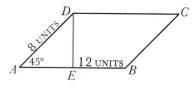

Fig. 392

Solution

  AB is the base of $\square ABCD$ and you know that its length is 12 units. To find the altitude, construct, or draw, a perpendicular, DE, to base AB. A right triangle is formed and the length of DE can be determined. The side opposite a 45° angle in a right triangle is equal to one-half the hypotenuse times $\sqrt{2}$. $DE=4\sqrt{2}$.

$$A=bh.$$
$$A=12(4\sqrt{2}).$$
$$A=48\sqrt{2} \text{ square units.}$$

Exercises

1. Find the area of a parallelogram whose base is $5x$ units and whose altitude is $3x$ units.

2. Two adjacent sides of a parallelogram are 12 units and 30 units and they include an angle of 150°. Find the area of the parallelogram.

3. The areas of two parallelograms are equal and their altitudes are 6 units and 9 units respectively. The base of the first parallelogram is 12 units. Find the length of the base of the second parallelogram.

4. In $\square ABCD$, $\angle A = 45°$, $AB = 25$ units, and $AD = 10$ units. Find the area of $\square ABCD$. Leave your answer in simplest radical form.

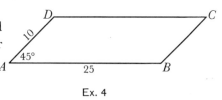

Ex. 4

5. Find the area of a parallelogram whose base is $(a+4)$ units and whose altitude is $(3a-2)$ units.

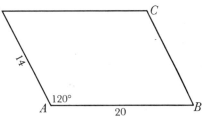

6. In $\square ABCD$, $\angle A = 120°$, $AD = 14$ units, and $AB = 20$ units. Find the area of $\square ABCD$. Leave your answer in simplest radical form.

Ex. 6

7. The sides of a parallelogram are 13 inches and 18 inches, respectively, and include an angle of 30°. Find the area of the parallelogram.

8. If the dimensions of a parallelogram are doubled, how does the area of the parallelogram change?

9. Two parallelograms have bases of 8 units and 12 units and their altitudes are 6 units and 9 units, respectively. Find the ratio of their areas.

10. What change occurs in the area of a parallelogram when the angle included between the base and a side changes but the length of the base and side remain the same?

11. Two parallelograms have equal altitudes and bases of 16 inches and 24 inches respectively. The area of the larger parallelogram is 120 square inches. Find the area of the smaller parallelogram.

12. A parallelogram is equal in area to a rectangle whose base is 14 inches and whose altitude is 8 inches. The base of the parallelogram exceeds the altitude drawn to the base by 9 inches. Find the lengths of the altitude and base of the parallelogram.

13. The altitudes of two parallelograms are equal and their bases are $6a$ units and $8a$ units. What is the ratio of their areas?

14. Construct a parallelogram. Then, by constructing lines parallel to one side of the parallelogram, divide the parallelogram into three equal parallelograms.

15. Two parallelograms have equal areas. If the ratio of their bases is $\frac{3}{2}$, what is the ratio of their altitudes?

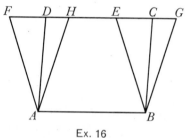

16. In the diagram $ABCD$, $ABEF$, and $ABGH$ are parallelograms with upper bases in the same straight line and with a common lower base. What generalization can you make concerning the parallelograms? Why?

Ex. 16

17. Find the length of the side of a square whose area is equal to the area of a parallelogram whose base is $24y$ inches and whose altitude is $6y$ inches.

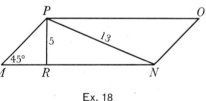

18. In $\square MNOP$, $\angle M = 45°$, altitude $PR = 5$ units, and diagonal $PN = 13$ units. Find the perimeter and the area of the parallelogram. Leave your answer in its simplest radical form.

Ex. 18

19. The area of a parallelogram is $(2x^2 + 3x - 12)$ square units and the base is $(2x - 3)$ units. Find the length of the altitude drawn to the base.

20. Prove that the line segment joining the midpoints of the bases of a parallelogram divides it into two equal parallelograms.

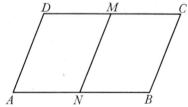

Ex. 20

THE AREA OF A TRIANGLE

The following exercise will help you discover a relationship for finding the area of a triangle. Construct a parallelogram and draw one of its diagonals dividing the parallelogram into two triangles. Then cut out the triangles and place one upon the other. You will notice that the triangles coincide since a diagonal of a parallelogram divides the parallelogram into two congruent triangles. You have also learned that congruent polygons are equal in area. Therefore, each triangle is equal to one-half the parallelogram. A deductive proof for this generalization is given in the following developmental exercises.

The aluminum dome of this convention hall is composed of many triangles. In order to determine its total area, the area of each triangle must be known.

Developmental Exercises

DE—1. Prove the following theorem:

THEOREM 124

The area of a triangle whose base measures b units and whose altitude to the base measures h units is $\frac{1}{2}bh$ square units.

Solution

> **Given:** $\triangle ABC$ with length of base BC denoted by b and length of altitude AE denoted by h.
> **Prove:** Area of $\triangle ABC = \frac{1}{2}bh$.

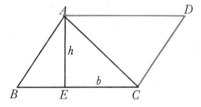

Fig. 393

> **Construction:** Through A construct $AD \parallel BC$; through C construct $CD \parallel AB$. AD and CD intersect at D.

Proof:

STATEMENTS	REASONS
1. $\triangle ABC$ with length of base BC denoted by b and length of altitude AE denoted by h.	1. Given.
2. Through A draw $AD \parallel BC$ and through C draw $CD \parallel AB$. AD and CD intersect at D.	2. Through a given point outside a given line one, and only one, line may be constructed parallel to a given line.
3. $ABCD$ is a parallelogram with base of b units and altitude of h units.	3. A quadrilateral whose opposite sides are parallel is a parallelogram.
4. $\triangle ABC = \frac{1}{2}\square ABCD$.	4. A diagonal divides a parallelogram into two congruent triangles.
5. Area of $\square ABCD = bh$.	5. The area of a parallelogram whose base measures b units and whose altitude to that base measures h units is bh square units.
6. $\therefore$ Area of $\triangle ABC = \frac{1}{2}bh$.	6. A quantity may be substituted for an equal quantity in an expression without altering the value of the expression.

‖**COROLLARY 1**

‖The ratio of the areas of two triangles is equal to the ratio of the
‖products of their bases and altitudes.

‖**COROLLARY 2**

‖Triangles having equal bases and equal altitudes are equal.

‖**COROLLARY 3**

‖The ratio of the areas of two triangles having equal altitudes is equal
‖to the ratio of their bases.

‖**COROLLARY 4**

‖The ratio of the areas of two triangles having equal bases is equal to
‖the ratio of their altitudes.

‖**COROLLARY 5**

‖The area of a triangle is equal to one-half the area of a parallelogram
‖having an equal base and altitude equal respectively to the base
‖and altitude of the triangle.

DE—2. Find the area of a triangle whose base measures $(2x-3)$ units and
whose altitude measures $6x$ units.

Solution

$$A = \tfrac{1}{2}bh.$$
$$A = \tfrac{1}{2}(2x-3)(6x).$$
$$A = (2x-3)(3x).$$
$$A = (6x^2 - 9x) \text{ square units.}$$

DE—3. Find the area of an equilateral triangle the length of whose side is
denoted by s.

Solution

$A = \tfrac{1}{2}\, bh.$

Before the area can be computed,
you must know the length of the
altitude. Construct the altitude AD
to CB. Recall Corollary 3 of Theorem
119. The length of the altitude of an
equilateral · triangle is equal to
$\dfrac{s}{2}\sqrt{3}$ where s represents the length
of a side. Therefore,

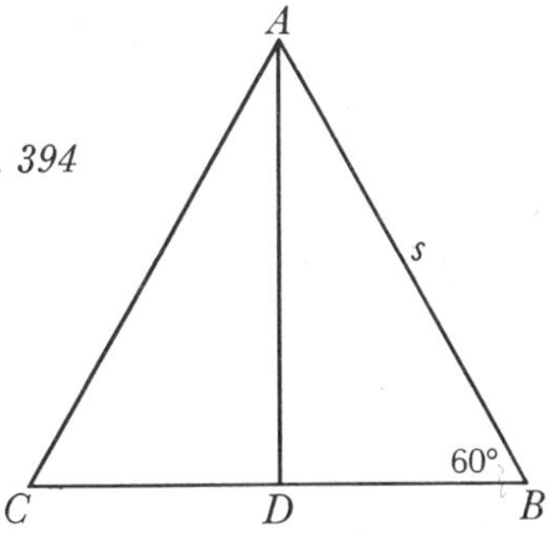

Fig. 394

$$A = \frac{s}{2}\left(\frac{s}{2}\sqrt{3}\right) \text{ or } A = \frac{s^2\sqrt{3}}{4}.$$

Exercises

In the following exercises leave your answers, if not whole numbers, in simplest radical form.

1. What is the ratio of the areas of two triangles that have altitudes of 6 inches and 8 inches if the base of each triangle measures 12 inches?

2. Find the area of an isosceles triangle whose vertex angle is $120°$ and whose base is 10 inches.

3. Find the base of a triangle whose area is 120 square feet and whose altitude is 12 feet.

4. Find the altitude of an equilateral triangle whose area is $36\sqrt{3}$ square units.

5. The base and altitude of one triangle are 14 inches and 8 inches and the base and altitude of a second triangle are 10 inches and 7 inches. What is the ratio of the area of the first triangle to the area of the second triangle?

6. D and E are midpoints of AB and AC in $\triangle ABC$. Find the following ratios:

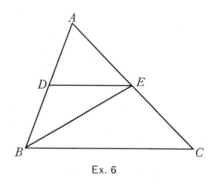

a. $\dfrac{\triangle ADE}{\triangle BDE}$.

b. $\dfrac{\triangle ADE}{\triangle ABE}$.

c. $\dfrac{\triangle ABE}{\triangle ABC}$.

d. $\dfrac{\triangle ADE}{\triangle ABC}$.

Ex. 6

7. The medians of a triangle divide it into six equal triangles. True or false? Give a reason for your answer.

8. Triangles are constructed with a given line segment as a base and their opposite vertices on a line parallel to the given line segment. What generalizations can you make about their areas? Why?

9. Find the area of an equilateral triangle whose altitude is $4\sqrt{3}$ units.

10. If the altitude of an isosceles triangle is doubled but the base remains the same, what change takes place in the area? If the base is doubled and the altitude remains the same? If both the base and the altitude are doubled? Are your answers correct if the triangle is not isosceles? Give a reason for your answer.

11. The altitude of a triangle is two-thirds the length of the base to which it is drawn. The area of a triangle is 27 square units. Find the lengths of the altitude and the base of the triangle.

12. The side of an equilateral triangle is 8 inches. Find the length of the side of an equilateral triangle with twice the area.

13. One leg of a right triangle measures 17 units and the hypotenuse is 19 units. Find the area of the triangle.

14. Find the area of $\triangle DEF$.

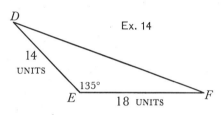

Ex. 14

15. Find the area of an isosceles right triangle whose hypotenuse is 8 inches.

16. Two sides of a triangle are 10 inches and 16 inches. The altitude of the third side is 8 inches. Find the area of the triangle.

17. Two sides of a triangle are 26 inches and 16 inches. The projection of the longer side on the shorter side is 10 inches. Find the area of the triangle.

18. Two equilateral triangles have an altitude of one equal to the side of the other. Find the ratio of their areas.

19. The area of a triangle is equal to one-half the product of its perimeter and the radius of its inscribed circle. True or false? Give a reason for your answer.

20. The length of the base of an isosceles triangle is denoted by b and the lengths of the equal sides are denoted by a. Find the area of the triangle.

THE AREA OF A TRAPEZOID

The previous formulas for the areas of a rectangle, parallelogram, and a triangle may be used in establishing a formula for the area of a trapezoid. In order to help you discover the relationships between a trapezoid and the other polygons you have studied, answer the following questions.

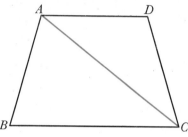

(*1*) In trapezoid *ABCD* what is the function of *AC*?

(*2*) How are sides *AD* and *BC* related? Why?

(*3*) How can you find the area of △*ADC*?

(*4*) What is the altitude of △*ADC*?

Fig. 395

(*5*) How can you find the area of △*ABC*?

(*6*) Compare the altitudes of △*ADC* and △*ABC*.

(*7*) How can you find the area of trapezoid *ABCD*?

Developmental Exercises

DE—1. Prove the following theorem:

> **THEOREM 125**
>
> **The area of a trapezoid whose bases measure *b* and *b'* units and whose altitude measures *h* units is $\frac{1}{2} h(b+b')$ square units.**

Solution

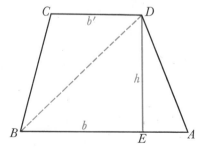

Given: Trapezoid *ABCD* with the length of the base *AB* denoted by *b*, the length of the base *CD* denoted by *b'*, and the length of the altitude *DE* denoted by *h*.

Prove: $A = \frac{1}{2} h(b+b')$.

Construction: Construct *DB*.

Fig. 396

Proof:

STATEMENTS	REASONS
1. Trapezoid *ABCD* with the length of base *AB* denoted by *b*, the length of base *CD* denoted by *b'*, and the length of the altitude *DE* denoted by *h*.	1. Given.
2. Draw *BD*.	2. Two points determine a line.
3. *h* denotes the length of the altitudes of $\triangle ABD$ and $\triangle BCD$.	3. Why?
4. Area of $\triangle ABD = \frac{1}{2}bh$. Area of $\triangle BCD = \frac{1}{2}b'h$.	4. The area of a triangle whose base measures *b* units and whose altitude to that base measures *h* units is $\frac{1}{2}bh$ square units.
5. $\triangle ABD + \triangle BCD = \frac{1}{2}bh + \frac{1}{2}b'h$.	5. If equals are added to equals, the sums are equal.
6. Trapezoid $ABCD = \triangle ABD + \triangle BCD$.	6. The whole is equal to the sum of its parts.
7. Area of trapezoid $ABCD = \frac{1}{2}h(b+b')$.	7. A quantity may be substituted for its equal in an expression without altering the value of the expression.

DE—2. The altitude of a trapezoid is 8 inches and its bases are 10 inches and 14 inches. Find the area of the trapezoid.

Solution

$$A = \frac{1}{2}h(b+b').$$
$$A = \frac{1}{2}(8)(10+14).$$
$$A = 4(24).$$
$$A = 96 \text{ square inches.}$$

Exercises

In the following exercises leave the answers that are not rational numbers in simplest radical form.

1. The altitude of a trapezoid is 6 inches. The area of the trapezoid is 111 square inches. If the difference of the bases is 11 inches, find the length of the longer base.

2. A trapezoid is inscribed in a circle whose diameter is 40 inches. The parallel sides are 12 inches and 16 inches from the center of the circle and on opposite sides of the center. Find the area of the trapezoid.

3. Find the area of a trapezoid cut off by a line segment joining the midpoints of two sides of an equilateral triangle whose side is 6 inches.

4. The altitude of a trapezoid is xy units, the upper base is $(3x-y)$ units, and the lower base is $(3x+y)$ units. Find the area of the trapezoid.

5. In trapezoid $ABCD$, $\angle A=30°$, base $CD=18$ units, base $AB=26$ units, and $AD=16$ units. Find the area of the trapezoid.

6. The bases of a trapezoid are 6 feet and 8 feet and the nonparallel sides form 45° angles with the lower base. What is the area of the trapezoid?

7. The area of a trapezoid is $\frac{3}{4}$ the area of a rectangle. The trapezoid and the rectangle have equal altitudes. The base of the rectangle and the lower base of the trapezoid each is 14 inches. Find the length of the upper base of the trapezoid.

8. A triangle and a trapezoid have equal altitudes of 8 inches. Find the length of the base of the triangle if the median of the trapezoid is 14 inches and the areas are equal.

9. Prove that the area of a trapezoid is equal to the product of the lengths of its altitude and median.

10. If the two bases and the altitude of a trapezoid are doubled, how is the area changed?

11. In $\triangle ABC$, $BC=25$ inches, altitude $AG=10$ inches, $AF=6$ inches, and $DE \parallel BC$. Find the area of $BCED$.

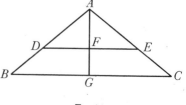

Ex. 11

12. In trapezoid $ABCD$, the nonparallel sides, AD and BC, are each 17 units and the bases, DC and AB, are 21 and 37 units, respectively. Find the area of trapezoid $ABCD$.

THE AREA OF A RHOMBUS

Recall that a rhombus is a parallelogram with a pair of equal adjacent sides. Since the rhombus is a parallelogram, the formula $A = bh$ may be used to find its area. It is possible though, to use another formula to find the area of a rhombus.

Developmental Exercises

DE—1. Prove the following theorem:

> **THEOREM 126**
> **The area of a rhombus is equal to one-half the product of the lengths of its diagonals.**

Solution

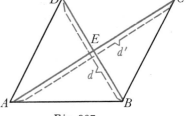

Fig. 397

> **Given:** Rhombus $ABCD$ with diagonals DB and AC intersecting at E. The length of DB is denoted by d. The length of AC is denoted by d'.
>
> **Prove:** $A = \frac{1}{2}dd'$.

Proof:

STATEMENTS	REASONS
1. Rhombus $ABCD$ with diagonals DB and AC intersecting at E.	1. Given.
2. $DB \perp AC$.	2. The diagonals of a rhombus are perpendicular to each other.
3. CE is the altitude of $\triangle BCD$.	3. Why?
4. Area of $\triangle BCD = \frac{1}{2}CE(BD)$, Area of $\triangle BAD = \frac{1}{2}AE(BD)$.	4. Why?
5. $\triangle BCD + \triangle BAD = \frac{1}{2}CE(BD) + \frac{1}{2}AE(BD)$.	5. If equals are added to equals the sums are equal.
6. Rhombus $ABCD = \triangle BCD + \triangle BAD$.	6. The whole is equal to the sum of its parts.
7. Area of rhombus $ABCD = \frac{1}{2}BD(AC)$ or $= \frac{1}{2}dd'$.	7. A quantity may be substituted for its equal in an expression without altering the value of the expression.

DE—2. Find the area of a rhombus whose diagonals are 12 feet and 16 feet.

Solution

$$A = \tfrac{1}{2}dd',$$
$$A = \tfrac{1}{2}(12)(16),$$
$$A = 6(16),$$
$$A = 96 \text{ square feet.}$$

Exercises

In the following exercises leave your answers that are not rational numbers in simplest radical form.

1. Find the area of a rhombus if its diagonals are $4x$ and $3y$.

2. The area of a rhombus is 192 square units and one diagonal is 16 units. How long is the other diagonal?

3. The perimeter of a rhombus is 40 inches and its shorter diagonal is 12 inches. Find its area.

4. The length of a side of a rhombus is denoted by s. The shorter diagonal is equal to a side. Represent the length of each diagonal and the area of the rhombus.

5. The diagonals of a rhombus are in the ratio 4:5 and the area of the rhombus is 20 square units. Find the length of each diagonal.

6. The area of a rhombus is 16 square inches. Find the length of the diagonals if one is one-half the other.

7. Find the area of a rhombus whose side is 15 units and one of whose diagonals is 18 units.

8. Find the length of a side of a rhombus whose area is 400 square units and diagonal is 16 units.

9. The diagonals of a rhombus are 16 inches and 20 inches. Find the perimeter of the rhombus.

10. The diagonals of a rhombus are in the ratio of 3:4 and the area of the rhombus is 108 square inches.
  a. Find the length of each diagonal.
  b. Find the length of a side of the rhombus.
  c. Find the perimeter of the rhombus.
  d. Find the length of the altitude of the rhombus.

CONSTRUCTING EQUAL FIGURES

In this section you will learn how to construct a polygon equal to a given polygon. Remember that for polygons to be equal it is only necessary that they have equal areas. All exercises should include the given data, an analysis, and the final construction.

Developmental Exercises

DE—1. Construct a rectangle, having a given base, equal to a given parallelogram.

Solution

    Given: b, the base of the rectangle to be constructed and $\square ABCD$ with altitude BE whose length is denoted by h'. Let b' denote the length of DC.

    Analysis:
Area of the rectangle $= bh$.
Area of the parallelogram $= b'h'$.

Since the two areas are to be equal $bh = b'h'$ or $\dfrac{b}{b'} = \dfrac{h'}{h}$. Knowing b, b', and h', can h be determined?

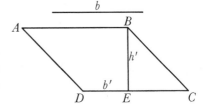

    Construction: Since b, b', and h' are known, to find h you can use the construction for a fourth proportional.

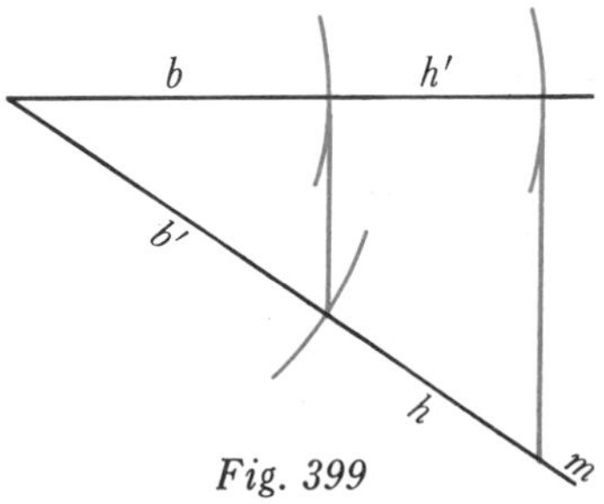

Fig. 399

The length of h is now determined. With b, the base, and h, the altitude, construct the required rectangle.

Rectangle $ABCD$ has an area equal to the given parallelogram.

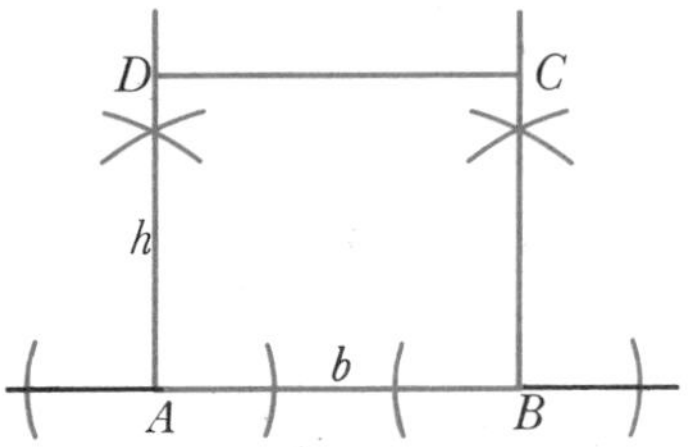

Fig. 400

DE—2. Construct a square equal to a given triangle.

  Solution

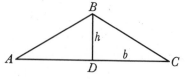

   Given: $\triangle ABC$ with the length of
       base AC denoted by b and
       the length of altitude BD
       denoted by h.

  Analysis:
  Area of the triangle $=\frac{1}{2}bh$.
  Area of the square $=s^2$.

Fig. 401

  Since the two areas are to be equal, $\frac{1}{2}bh=s^2$ or $\dfrac{\frac{1}{2}b}{s}=\dfrac{s}{h}$.

  Since b and h are known, can s be determined?

  Construction: From the analysis
you see that the side of the square
is the mean proportional between
one-half the base of the triangle and
the altitude of the triangle. Therefore
to determine s you may use the construction for the mean proportional.

  Square $ABCD$ has an area equal to
the area of the given triangle.

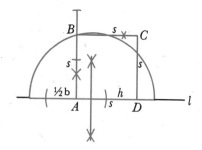

Exercises

Fig. 402

 1. Construct a rectangle with a given base equal to a given rhombus.

 2. Construct an equilateral triangle. Construct a square equal to
that triangle.

 3. Construct a rectangle with a given base equal to a given square.

 4. Construct a square equal to a given rectangle.

 5. Construct an oblique, scalene triangle equal to a given square.

 6. Construct a right triangle equal to a given square.

 7. Construct an isosceles triangle equal to a given square.

 8. Given the altitude and an obtuse angle, construct a parallelogram
equal to a given rectangle.

 9. Construct a triangle equal to twice the area of a given square.

 10. Construct a rectangle equal to a given irregular quadrilateral.

DE—3. Construct a triangle equal to a given polygon.

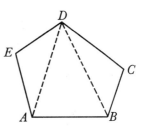

Solution
   Given: Polygon *ABCD*.

Fig. 403

Analysis:
   Polygon *ABCDE* can be divided into three triangles. A triangle is to be constructed equal to the sum of these three triangles.

Construction:
● Extend *AB* in both directions.
● Through *C* construct *CF* parallel to *DB*.
● Draw *DF*.
● Through *E* construct *EG* parallel to *AD*.
● Draw *GD*.
● △*DFG* is equal in area to polygon *ABCDE*.

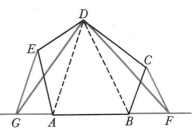

Fig. 404

   Notice that △*DGF* is formed by three triangles, *AGD*, *ABD*, and *BFD*. The polygon also contains three triangles *AED*, *ABD*, and *BCD*.
   △*DGF* = △*AGD* + △*ABD* + △*BFD*.
   ABCDE = △*AED* + △*ABD* + △*BCD*.
   △*AED* = △*AGD* since both triangles have the same base, *AD*, and equal altitudes. (Two parallel lines, *EG* and *AD*, are everywhere equidistant.)
   △*ABD* = △*ABD* by identity.
   △*BFD* = △*BCD* since both triangles have the same base, *DB*, and equal altitudes. How do you know that the altitudes of these triangles are equal?
   Therefore, △*DGF* = *ABCDE*.

Exercises

   1. Construct a rectangle with a given base equal to another given rectangle.

   2. Construct a parallelogram with a given base and acute angle equal to a given square.

3. Construct an isosceles triangle equal to a given triangle.

4. Construct a square equal to a given trapezoid.

5. Construct a square equal to a given parallelogram.

6. Construct a square equal to a given quadrilateral.

7. Construct a triangle with a given base equal to a given parallelogram.

8. Construct a triangle with a given altitude equal to a given triangle.

9. Construct a triangle equal to a given quadrilateral.

10. Construct a triangle equal to a given hexagon.

11. Construct a square equal to the sum of two given squares.

12. Construct a right triangle with a given hypotenuse equal to a given rectangle.

13. Given one diagonal of a rhombus, construct the rhombus equal to a given parallelogram.

14. Construct a square equal in area to a rhombus whose diagonals are given line segments, a and b, of unequal lengths.

AREAS OF SIMILAR POLYGONS

If each side of a square is four units, into how many one unit squares can it be divided? Each of the small squares is similar to the original square. What is the ratio of their sides? What is the ratio of their areas? In order to compare the areas of similar polygons, study the following developmental exercises.

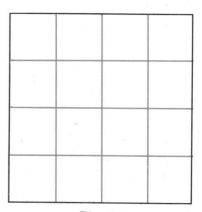

Fig. 405

Developmental Exercises

DE—1. Prove the following theorem:

THEOREM 127

The areas of two similar triangles have the same ratio as the squares of the length of any two corresponding sides.

Solution

Given: $\triangle ABC$ with altitude CD whose length is denoted by h.
$\triangle A'B'C'$ with altitude $C'D'$ whose length is denoted by h'.

Prove: $\dfrac{\text{Area of } \triangle ABC}{\text{Area of } \triangle A'B'C'} = \dfrac{(AB)^2}{(A'B')^2} = \text{etc.}$

Fig. 406

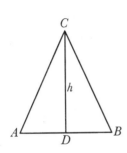
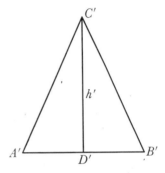

Proof:

STATEMENTS	REASONS
1. $\triangle ABC \sim \triangle A'B'C'$.	1. Given.
2. Area of $\triangle ABC = \frac{1}{2}h \cdot AB$. Area of $\triangle A'B'C' = \frac{1}{2}h' \cdot A'B'$.	2. The area of a triangle whose base measures b units and whose altitude measures h units is $\frac{1}{2}bh$ square units.
3. $\dfrac{\text{Area of } \triangle ABC}{\text{Area of } \triangle A'B'C'} = \dfrac{h \cdot AB}{h' \cdot A'B'}$.	3. If equals are divided by equals the quotients are equal.
4. $\dfrac{h}{h'} = \dfrac{AB}{A'B'}$.	4. If two triangles are similar, the corresponding altitudes have the same ratio as any two corresponding sides.
5. $\dfrac{\text{Area of } \triangle ABC}{\text{Area of } \triangle A'B'C'} = \dfrac{AB}{A'B'} \times$ $\dfrac{AB}{A'B'} = \dfrac{(AB)^2}{(A'B')^2} = \text{etc.}$	5. A quantity may be substituted for its equal.

DE—2. Prove the following theorem:

| **THEOREM 128**

The areas of two similar polygons have the same ratio as the squares of any two corresponding sides.

Solution

Given: Any similar polygons $ABCDE$ and $A'B'C'D'E'$ with corresponding vertices A and A', etc. and corresponding sides AB and $A'B'$, etc.

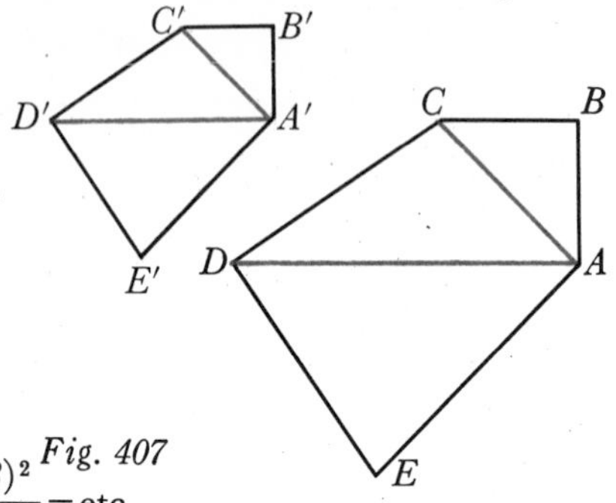

Prove: $\dfrac{\text{Area of } ABCDE}{\text{Area of } A'B'C'D'E'} = \dfrac{(AB)^2}{(A'B')^2} = \text{etc.}$

Fig. 407

Construction: Draw diagonals AC, AD, $A'C'$, and $A'D'$.

Proof:

STATEMENTS	REASONS
1. AC, AD, $A'C'$, and $A'D'$ exist.	1. Two points determine a line.
2. $\triangle ABC \sim \triangle A'B'C'$, $\triangle CAD \sim \triangle C'A'D'$, $\triangle ADE \sim \triangle A'D'E'$.	2. Why?
3. Supply the necessary proportions.	3. The areas of two similar triangles have the same ratio as the squares of any two corresponding sides.
4. $\dfrac{\text{Area of } \triangle ABC}{\text{Area of } \triangle A'B'C'} =$ $\dfrac{\text{Area of } \triangle CAD}{\text{Area of } \triangle C'A'D'} =$ $\dfrac{\text{Area of } \triangle ADE}{\text{Area of } \triangle A'D'E'}$.	4. Quantities equal to the same or equal quantities are equal to each other.
5. Area of $ABCDE = $ Area of $(\triangle ABC + \triangle CAD + \triangle ADE)$. Area of $A'B'C'D'E' = $ Area of $(\triangle A'B'C' + \triangle C'A'D' + \triangle A'D'E')$.	5. The whole is equal to the sum of its parts.
6. $\dfrac{\text{Area of } ABCDE}{\text{Area of } A'B'C'D'} = \dfrac{(AB)^2}{(A'B')^2} =$ etc.	6. Why?

DE—3. The areas of two similar triangles are in the ratio of 25:9. A side of the larger triangle is 10 units. Find the length of the corresponding side in the smaller triangle.

Solution

$$\frac{A}{A'} = \frac{s^2}{(s')^2}.$$

$$\frac{25}{9} = \frac{(10)^2}{(s')^2}.$$

$$\frac{25}{9} = \frac{100}{(s')^2}.$$

$$25(s')^2 = 900.$$

$$(s')^2 = 36.$$

$$s' = 6 \text{ units.}$$

DE—4. In two similar polygons, two corresponding sides are 5 units and 30 units. The area of the smaller polygon is 50 square units. Find the area of the larger polygon.

Solution

$$\frac{A}{A'} = \frac{s^2}{(s')^2}.$$

$$\frac{50}{A'} = \frac{(5)^2}{(30)^2}.$$

$$\frac{50}{A'} = \frac{25}{900}.$$

$$25A' = 45000.$$

$$A' = 1800 \text{ square units.}$$

Exercises

1. The corresponding sides of two similar polygons are in the ratio of 4:5. Find the ratio of their areas.

2. The corresponding sides of two similar polygons are in the ratio of 1:3. Find the ratio of their perimeters and of their areas.

3. Two polygons are similar. The area of the first polygon is 208 square feet and one of its sides is 12 feet. If the corresponding side of the second polygon is 16 feet, determine the area of the larger polygon.

4. The ratio of the areas of two similar polygons is 8:3. If the longest side of the smaller polygon measures 6 feet, find the length of the longest side of the larger polygon.

5. By what number must the side of a square be multiplied to triple its area?

6. If the side of a square is multiplied by 16, by what number is its area multiplied?

7. Construct a triangle that is similar to a given triangle and equal to one-fourth of it.

8. Construct a quadrilateral similar to a given irregular quadrilateral and nine times as large.

9. The areas of two similar polygons are 128 square inches and 200 square inches. If a side of the first is 12 inches, find the length of the corresponding side of the second.

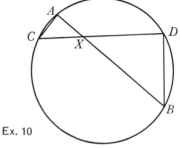

10. If $CX=3$ units and $CD=8$ units, what is the ratio of the area of $\triangle XAC$ to $\triangle XBD$?

Ex. 10

11. Given: $AB \perp BC$, $DE \perp BC$, $DE = 2\sqrt{2}$ units, $CE = \dfrac{3\sqrt{2}}{2}$ units, and $BE = \sqrt{2}$ units. Find the lengths of AB, BC, and AC.

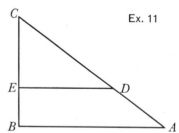

Ex. 11

12. If the altitude of one equilateral triangle is equal to the side of another equilateral triangle, find the ratio of their areas.

13. The ratio of the sides of two squares is 1:3. If the difference of the areas of the two squares is 288 inches, find the length of the side of the largest square.

14. The sum of the corresponding sides of two similar triangles is 12 inches. If the ratio of their areas is 3:1, find the length of the above mentioned sides.

THE AREA OF A REGULAR POLYGON

Recall that *a regular polygon is both equiangular and equilateral.* Two regular polygons having the same number of sides are similar. Consequently, all of the theorems pertaining to similar polygons apply to these regular polygons.

Every regular polygon of *n* sides can be divided into *n* congruent triangles. Each of these is an isosceles triangle with a side of the polygon as a base and the common center of the inscribed and circumscribed circles as the vertex. This common center is called the *center of the polygon.* The radius of the circumscribed circle is the *radius of the polygon.* The radius of the inscribed circle is the *apothem of the polygon.* The angle formed by radii to any two consecutive vertices of the polygon is called the *central angle of the polygon.* Each of these central angles measures $\dfrac{360°}{n}$, where *n* denotes the number of sides of the polygon.

Fig. 408

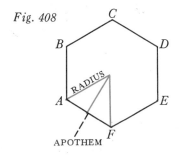

The Pentagon Building in Arlington, Virginia, is the largest office building in the world. It has an area of 3,695,130 square feet.

Developmental Exercises

DE—1. Prove the following theorem:

> ### THEOREM 129
>
> **The area of a regular polygon is equal to one-half the product of its perimeter and the length of its apothem.**

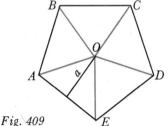

Solution

Given: Any regular polygon *ABCDE* with the length of the apothem denoted by *a* and the perimeter denoted by *p*.

Prove: Area of $ABCDE = \frac{1}{2}ap$.

Fig. 409

Construction: Draw radii *OA, OB, OC, OD*.

Proof:

STATEMENTS	REASONS
1. Draw *OA, OB, OC, OD,* and *OE*.	1. Two points determine a line.
2. $\triangle AOB \cong \triangle BOC$, $\triangle BOC \cong \triangle COD$, $\triangle COD \cong \triangle DOE$, $\triangle DOE \cong \triangle EOA$, $\triangle EOA \cong \triangle AOB$.	2. **s.s.s. = s.s.s.** You supply the missing steps.
3. All of the triangles are congruent.	3. Why?
4. The altitudes (apothems) of these triangles are equal.	4. Why?
5. $\triangle AOB = \frac{1}{2}a(AB)$, $\triangle BOC = \frac{1}{2}a(BC)$, $\triangle COD = \frac{1}{2}a(CD)$, $\triangle DOE = \frac{1}{2}a(DE)$, $\triangle EOA = \frac{1}{2}a(EA)$.	5. The area of a triangle having a base of *b* units and an altitude of *h* units is $\frac{1}{2}bh$ square units.
6. $\triangle AOB + \triangle BOC + \triangle COD + \triangle DOE + \triangle EOA = ABCDE$.	6. The whole is equal to the sum of its parts.
7. $\triangle AOB + \triangle BOC + \triangle COD + \triangle DOE + \triangle EOA = \frac{1}{2}a(AB) + \frac{1}{2}a(BC) + \frac{1}{2}a(CD) + \frac{1}{2}a(DE) + \frac{1}{2}a(EA)$.	7. If equals are added to equals the sums are equal.
8. Polygon $ABCDE = \frac{1}{2}ap$.	8. Supply the missing statements and reasons.

DE—2. The perimeter of a regular polygon is 20 inches and the length of its apothem is 3 inches. Find the area of the polygon.

Solution

$$A = \tfrac{1}{2}ap,$$
$$A = \tfrac{1}{2}(3)(20),$$
$$A = 30 \text{ square inches.}$$

Exercises

1. The sides of two regular pentagons are 4 inches and 6 inches, respectively. How does the area of the smaller pentagon compare with the area of the larger one?

2. Find the length of the apothem and the area of an equilateral triangle which is circumscribed about a circle the length of whose radius is 5 units. Leave your answer in simplest radical form.

3. The ratio of the areas of two regular polygons of the same number of sides is 1:4. If a side of the larger polygon is 6 units, find the length of the corresponding side of the smaller polygon.

4. Find the area of a regular hexagon which is circumscribed about a circle whose radius is 4 units.

5. A regular decagon has a side of length x and an apothem of length a. Write a formula for finding its area in terms of x and a.

6. The area of a regular octagon is 36 times the area of another regular octagon. If the length of a side of the smaller polygon is 3 inches, find the length of a side of the larger polygon.

7. Find the length of the apothem of a regular polygon whose area is 138 square units and whose perimeter is 46 units.

8. The length of the side and the length of the radius of a regular polygon of x sides are given. If the number of sides is doubled but the length of the radius remains constant, what change takes place in the length of the side?

9. The area of a regular octagon is $6\tfrac{1}{4}$ times the area of another regular octagon. What is the ratio of their perimeters?

10. A regular hexagon is inscribed in a circle having a 5 inch radius. Find the perimeter and the area of the hexagon.

THE AREA OF A CIRCLE

Inscribe a regular hexagon in a large circle. Then bisect the sides of the hexagon and locate the midpoint of the arc of each side. Connect these midpoints to the vertices of the hexagon. What new figure is formed? If you continued this process, how many sides would the next figure contain? What geometric figure would be approached as a limit if this process was continued indefinitely? What is its perimeter? Draw the apothem in each polygon. What length do these approach as a limit as the number of sides of the polygon increases?

Fig. 410

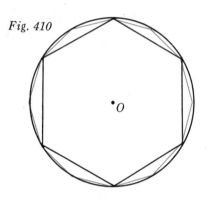

In the previous lesson you discovered that **the area of a regular polygon is equal to one-half the product of its perimeter and the length of its apothem.** It might be concluded that *a circle is a polygon with an infinite number of sides and whose apothem is the radius of the circumscribed circle.* Thus, **the area of a circle would be equal to one-half the product of its circumference and the length of its radius.** This conclusion is correct and will be accepted as an assumption.

ASSUMPTION 44

The area of a circle is equal to one-half the product of the length of the radius and its circumference.

It can also be shown that the circumference of a circle varies directly as the diameter. That is, as a diameter increases in length, the circumference increases; as a diameter decreases in length, the circumference decreases. The constant of variation is called π (pronounced pī).

ASSUMPTION 45

The ratio of the circumference of any circle to the length of its diameter is the constant π.

From these relationships many new formulas may be obtained.

Developmental Exercises

DE—1. Obtain a formula for the circumference of any circle in terms of the length of its radius.

Solution

Let r represent the length of the radius; d represent the length of the diameter; and C the circumference.

$$\frac{C}{d} = \pi.$$
$$C = \pi d.$$
$$C = 2\pi r.$$

Thus, the following corollary has been proved.

COROLLARY 1

The circumference of any circle is equal to the product of 2π and the length of its radius.

DE—2. Obtain a formula for the area of any circle in terms of the length of its **a.** radius **b.** diameter.

Solution

Let A represent the area of any circle, C represent its circumference, r represent the length of its radius, and d represent the length of its diameter.

a. $A = \frac{1}{2}rC.$
$C = 2\pi r.$
$A = \frac{1}{2}r(2\pi r).$
$A = \pi r^2.$

Thus, the following corollary has been proved.

COROLLARY 2

The area of any circle is equal to the product of the square of the length of its radius and π.

b. $A = \pi r^2.$
$r = \frac{1}{2}d.$
$A = \pi(\frac{1}{2}d)^2.$
$A = \frac{1}{4}\pi d^2.$

Thus, the following corollary has been proved.

COROLLARY 3

The area of any circle is equal to the product of the square of the length of its diameter and $\frac{1}{4}\pi$.

DE—3. Prove the following corollary:

> ‖**COROLLARY 4**
> The ratio of the areas of two circles is equal to the ratio of the squares of the lengths of their radii and to the ratio of the squares of the lengths of their diameters.

Solution

Let A represent the area of a circle, r being the length of its radius, and d being the length of its diameter.

Let A' represent the area of another circle, r' being the length of its radius and d' being the length of its diameter.

(*1*) $A = \pi r^2$.

(*2*) $A' = \pi r'^2$.

(*3*) $\dfrac{A}{A'} = \dfrac{r^2}{r'^2}$.

(*1*) $A = \frac{1}{4}\pi d^2$.

(*2*) $A' = \frac{1}{4}\pi d'^2$.

(*3*) $\dfrac{A}{A'} = \dfrac{d^2}{d'^2}$.

Statement 3 is obtained by dividing the members of the equation in statement 1 by the members of the equation in statement 2. If equals are divided by equals, the quotients are equal.

DE—4. Find the area of a circle whose radius is 8 units.

Solution

$A = \pi r^2$,
$A = \pi (8)^2$,
$A = 64\pi$ square units.

DE—5. The diameter of a circle is 10 inches. Find the area of the circle.

Solution

$A = \frac{1}{4}\pi d^2$.
$A = \frac{1}{4}\pi (10)^2$.
$A = \frac{1}{4}\pi (100)$.
$A = 25\pi$ square inches.

DE—6. The circumference of a circle is 36π. Find the area of the circle.

Solution

$C = 2\pi r$,
$36\pi = 2\pi r$,
$2\pi r = 36\pi$,
$r = 18$ units.

$A = \frac{1}{2}rC$,
$A = \frac{1}{2}(18)(36\pi)$,
$A = 324\pi$ square units.

Exercises

1. Find the area of a circle having a circumference of 2π units.

2. The radius of a circle is 5 inches. Find the area.

3. The diameter of a circle is 2 feet 8 inches. Find the area.

4. If the radius of a circle is tripled, by what number is the area multiplied?

5. The area of a circle is 121π square units. What is the length of the radius of the circle?

6. The diameter of one circle is $\frac{1}{6}$ the diameter of another circle. What is the ratio of the area of the smaller circle to the area of the larger?

7. The hypotenuse of a right triangle inscribed in a circle is $3\sqrt{2}$ units. Find the area of the circle. (Leave your answer in terms of π.)

8. The radius of one circle is 7 inches, the radius of a second circle is 7 feet 7 inches. What is the ratio of their areas?

9. The ratio of the areas of two circles is 5 to 9. What is the ratio of their radii?

10. The area of a circle is $38\frac{1}{2}$ square feet. Find the length of the diameter to the nearest foot. (Use $\pi = \frac{22}{7}$.)

11. The diameter of one circle is 16 inches, while the radius of a second circle is 3 feet. What is the ratio of their areas?

12. What is the effect on the circumference of a circle
    a. if the radius is multiplied by $\frac{1}{3}$?
    b. if the area is multiplied by $\frac{1}{3}$?
    c. if the radius is divided by $\frac{1}{2}$?
    d. if the area is divided by $\frac{1}{2}$?

13. If the diameter of a circle is decreased by $\frac{1}{4}$ its length, the area is reduced by what fraction of the original?

14. If the radius of a circle is decreased by $\frac{1}{2}$ its length, the area is reduced by what fraction of the original?

THE AREA OF A SECTOR AND OF A SEGMENT OF A CIRCLE

The sector of a circle is a part of the interior of a circle bounded by two radii and their intercepted arc. The central angle, AOB, is called the *angle of the sector.* A sector is classified as *minor* if its intercepted arc is a minor arc of the circle. The sector is classified as *major* if its intercepted arc is a major arc of the circle.

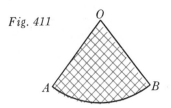

Fig. 411

Since a sector is part of the interior of a circle its area depends upon the size of its central angle and the length of the radius of the circle.

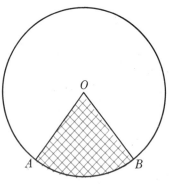

Fig. 412

ASSUMPTION 46

The ratio of the area of a sector to the area of the circle is equal to the ratio of the measure of the angle of the sector to 360°.

Let n represent the number of degrees in the angle of the sector.

$$\frac{\text{Area of sector}}{\text{Area of circle}} = \frac{n}{360}.$$

Solving for the area of the sector

$$\text{Area of sector} = \frac{n}{360} \, (\text{Area of circle}).$$

But the area of any circle is equal to πr^2 where r represents the length of the radius of the circle.

$$\text{Area of sector} = \frac{n}{360} \pi r^2.$$

A segment of a circle is a part of the interior of a circle formed by a chord and its intercepted arc. A segment is classified as *minor* if its intercepted arc is a minor arc of the circle. It is classified as *major* if its intercepted arc is a major arc of the circle. Notice that the segment is a part of sector AOB. To find the area of the segment subtract the area of $\triangle AOB$ from the area of sector AOB.

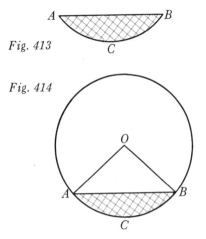

Fig. 413

Fig. 414

ASSUMPTION 47

The area of a segment of a circle is equal to the area of the corresponding sector minus the area of the triangle formed by the chord and the radii drawn to its ends.

Developmental Exercises

DE—1. Find the area of a sector of a circle whose central angle is 40° if the length of the radius of the circle is 8 inches. Leave your answer in terms of π.

Solution

Area of sector $= \dfrac{n}{360}\pi r^2$.

Area of sector $= \frac{40}{360}\pi(8)^2$.

Area of sector $= \frac{1}{9}\pi(64)$.

Area of sector $= 7\frac{1}{9}\pi$ square inches.

DE—2. Find the area of a segment of a circle whose arc has a central angle of 60° in a circle whose radius is 12.0 inches. Use $\pi = 3.14$ and $\sqrt{3} = 1.73$. Give your answer to the nearest tenth.

Solution

Area of sector $= \dfrac{n}{360}\pi r^2$.

Area of sector $= \frac{60}{360}(3.14)(12)^2$.

Area of sector $= \frac{1}{6}(3.14)(144)$.

Area of sector $= 75.36$ square inches.

Area of triangle $= \dfrac{s^2\sqrt{3}}{4}$.

Area of triangle $= \dfrac{(12)^2(1.73)}{4}$.

Area of triangle $= \dfrac{144(1.73)}{4}$.

Area of triangle $= 62.28$ square inches.

Area of segment $=$ area of sector $-$ area of triangle.

Area of segment $= 75.36$ square inches $- 62.28$ square inches.

Area of segment $= 13.08$ square inches or 13.1 square inches.

In this example the triangle was equilateral so we used the special formula $A = \dfrac{s^2\sqrt{3}}{4}$ for finding its area. The formula $A = \frac{1}{2}bh$ may be used for other triangles.

Exercises

In the following exercises leave your answers in terms of π and in simplest radical form unless otherwise instructed.

1. Find the area of a circle the length of whose radius is $3x$ units.

2. Two circles have radii of a units and 4 units, respectively. Find the length of the radius of a circle whose area is equal to the sum of the areas of these two circles.

3. Find the area of a circular mirror whose diameter is 3 feet.

4. Find the measure of the central angle of a sector that has an area of 25π square inches and a radius of 12 inches.

5. The circumference of a circle is 12π inches. What is the area of the circle?

6. Find the area of a circle if an arc of $45°$ is 2π inches in length.

7. What is the ratio of the areas of two circles that have radii of 2 inches and 4 inches respectively?

8. What is the area of a segment bounded by a 10 inch chord and its minor arc in a circle having a radius of 10 inches?

9. If the radius of a circle is 6 inches and a central angle is $120°$, find the area of the segment cut off by the chord of the angle.

10. If the radius of a circle is multiplied by 2, by what number is the area multiplied?

11. One circle has a radius three times as great as the radius of another circle. How do their areas compare?

12. The chord of a segment is 20 inches long and is 10 inches from the center of the circle. Find the area of the segment.

13. The area of a sector is 9π and the central angle of the sector is $40°$. Find the length of the radius of the circle.

14. The area of a $60°$ sector is 150π square inches. Find the length of the intercepted arc.

15. The radius of one circle is twice that of another circle. If the area of the smaller circle is 16 square inches, find the area of the larger circle.

16. A $30°$ angle is inscribed in a circle. One side of the angle is a diameter 8.0 inches long. Find the area of the sector included by the sides of the angle and its intercepted arc. (Use $\pi = 3.14$ and $\sqrt{3} = 1.73$.) Give your answer to the nearest tenth.

17. A circle is inscribed in a square the length of whose side is denoted by x. Find the area of the circle.

18. Two tangents drawn to a circle from the same external point form an angle of $60°$. If the length of the radius of the circle is 6.0 inches, find the area of the segment formed by the minor arc and its chord. (Use $\pi = 3.14$ and $\sqrt{3} = 1.73$. Give your answer to the nearest tenth.)

19. The area of the cross section of a pipe determines the volume of water that flows through the pipe. The inside diameters of two pipes are 2.0 inches and 1.5 inches respectively. Compare the amounts of water that flow through the two pipes.

20. Prove that the area of the circle constructed upon the hypotenuse of a right triangle as a diameter is equal to the sum of the areas of the circles constructed upon the legs as diameters.

Ex. 20

THE AREA OF A COMBINATION OF FIGURES

You will now proceed to find the areas of surfaces that combine two or more geometric figures. First study the list of suggestions to follow in solving more complex area problems.

(*1*) Make a careful drawing from data in the given original problem.

(*2*) Identify the separate geometric figures contained in the diagram.

(*3*) Write the area formula for each figure.

(*4*) Determine the numerical or literal values for the letters contained in the formulas.

(*5*) **a.** Solve each area formula separately or

    b. write a combined area formula in simplest form for the original problem.

(*6*) **a.** Combine the separate areas results by addition or subtraction.

    b. Solve the combined area formula.

Sometimes it is easier to combine results containing the symbol π and then to multiply by the value of π to obtain the final numerical result rather than use two separate multiplications and then add or subtract.

‖*Developmental Exercises*

DE—1. *A ring is a figure bounded by two concentric circles.* Find the area of a ring if the radius of the larger circle is 12 units and the radius of the smaller circle is 8 units. (Use $\pi = 3.14$.)

Solution
Method 1

    Area of ring = area of larger circle − area of smaller circle.

Area of the larger circle:	Area of the smaller circle:
$A = \pi r^2,$	$A = \pi r^2,$
$A = \pi (12)^2,$	$A = \pi (8)^2,$
$A = 144\pi$ square units.	$A = 64\pi$ square units.

    Area of ring = 144π square units − 64π square units.
    Area of ring = 80π square units.
    Area of ring = $80(3.14)$ square units.
    Area of ring = 251.2 square units.

Method 2

Area of ring = area of larger circle — area of smaller circle.

Area of larger circle = $\pi r^2 = \pi(12)^2$ square units.

Area of smaller circle = $\pi r^2 = \pi(8)^2$ square units.

Area of ring = $\pi(12)^2$ square units — $\pi(8)^2$ square units.

Area of ring = $\pi(12^2 - 8^2)$ square units.

Area of ring = 80π square units.

Area of ring = $80(3.14)$ square units.

Area of ring = 251.2 square units.

Fig. 415

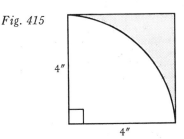

DE—2. Find the area of the shaded section in the diagram. Leave your answer in terms of π.

Solution

Area of square = s^2 where s represents the length of a side.

Area of sector = $\dfrac{n}{360}\pi r^2$ where r represents the length of the radius.

Area of shaded section = area of square — area of sector.

Area of shaded section = s^2 square inches — $\dfrac{n}{360}\pi r^2$ square inches.

Area of shaded section = $(4)^2$ square inches — $\dfrac{90}{360}\pi(4)^2$ square inches.

Area of shaded section = 16 square inches — $\frac{1}{4}\pi(16)$ square inches.

Area of shaded section = $16 - 4\pi$ square inches.

Exercises

Leave your answers in terms of π in the following exercises unless otherwise instructed.

1. Chord AC in $\odot O$ intercepts arc ABC equal to 240°. Find the area bounded by ABC and chord AC if the radius of the circle is 6 units.

2. The side of a square is 10 inches. Find the area of the section included between the square and the circumscribed circle.

Ex. 3

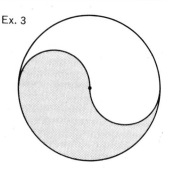

3. In the diagram the diameter of the large circle is 20 inches. The curved line inside the circle is formed by two equal semicircles. The diameter of each semicircle is equal to the radius of the large circle. Find the area of the shaded section.

Ex. 4

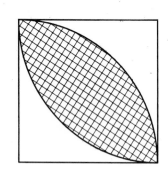

4. Find the area of the shaded section in the square the length of whose side is denoted by y. (Use $\pi = 3.14$.)

5. The circumferences of two concentric circles are 2π inches and 16π inches, respectively. Find the area of the ring between them.

Ex. 5

6. Find the total area of the diagram. $GF \parallel AE$, $GB \perp AE$, $CK \perp AE$, $FL \perp AE$, $DM \perp AE$, $AG = 5$ units, $GH = 4$ units, $HB = 4$ units, $KL = 1$ unit, $HL = 7$ units, $KC = 2$ units, $DM = 3$ units, $ME = 2$ units, and $LM = 2$ units.

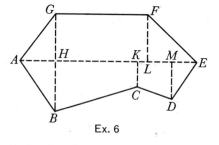

Ex. 6

7. In the diagram AB is a diameter of the large semicircle. $AO = OB$ and $AB = 24$ units. Find the area of the shaded section.

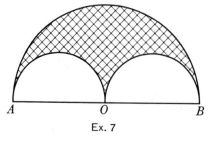

Ex. 7

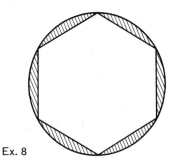

Ex. 8

8. A regular hexagon, *ABCDEF*, is inscribed in $\odot O$ whose radius is 7 units. Find the area bounded by the circle and the hexagon to the nearest square unit. (Use $\pi = \frac{22}{7}$ and $\sqrt{3} = 1.73$.)

9. Find the area of the shaded section in the square whose side is $2r$. (Use $\pi = 3.14$.)

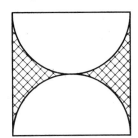

Ex. 9

10. In $\odot O$ chord *AB* is parallel to chord *CD*. If radius *OC* is 6 inches and *AB* and *CD* are each 4 inches, find the area between the chords and bounded by the circle.

11. *ABCD* is a square whose side is 1 inch. Semicircles are constructed upon the sides of the square. Find the total area.

Ex. 11

12. Two equal circles having a radius of 7 inches intersect so that their common chord is equal to the radius. Find the area of the section that lies within both circles. (Use $\pi = \frac{22}{7}$ and $\sqrt{3} = 1.7$. Give your answer to the nearest integer.)

13. The equilateral triangle in this diagram has a side of 2 inches. The circles have equal radii. Find the area of the shaded section of the diagram.

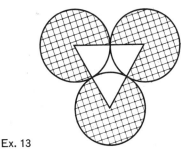

Ex. 13

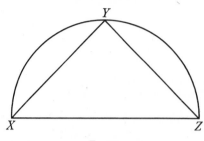

Ex. 14

14. The top of a stained glass window has the shape of an equilateral arch. Find the entire area of the arch if the length of the radius of each arc is 3.0 feet. (Use $\pi = 3.14$ and $\sqrt{3} = 1.73$.)

Ex. 15

15. Find the area of the shaded section in the equilateral triangle the length of whose side is denoted by $2x$. (Use $\pi = 3.14$ and $\sqrt{3} = 1.73$.)

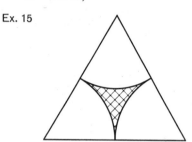

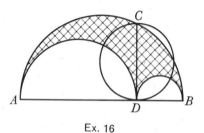

Ex. 16

16. In the diagram if $CD \perp AB$, prove that the area of the shaded part bounded by the semicircles is equal to the area of the circle whose diameter is CD.

17. The top of a washing machine agitator has a hexagonal cross section as shown in the diagram. The length of the side of the regular hexagon is equal to the one inch diameter of the circle in the diagram. Find the shaded section correct to the nearest square inch. (Use $\pi = 3.14$ and $\sqrt{3} = 1.73$.)

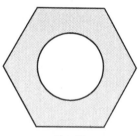

Ex. 17

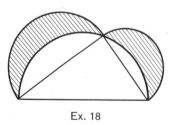

Ex. 18

18. Prove that if three semicircles are drawn upon the three sides of a right triangle, the area of the right triangle is equal to the sum of the areas of the two crescents (shaded sections in the diagram).

SOLID GEOMETRY

Recall that *a **prism** is a polyhedron, two faces of which are polygons in parallel planes while the other faces are parallelograms. The **area of a prism** is the sum of the areas of all the faces. The **lateral area** is the sum of the areas of the lateral faces.* Thus, in the diagram the total area is the sum of the areas of *ABCD, BCEF, EFGH, GHDA, ABFG,* and *CDHE,* while the lateral area is the sum of the areas of *ABCD, BCEF, EFGH,* and *GHDA.*

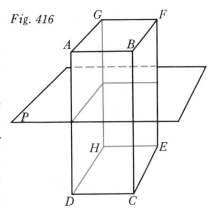

Fig. 416

A *right section* of a prism is a section made by a plane perpendicular to the lateral edges. The lateral area of a prism may also be obtained as the product of the length of the lateral edge and the perimeter of a right section of the prism.

**Lateral Area of Prism = Lateral Edge ×
Perimeter of Right Section.**

The measure of the space bounded by the solid is referred to as the *volume* of the solid. To determine the volume of any solid, a unit of measure must first be determined. *A unit of measure of volume is the portion of space bounded by a cube whose edge is one unit of length.* The volume of a geometric solid is the number of these cubic units in the interior of the solid. To determine the volume of a prism, multiply the area of the base by the altitude of the prism.

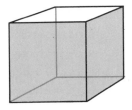

1 CUBIC UNIT

Fig. 417

Volume of Prism = Area of Base × Altitude.

The volume of a pyramid is equal to the product of one-third the area of the base and the altitude of the pyramid.

Volume of Pyramid = $\frac{1}{3}$ Area of Base × Altitude.

The formulas for the lateral area and the volume of solids having curved surfaces, the cylinder, cone, and sphere, are similar to the formulas for the lateral area and volume of prisms.

Fig. 418

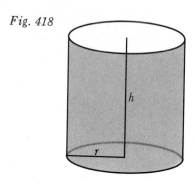

The lateral area of a right circular cylinder is the product of its circumference and the length of its altitude. If the cylinder has a base of radius r and an altitude h, the lateral area may be expressed as $2\pi rh$.

Lateral Area of Right Circular Cylinder $= 2\pi rh$.

The volume of a right cylinder is the product of the area of the base and the length of the altitude. Since the base of a right circular cylinder is always a circle, the volume of the right circular cylinder may also be expressed as $\pi r^2 h$, where r is the length of the radius of the base and h is the length of the altitude.

Volume of Right Circular Cylinder $= \pi r^2 h$.

The lateral area of a right circular cone is one-half the length of the slant height times the circumference. The volume of any cone is the product of one-third the area of the base, a circle, and the length of the altitude, or $\frac{1}{3}\pi r^2 h$, where r represents the length of the radius of the base and h represents the length of the altitude.

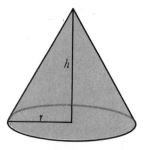

Fig. 419

Volume of a Right Circular Cone $= \frac{1}{3}\pi r^2 h$.

The area of a sphere is $4\pi r^2$ and its volume is $\frac{4}{3}\pi r^3$, where r denotes the length of the radius.

Area of a Sphere $= 4\pi r^2$. Volume of a Sphere $= \frac{4}{3}\pi r^3$.

Developmental Exercises

DE—1. Find the **a.** lateral area and **b.** total area for the given right rectangular prism.

Solution

  a. The lateral faces are four rectangles—8 units by 3 units, 8 units by 5 units, 8 units by 3 units, and 8 units by 5 units.
$A = bh$ for each face.
$A = 8(3)$.
$A = 24$ square units (the area for each of two faces).
$A = 8(5)$.
$A = 40$ square units (the area for each of the other two faces).
The lateral area $= 24 + 24 + 40 + 40 = 128$ square units.

  b. The bases are rectangles 5 units by 3 units.
$A = bh$.
$A = 5(3)$.
$A = 15$ square units (the area for each base).
Total area $= 15 + 15 + 128 = 158$ units.

DE—2. Find the lateral area of a right triangular prism whose altitude is 7 units and whose base has sides of 10 units, 11 units, and 12 units.

Solution

  The lateral area of a prism may be obtained as the product of the length of a lateral edge and the perimeter of a right section. Since this is a right triangular prism, the base is a right section.
Perimeter of the base $= 10$ units $+ 11$ units $+ 12$ units or 33 units.
$A = (33)7 = 231$ square units.

DE—3. Find the volume of a right circular cylinder having a radius of 3 inches and an altitude of 7 inches.

Solution

$$V = \pi r^2 h.$$
$$V = \pi(3)^2(7).$$
$$V = 63\pi \text{ cubic inches.}$$

Exercises

1. The base of a regular pyramid is an equilateral triangle with a side of 18 inches. Each slanting edge of the pyramid is 18 inches. Compute the lateral area of the pyramid.

2. Explain how the lateral area of a regular pyramid changes when both the perimeter of the base and each slanting edge are doubled.

3. Find the total area of a right prism whose lateral edge is 14 inches and whose base is a right triangle with legs of 5 inches and 12 inches, respectively.

4. Find the area of a right circular cylinder with a base radius of 5 inches and an altitude of 9 inches.

5. Find the length of the slant height of a right circular cone having a lateral area of 159π square inches and a base radius of 3 inches.

6. The lateral area of a right circular cylinder is 1000 square inches and the latitude is 18 inches. What is the length of the diameter of either base?

7. The earth's diameter is approximately 7920 miles. The area of the United States is approximately 3 million square miles. What per cent of the earth's surface is our country?

8. The radius of the moon is approximately 1080 miles. The radius of our earth is 3960 miles. Compare their surfaces.

9. The base of an ornamental spherical cone has an area of 15 square inches. It was carved from a sphere having a radius of 9 inches. Compute the volume of the cone. Compare the volume of the cone to the volume of the sphere.

10. Find the volume of a pyramid whose base is a square of a side 8 inches and whose altitude is 12 inches.

11. Find the length of the radius of a right circular cylinder whose volume is 128π cubic feet and whose altitude is 8 feet.

12. Find the volume of the right circular cone having the same radius and altitude as the cylinder in Exercise **11.**

13. Find the lateral area of a sphere whose radius is 8 feet.

14. Find the volume of the sphere in Exercise **13.**

15. Compare the volume of a pyramid to the volume of a prism having the same base and altitude.

16. Compare the volume of a right circular cone to the volume of a right circular cylinder having the same radius and altitude.

EXTEND YOUR HORIZON

In this chapter we considered only two area formulas for triangles. $A = \frac{1}{2}bh$ was used when the base and the altitude of any triangle could be determined. $A = \frac{s^2\sqrt{3}}{4}$ was used to find the area of an equilateral triangle when a side was known.

If only the three sides of a triangle are given we can find the area of the triangle by a third method. The theorem which established this formula is attributed to Hero, a mathematician of Alexandria, who used the principle about 2000 years ago. Follow the algebraic steps closely in the following proof and supply the reasons.

HERO'S FORMULA

The area of a triangle whose sides are a, b, and c is equal to $\sqrt{s(s-a)(s-b)(s-c)}$ where $s = \frac{1}{2}(a+b+c)$.

Given: $\triangle ABC$ with the length of the sides AB, BC, and AC denoted by c, a, and b respectively. $s = \frac{1}{2}(a+b+c)$.

Prove: Area of $\triangle ABC = \sqrt{s(s-a)(s-b)(s-c)}$.

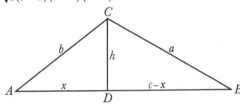

Fig. 420

Proof:

In order to prove this formula, h, the altitude of the triangle, must first be determined.

1. $\triangle ABC$ with sides AB, BC, and AC denoted by c, a, and b, respectively.
2. Construct $CD(h) \perp AB$.
3. $\angle CDB$ is a right angle; $\angle CDA$ is a right angle.
4. $\triangle CDB$ is a right triangle; $\triangle CDA$ is a right triangle.
5. $h^2 + (c-x)^2 = a^2$.
6. $h^2 + c^2 - 2cx + x^2 = a^2$.
7. $h^2 + x^2 = b^2$.
8. $c^2 - 2cx = a^2 - b^2$.
9. $-2cx = a^2 - b^2 - c^2$.
10. $x = \dfrac{b^2 - a^2 + c^2}{2c}$.

11. Substituting in Statement 7, we obtain: $h^2 + \left(\dfrac{b^2 - a^2 + c^2}{2c}\right)^2 = b^2$.

12. $h^2 + \dfrac{(b^2 - a^2 + c^2)^2}{4c^2} = b^2$.

13. $h^2 = b^2 - \dfrac{(b^2 - a^2 + c^2)^2}{4c^2}$.

14. $h^2 = \dfrac{4b^2c^2 - (b^2 - a^2 + c^2)^2}{4c^2}$.

15. $h^2 = \dfrac{[2bc + (b^2 - a^2 + c^2)][2bc - (b^2 - a^2 + c^2)]}{4c^2}$.

16. $h^2 = \dfrac{(2bc + b^2 - a^2 + c^2)(2bc - b^2 + a^2 - c^2)}{4c^2}$ or

$h^2 = \dfrac{(2bc + b^2 + c^2 - a^2)(2bc - b^2 - c^2 + a^2)}{4c^2}$.

17. $h^2 = \dfrac{[(b+c)^2 - a^2][a^2 - (b-c)^2]}{4c^2}$.

18. $h^2 = \dfrac{(b+c+a)(b+c-a)(a-b+c)(a+b-c)}{4c^2}$ or

$h^2 = \dfrac{(a+b+c)(b+c-a)(a+c-b)(a+b-c)}{4c^2}$.

19. $a + b + c = 2s$.

20. $b + c - a = 2s - 2a = 2(s-a)$; $a + c - b = 2s - 2b = 2(s-b)$; $a + b - c = 2s - 2c = 2(s-c)$.

21. Substituting in Statement 18: $h^2 = \dfrac{2s \cdot 2(s-a) \cdot 2(s-b) \cdot 2(s-c)}{4c^2}$.

22. $h^2 = \dfrac{16s(s-a)(s-b)(s-c)}{4c^2}$ or $h^2 = \dfrac{4s}{c^2}(s-a)(s-b)(s-c)$.

23. $h = \dfrac{2}{c}\sqrt{s(s-a)(s-b)(s-c)}$.

24. Area of $\triangle ABC = \tfrac{1}{2}ch$.

25. Area of $\triangle ABC = \tfrac{1}{2}c\dfrac{2}{c}\sqrt{s(s-a)(s-b)(s-c)}$.

26. $\therefore$ Area of $\triangle ABC = \sqrt{s(s-a)(s-b)(s-c)}$.

(*1*) Find the area of a triangle whose sides are 9, 12, and 15 units.

Solution

$a = 9$ units.	$s = \tfrac{1}{2}(a+b+c)$.	$s-a = 18-9 = 9$.
$b = 12$ units.	$s = \tfrac{1}{2}(9+12+15)$.	$s-b = 18-12 = 6$.
$c = 15$ units.	$s = \tfrac{1}{2}(36)$.	$s-c = 18-15 = 3$.
	$s = 18$.	

$$A = \sqrt{s(s-a)(s-b)(s-c)}.$$
$$A = \sqrt{18(9)(6)(3)}.$$

Method 1

$$A = \sqrt{2916}.$$
$$A = \sqrt{9} \cdot \sqrt{324}.$$
$$A = 3(18).$$
$$A = 54 \text{ square units.}$$

Method 2

$$A = \sqrt{18(9)(18)}.$$
$$A = 18(3).$$
$$A = 54 \text{ square units.}$$

(*2*) Find the area of a triangle whose sides are 13 units, 14 units, and 15 units.

Solution

$$a = 13 \text{ units.}$$
$$b = 14 \text{ units.}$$
$$c = 15 \text{ units.}$$

$$s = \tfrac{1}{2}(a+b+c).$$
$$s = \tfrac{1}{2}(13+14+15).$$
$$s = \tfrac{1}{2}(42).$$
$$s = 21.$$

$$s-a = 21-13 = 8.$$
$$s-b = 21-14 = 7.$$
$$s-c = 21-15 = 6.$$

$$A = \sqrt{s(s-a)(s-b)(s-c)}.$$
$$A = \sqrt{21(8)(7)(6)}.$$

Method 1

$$A = \sqrt{7056}.$$
$$A = \sqrt{84} \cdot \sqrt{84}.$$
$$A = 84 \text{ square units.}$$

Method 2

$$A = \sqrt{3 \cdot 7 \cdot 2 \cdot 2 \cdot 2 \cdot 7 \cdot 2 \cdot 3}.$$
$$A = 3 \cdot 7 \cdot 2 \cdot 2.$$
$$A = 84 \text{ square units.}$$

Now try these practice exercises.

If the results are not rational numbers in the following problems, leave the answers in simplest radical form.

(*1*) Find the area of a triangle whose sides are
    a. 5 inches, 12 inches, and 13 inches.
    b. 8 units, 15 units, and 17 units.
    c. 4 feet, 5 feet, and 7 feet.
    d. $(x+y)$, $(x+m)$, and $(y+m)$.

(*2*) Using Hero's area formula, show that the area of an equilateral triangle having a side s is $\dfrac{s^2\sqrt{3}}{4}$.

CHAPTER SUMMARY

The area of a quadrilateral

1. that is a rectangle whose sides measure b units and h units is bh square units.   (page 451)

2. that is a parallelogram whose base measures b units and whose altitudes to that base measures h units is bh square units.
(page 456)

3. that is a trapezoid whose bases measure b and b' units and whose altitude measures h units is $\frac{1}{2}h(b+b')$ square units.   (page 466)

4. that is a rhombus is equal to one-half the product of the lengths of its diagonals.   (page 469)

The area of a triangle

1. whose bases measures b units and whose altitude measures h units is $\frac{1}{2}bh$ square units.   (page 462)

2. is equal to one-half the area of a parallelogram having an equal base and an equal altitude.   (page 461)

3. having equal sides denoted by s is $\dfrac{s^2\sqrt{3}}{4}$ square units.

(page 463)

The area of

1. a regular polygon is equal to one-half the product of its perimeter and the length of its apothem.   (page 480)

2. a circle is equal to one-half the product of the length of its radius and its circumference.   (page 482)

3. a circle is equal to the product of the square of the length of its radius and π.   (page 483)

4. a circle is equal to the product of the length of its diameter and $\frac{1}{4}\pi$.
(page 483)

5. a segment of a circle is equal to the area of the corresponding sector minus the area of the triangle formed by the chord and the radii drawn to its ends.   (page 487)

The circumference of any circle

    1. is equal to the length of its diameter times π.   (page 482)

    2. is equal to the products of 2π and the length of its radius. (page 483)

The ratio of the areas

    1. of two rectangles is equal to the ratio of the products of the lengths of their bases and altitudes.   (page 452)

    2. of two rectangles having equal bases is equal to the ratio of their altitudes.   (page 452)

    3. of two rectangles having equal altitudes is equal to the ratio of their bases.   (page 453)

    4. of two parallelograms is equal to the ratio of the products of the lengths of their bases and altitudes.   (page 457)

    5. of two parallelograms having equal altitudes is equal to the ratio of their bases.   (page 458)

    6. of two parallelograms having equal bases is equal to the ratio of their altitudes.   (page 458)

    7. of two triangles is equal to the ratio of the products of their bases and altitudes.   (page 463)

    8. of two triangles having equal altitudes is equal to the ratio of their bases.   (page 463)

    9. of two triangles having equal bases is equal to the ratio of their altitudes.   (page 463)

    10. of two similar triangles is equal to the squares of the lengths of any two corresponding sides.   (page 475)

    11. of two similar polygons is equal to the squares of the lengths of any two corresponding sides.   (page 476)

    12. of two circles is equal to the ratio of the squares of the lengths of their radii and to the ratio of the squares of the lengths of their diameters. (page 484)

    13. of a sector to a circle is equal to the ratio of the measure of the angle of the sector to $360°$.   (page 486)

CHAPTER REVIEW

Vocabulary

Match the word in the left hand column with its correct definition in the right hand column.

1. Area

2. Equal Figures

3. Apothem

4. π (pi)

5. Segment of a Circle

6. Sector of a Circle

7. Center of a Regular Polygon

8. Radius of a Polygon

9. Central Angle of a Polygon

10. Ring

a. Area bounded by two circles.

b. An angle formed by the radii of the circumscribed circle to two consecutive vertices.

c. An angle formed by the radii of the inscribed circle to two consecutive vertices.

d. The ratio of the circumference of a circle to its diameter.

e. Area bounded by two concentric circles.

f. The measure of the portion of the plane enclosed by a geometric figure.

g. The common center of the inscribed and circumscribed circles.

h. The radius of the inscribed circle.

i. The radius of the circumscribed circle.

j. Figures that have the same area.

k. Part of the interior of a circle bounded by a chord and its intercepted arc.

l. Part of the interior of a circle bounded by two radii and their intercepted arc.

Exercises

1. Column 1 contains a list of formulas and Column 2 gives a brief description to identify the formulas. On your paper copy the numbers from Column 1 and match them with the correct letters from Column 2.

(1) $A = s^2$

(2) $A = \frac{1}{2}h(b+b')$

(3) $A = \frac{1}{2}ap$

(4) $A = bh$

(5) $A = \pi r^2$

(6) $A = \dfrac{n}{360°}\,\pi r^2$

(7) $A = \frac{1}{2}dd'$

(8) $A = \dfrac{s^2\sqrt{3}}{4}$

(9) $A = \dfrac{n}{360}\pi r^2 - \frac{1}{2}bh$

(10) $A = \frac{1}{2}bh$

a. The area of a triangle when its base and altitude are known.

b. Area of a parallelogram.

c. Area of a circle.

d. Area of a square.

e. Area of a trapezoid.

f. Area of an equilateral triangle.

g. Area of a regular polygon.

h. Area of a sector.

i. Area of a rhombus.

j. Area of a segment.

2. *ABCD* is a rectangle. Diagonal $AC = x$ units and side $AD = y$ units. Find the area of the rectangle.

3. *MNOP* is a trapezoid. $PO \parallel MN$, $PO = 8$ units, $MN = 13$ units. *PR*, the altitude to base *MN*, is 6 units. Find the area of the trapezoid.

4. In $\triangle ABC$, $\angle A = 30°$, $AC = 10$ units, $AB = 16$ units. Find the area of $\triangle ABC$.

5. *RSTU* is a square. Diagonal *RT* is *x* units. Find the area of the square.

6. $\triangle DEF$ is an equilateral triangle whose side is 12 units. Find the area of the triangle. Leave your answer in simplest radical form.

7. *ABCD* is a parallelogram. $\angle A = 45°$, $AD = 4$ units, $AB = 7$ units. Find the area of $\square ABCD$. Leave your answer in simplest radical form.

8. The area of a regular octagon is 96 square inches and the length of its apothem is 6 inches. Find the length of its side.

9. The length of the radius of a circle is 7 inches. Find the length of the radius of a circle whose area is 9 times as large.

10. Find the area of a regular hexagon inscribed in a circle whose radius is 4 units. Leave your answer in simplest radical form.

11. Find the area of an 80° sector in a circle whose radius is 18 inches. Leave your answer in terms of π.

12. Prove that the area of a trapezoid is equal to the product of one leg and the distance from the leg to the midpoint of the other leg.

13. Two circles are concentric. The smaller circle has a radius of 14 units and the larger circle has a radius of 28 units. Find the area of the ring. (Use $\pi = \dfrac{22}{7}$.)

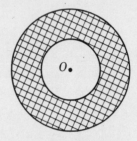

Ex. 13

14. The side of a square is $9\sqrt{2}$ units. Find the area included between the square and the circumscribed circle. (Use $\pi = 3.14$ and give the answer correct to the nearest square unit.)

15. Find the area of a segment whose arc is 90° in a circle whose radius is 12 inches. Leave your answer in terms of π.

16. The lengths of the radii of two regular hexagons are denoted by x and y. Express the ratio of their areas.

17. Construct a square equal in area to a given rectangle.

18. Given: *EG* and *FH* are medians in $\triangle DEF$.
   Prove: $\triangle DFH = \triangle DEG$.

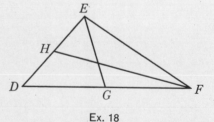

Ex. 18

19. Find the area of a rhombus having one diagonal of 16 inches and a perimeter of 40 inches.

20. Construct a triangle equal to a given pentagon.

CHAPTER TEST

1. *MNOP* is a parallelogram with diagonals *MO* and *PN*. Prove that triangle *MNP* and triangle *OMN* are equal.

2. The sides of a triangle are 4 units, 5 units, and 6 units. Find the length of the sides of a similar triangle whose area is 4 times as large as that of the first triangle.

3. The sum of the diagonals of a rhombus is 34 inches. If the difference between the diagonals is 14 inches, find the area of the rhombus.

4. The lengths of two adjacent sides of a rectangle can be found by solving for the roots of the equation $x^2 - 11x + 24 = 0$. Find the area of the rectangle.

5. Find the area of a square whose perimeter is $(8a - 8b)$ units.

6. *AB* is a diameter and *BC* is a chord in $\odot O$. $\angle ABC = 60°$ and $AB = 16''$. Find the area bounded by the angle and arc *AC*. (Leave your answer in terms of π and in simplest radical form.)

7. Find the area of a segment cut off by a side of an equilateral triangle inscribed in a circle whose radius is $6''$. (Leave your answer in terms of π and in simplest radical form.)

8. Find the area of the shaded section in the diagram if the diameter of the larger circle is denoted by a and the diameter of the smaller circle is denoted by b. (Leave your answer in terms of π.)

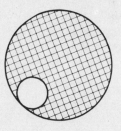

Ex. 9   Ex. 8

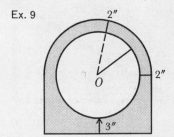

9. Find the area of the shaded section in the diagram. *O* is the center of a circle whose radius is one foot.

10. Construct a triangle equal to a given trapezoid.

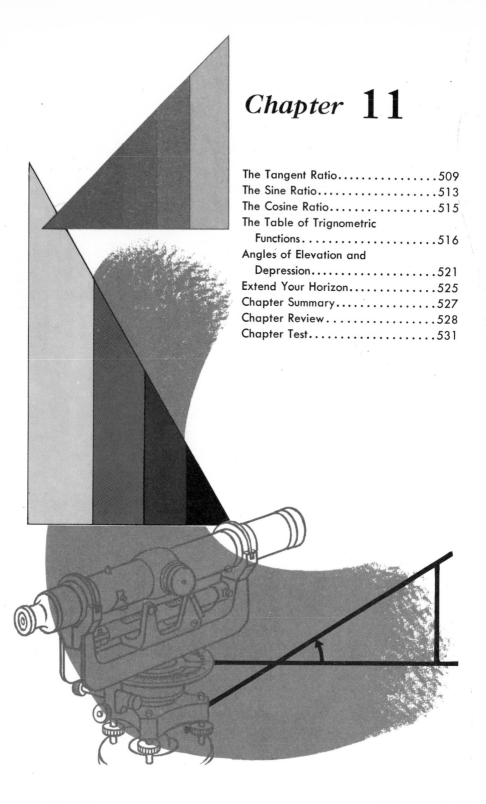

Chapter 11

NUMERICAL TRIGONOMETRY

THE TANGENT RATIO

In your study of congruent polygons, you discovered that in many instances indirect measurement was much more practical and desirable than direct measurement. You will now investigate a method of indirect measurement that applies the principles of similarity. This method is based on the fact that the sides of similar triangles have a constant ratio. The branch of mathematics in which this method is studied is called *trigonometry*. Our discussion will be limited to right triangles, though trigonometry applies to all triangles.

Trigonometry developed as a special tool or aid to be used in the solution of surveying problems. Its practical applications preceded the theoretical study of the subject. A study of the Ahmes Papyrus has led some authorities to speculate that the Egyptians made use of trigonometry in building the pyramids. A knowledge of trigonometry is essential in the study of modern surveying, navigation, and astronomy.

Recall that in any right triangle the three sides in the triangle are denoted by a, b, and c according to their positions opposite $\angle A$, $\angle B$, and $\angle C$, respectively. The side opposite the right angle in the triangle, usually side c, is called the *hypotenuse* and the sides which form the right angle, usually sides a and b, are called the *legs*. Therefore, the

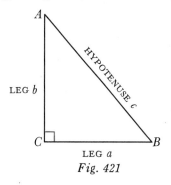

Fig. 421

side opposite angle A is leg a. The side adjacent to angle A is leg b. The "adjacent side" in a right triangle will always refer to one of the legs that forms the acute angle mentioned in the problem and never to the hypotenuse. The side opposite angle B is leg b and the side adjacent to angle B is leg a.

Developmental Exercises

DE—1. In right triangle *DEF*
    a. which side is opposite ∠ *D?*
    b. which side is adjacent to ∠ *D?*
    c. which side is opposite ∠ *F?*
    d. which side is adjacent to ∠ *F?*

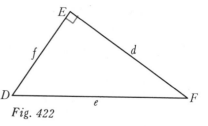

Fig. 422

Solution

    In the right triangle, *DEF,* ∠ *E* is the right angle. Therefore, *DF* is the hypotenuse.
    a. Side *EF* (*d*) is opposite ∠ *D*.
    b. Side *DE* (*f*) is adjacent to ∠ *D*.
    c. Side *DE* (*f*) is opposite ∠ *F*.
    d. Side *EF* (*d*) is adjacent to ∠ *F*.

DE—2. In the diagram at the right, ∠ *ABC* is any acute angle. *D, E,* and *F* are any points on *AB*. *DG, EH,* and *FJ* are perpendiculars to *BC*.
    Prove that $\dfrac{DG}{BG} = \dfrac{EH}{BH} = \dfrac{FJ}{BJ}$.

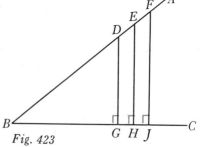

Fig. 423

Solution

    Since ∠ *B* = ∠ *B* by identity and ∠ *DGB*, ∠ *EHB*, and ∠ *FJB* are all right angles, △*BDG* ∼ △*BEH* ∼ △*BFJ*. The corresponding sides are therefore in proportion. Using the principles of proportion, it can be shown that $\dfrac{DG}{BG} = \dfrac{EH}{BH} = \dfrac{FJ}{BJ}$.

    The ratio of the perpendicular distance to the horizontal distance is the same for any point of *AB*. Thus, you may conclude that this constant ratio depends on the size of the angle (∠ *B* in this instance) and not upon the length of the legs of the triangle. The ratio of the length of the leg opposite an acute angle in a right triangle to the length of the leg adjacent to the angle is called the *tangent of the angle*. This ratio is constant for equal angles. The abbreviation for tangent of ∠ *A* is *tan A*.

‖ **In a right triangle the tangent of an acute angle is the ratio of the length of the opposite leg to the length of the adjacent leg.**

$$\tan B = \frac{\text{leg opposite} \angle B}{\text{leg adjacent to} \angle B}.$$

DE—3. In right triangle ABC, $\angle C$ is the right angle. Determine the tangent of $\angle A$ and $\angle B$.

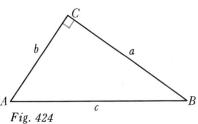

Fig. 424

Solution

$$\tan A = \frac{\text{leg opposite } \angle A}{\text{leg adjacent to } \angle A} = \frac{a}{b}.$$

$$\tan B = \frac{\text{leg opposite } \angle B}{\text{leg adjacent to } \angle B} = \frac{b}{a}.$$

DE—4. In right triangle MNO where $\angle M$ is the right angle, leg $MN = 4''$ and leg $MO = 3''$. Determine the numerical values of the tangents of $\angle O$ and $\angle N$.

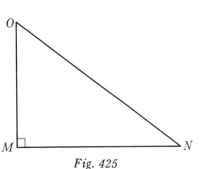

Fig. 425

Solution

$$\tan O = \frac{\text{leg opposite } \angle O}{\text{leg adjacent to } \angle O} = \frac{MN}{MO} = \frac{4}{3}.$$

$$\tan N = \frac{\text{leg opposite } \angle N}{\text{leg adjacent to } \angle N} = \frac{MO}{MN} = \frac{3}{4}.$$

DE—5. In right triangle ABC of Developmental Exercise **3**, where C is the right angle, leg $AC = 12$ units and hypotenuse $AB = 13$ units. Determine the numerical values of the tangents of $\angle A$ and $\angle B$.

Solution

Before the tangent values can be determined, the length of BC must be found. Using the corollary of the Pythagorean Theorem, you know that

$$a^2 = c^2 - b^2.$$

$$\text{Therefore, } a^2 = (13)^2 - (12)^2,$$
$$a^2 = 169 - 144,$$
$$a^2 = 25,$$
$$a = 5.$$

Now you can express the tangent values for $\angle A$ and $\angle B$.

$$\tan A = \frac{5}{12}.$$
$$\tan B = \frac{12}{5}.$$

Exercises

1. Complete: If two angles are equal, their tangents _____ _____. Write the converse of the proposition you completed above. Is it valid?

2. Complete: As the size of an angle decreases the value of the tangent of the angle _____.

3. In $\triangle XYZ$, $\angle Y$ is a right angle, $ZY = 6$ units, and $XY = 13$ units. Find the numerical values of the tangents of the acute angles.

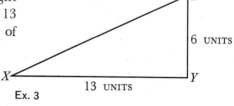

Ex. 3

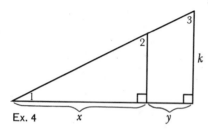

Ex. 4

4. Use the letters in the diagram to express the tangent of $\angle 1$ in two ways. Express the tangent of $\angle 3$. Of $\angle 2$.

5. In any right triangle, ABC, if $\angle C$ is the right angle and the tangent of $\angle A = \dfrac{\sqrt{3}}{2}$, determine the tangent of $\angle B$.

6. Prove that if the tangent of $\angle A$ is 1, the right triangle is isosceles.

7. If $AB \perp BD$ and $ED \perp BD$, prove that the tangent of $\angle A$ is equal to the tangent of $\angle E$.

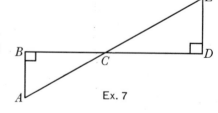

Ex. 7

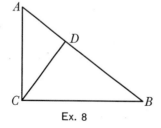

Ex. 8

8. In right $\triangle ABC$, $\angle C$ is a right angle and $CD \perp AB$. If $AC = 6$ feet, $BC = 8$ feet and $AD = 3.6$ feet, use tangent-function concepts to find the lengths of DC and BD.

THE SINE RATIO

Given that $\triangle BDG$, $\triangle BEH$, and $\triangle BFJ$ are right triangles, you proved in Developmental Exercise 2 of the previous section that $\triangle BDG \sim \triangle BEH \sim \triangle BFJ$. From this, using the principles of proportion, you may conclude that $\dfrac{DG}{BD} = \dfrac{EH}{BE} = \dfrac{FJ}{BF}$.

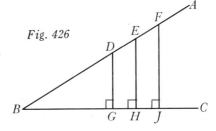

Fig. 426

The ratio of the perpendicular distance to the length of the hypotenuse on AB is the same for any point on AB. This constant ratio depends on the size of $\angle B$. It is called the *sine* of $\angle B$. The abbreviation for sine of $\angle B$ is *sin B*.

> **In a right triangle the sine of an acute angle is the ratio of the length of the opposite leg to the length of the hypotenuse.**
>
> $$\sin B = \frac{\text{leg opposite } \angle B}{\text{hypotenuse}}.$$

Developmental Exercises

DE—1. In $\triangle ABC$, $\angle C$ is a right angle. Determine the sine of $\angle A$ and $\angle B$.

Solution

$$\sin A = \frac{\text{leg opposite } \angle A}{\text{hypotenuse}} = \frac{a}{c}.$$

$$\sin B = \frac{\text{leg opposite } \angle B}{\text{hypotenuse}} = \frac{b}{c}.$$

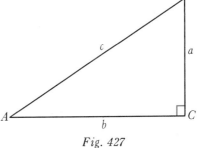

Fig. 427

DE—2. In right triangle MNO where $\angle M$ is the right angle, side $MN = 4$ units, side $MO = 3$ units, and hypotenuse $ON = 5$ units, determine the numerical values of the sines of angles O and N.

Solution

$$\sin O = \frac{MN}{ON} = \frac{4}{5} \text{ or } .8.$$

$$\sin N = \frac{MO}{ON} = \frac{3}{5} \text{ or } .6.$$

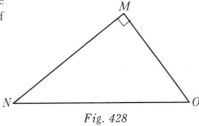

Fig. 428

Exercises

1. Complete: If two angles are equal, their sines _____ _____. Write the converse of the proposition you completed above. Is it valid?

2. Complete: As the size of an angle decreases the value of the sine of the angle _____.

3. In $\triangle MNO$, $\angle N$ is a right angle. If $NO = 5$ units and $MN = 12$ units, find the numerical values of the sines of the acute angles.

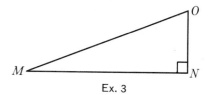

Ex. 3

4. Use the letters in the diagram to express the sine of $\angle 1$ and $\angle 2$ in two ways.

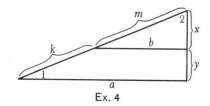

Ex. 4

5. In the diagram, BD bisects $\angle B$, $AD \perp BD$, $CE \perp DB$, $\sin C = \frac{4}{7}$.
   a. If $DB = 52$ feet, find the length of AB.
   b. If $AB = 3'6''$, find the length of DB.

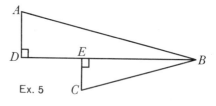

Ex. 5

6. In the diagram, $NL \perp KM$, $KN \perp MN$. If $\sin K = \frac{3}{5}$, find the numerical value of $\sin \angle M$.

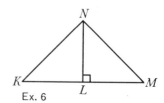

Ex. 6

THE COSINE RATIO

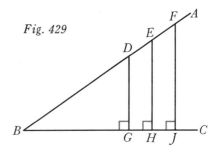

Fig. 429

The third trigonometric ratio to be studied is the ratio of the length of the side adjacent to the acute angle to the length of the hypotenuse of the right triangle. From the diagram, the given data, and the conclusions proved in establishing the tangent and sine functions, you can now conclude that $\dfrac{BG}{BD} = \dfrac{BH}{BE} = \dfrac{BJ}{BF}$.

The ratio of the length of the adjacent side on BC to the length of the hypotenuse on AB is the same for any point on AB. This constant ratio is called the *cosine* of the angle. The abbreviation for cosine of $\angle B$ is *cos B*.

> **The cosine of an acute angle in a right triangle is the ratio of the length of the adjacent leg to the length of the hypotenuse.**
>
> $$\cos B = \frac{\text{leg adjacent to } \angle B}{\text{hypotenuse}}.$$

Developmental Exercises

DE—1. In right triangle ABC, $\angle C$ is the right angle. Determine the cosines of $\angle A$ and $\angle B$.

Solution

$$\cos A = \frac{\text{leg adjacent to } \angle A}{\text{hypotenuse}} = \frac{b}{c}.$$

$$\cos B = \frac{\text{leg adjacent to } \angle B}{\text{hypotenuse}} = \frac{a}{c}.$$

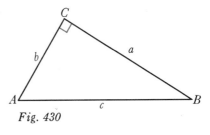

Fig. 430

DE—2. In the right triangle ABC in Developmental Exercise **1**, where C is the right angle, side $BC = 4''$, side $AC = 3''$, and hypotenuse $AB = 5''$. Determine the numerical values of the cosines of $\angle A$ and $\angle B$.

Solution

$$\cos A = \frac{AC}{AB} = \frac{3}{5}.$$

$$\cos B = \frac{BC}{AB} = \frac{4}{5}.$$

Exercises

1. Complete: If two angles are equal, their cosines _____
_____. Write the con-
verse of the proposition you just completed. Is it valid?

2. Complete: As the size of an angle decreases, the value of the
cosine of the angle_____.

3. In $\triangle MNO$, $\angle O$ is the right
angle. If $MO = 5$ units and $MN =$
13 units, find the numerical values
of the cosines of the acute angles.

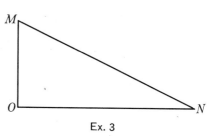

Ex. 3

4. Use the letters in the drawing
to express the cosine of $\angle 1$ and $\angle 2$
in two ways.

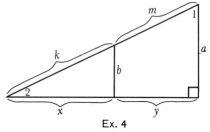

Ex. 4

5. In $\triangle ABC$, $\angle C$ is a right angle. Determine and compare the
    a. sine of $\angle a$ and the cosine of $\angle B$.
    b. the sine of $\angle B$ and the cosine of $\angle A$.

6. Using the answers from Exercise **5,** state a generalization comparing the sine of $\angle A$ to the cosine of $\angle B$ and the reverse.

THE TABLE OF TRIGONOMETRIC FUNCTIONS

Since the value of the tangent, sine, and cosine, depend on the size
of the angle, their ratios are functions of the angle. Hence they are
called *trigonometric functions*. Every angle of x degrees will have the same
numerical values for each trigonometric function. Why? In the developmental exercises below, you will determine the numerical values of
the trigonometric functions for angles of a given size.

Developmental Exercises

DE—1. Determine the **a.** tangent, **b.** sine, and **c.** cosine functions for any 30° angle in any right triangle.

Solution

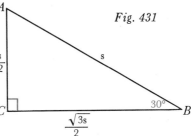

Fig. 431

From Theorem 119 and its corollaries

a. If s represents the length of the hypotenuse, AB, then $AC = \dfrac{s}{2}$, and $BC = \dfrac{\sqrt{3}s}{2}$. The tangent of $\angle B$ (the 30° angle) is $\dfrac{AC}{BC}$ or $\dfrac{\frac{s}{2}}{\frac{\sqrt{3}s}{2}}$. This is equivalent to $\dfrac{\sqrt{3}}{3}$ or .5774.

b. The sine of $\angle B$ is $\dfrac{AC}{AB}$ or $\dfrac{\frac{s}{2}}{s}$. This is equivalent to $\frac{1}{2}$ or .5000.

c. The cosine of $\angle B$ is $\dfrac{BC}{AB}$ or $\dfrac{\frac{\sqrt{3}s}{2}}{s}$. This is equivalent to $\dfrac{\sqrt{3}}{2}$ or .8660.

DE—2. Determine the **a.** tangent, **b.** sine, and **c.** cosine functions for any 86° angle in any right triangle.

Solution

Since we do not know any specific relationships concerning the legs of a right triangle containing an 86° angle, we cannot use the method shown in Developmental Exercise **1.** We must develop a method for determining the functions for any acute angle of a right triangle.

The approximate values of the trigonometric functions for any 86° angle may be found by using scale drawing. To do this for every angle 1° to 90° would be extremely time consuming. Therefore, a table has been constructed showing the numerical values of the functions for angles of 1° to 90°. See page 519.

a. In the column headed "Angle" find 86°. To the right of 86°, in the column headed "Tan" read 14.3007. Tan 86° = 14.3007. This is the tangent ratio for any angle of 86°.

b. Opposite 86°, in the column headed "Sin," .9976 is found. Thus, sin 86° = .9976.

c. In the column headed "Cos," opposite 86°, you find that cos 86° = .0698.

DE—3. In right triangle PQR, $\angle P =$ 90°. The length of PR is 20″, the length of PQ is 8.08″. Determine the measure of $\angle R$.

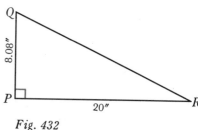

Solution   *Fig. 432*

The tangent of $\angle R = \dfrac{PQ}{PR} = \dfrac{8.08}{20}$ or .4040.

Using the table, you can find the measure of the angle having a tangent of .4040.

In the column headed "Tan" find .4040. Opposite this, to the left in the column headed "Angle," read the angle measure, tan $\angle 22° = .4040$. Therefore, $\angle R = 22°$.

DE—4. In right triangle ABC, $\angle C$ is the right angle, $\angle A = 53°$, and $AB = 20'$. Find the length of BC correct to the nearest foot.

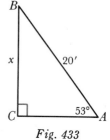

Fig. 433

Solution

We must use the function of the given angle ($\angle A$) which involves the unknown length (BC) and a known length (AB). This must be the sine function.

$$\sin A = \frac{BC}{AB}.$$

Let x represent the length of BC in feet.

$$\sin 53° = \frac{x}{20},$$

$$.7986 = \frac{x}{20},$$

$$x = 15.972.$$

$$BC = 16 \text{ feet.}$$

The value of sin 53° was obtained from the trigonometric tables.

Could you have solved this problem using either the tangent or cosine functions? Why not? Could you have used $\angle B$? Why not? Without solving for it first?

TABLE OF TRIGONOMETRIC RATIOS

Angle	Sin	Cos	Tan	Angle	Sin	Cos	Tan
1°	.0175	.9998	.0175	46°	.7193	.6947	1.0355
2°	.0349	.9994	.0349	47°	.7314	.6820	1.0724
3°	.0523	.9986	.0524	48°	.7431	.6691	1.1106
4°	.0698	.9976	.0699	49°	.7547	.6561	1.1504
5°	.0872	.9962	.0875	50°	.7660	.6428	1.1918
6°	.1045	.9945	.1051	51°	.7771	.6293	1.2349
7°	.1219	.9925	.1228	52°	.7880	.6157	1.2799
8°	.1392	.9903	.1405	53°	.7986	.6018	1.3270
9°	.1564	.9877	.1584	54°	.8090	.5878	1.3764
10°	.1736	.9848	.1763	55°	.8192	.5736	1.4281
11°	.1908	.9816	.1944	56°	.8290	.5592	1.4826
12°	.2079	.9781	.2126	57°	.8387	.5446	1.5399
13°	.2250	.9744	.2309	58°	.8480	.5299	1.6003
14°	.2419	.9703	.2493	59°	.8572	.5150	1.6643
15°	.2588	.9659	.2679	60°	.8660	.5000	1.7321
16°	.2756	.9613	.2867	61°	.8746	.4848	1.8040
17°	.2924	.9563	.3057	62°	.8829	.4695	1.8807
18°	.3090	.9511	.3249	63°	.8910	.4540	1.9626
19°	.3256	.9455	.3443	64°	.8988	.4384	2.0503
20°	.3420	.9397	.3640	65°	.9063	.4226	2.1445
21°	.3584	.9336	.3839	66°	.9135	.4067	2.2460
22°	.3746	.9272	.4040	67°	.9205	.3907	2.3559
23°	.3907	.9205	.4245	68°	.9272	.3746	2.4751
24°	.4067	.9135	.4452	69°	.9336	.3584	2.6051
25°	.4226	.9063	.4663	70°	.9397	.3420	2.7475
26°	.4384	.8988	.4877	71°	.9455	.3256	2.9042
27°	.4540	.8910	.5095	72°	.9511	.3090	3.0777
28°	.4695	.8829	.5317	73°	9563	.2924	3.2709
29°	.4848	.8746	.5543	74°	.9613	.2756	3.4874
30°	.5000	.8660	.5774	75°	.9659	.2588	3.7321
31°	.5150	.8572	.6009	76°	.9703	.2419	4.0108
32°	.5299	.8480	.6249	77°	.9744	.2250	4.3315
33°	.5446	.8387	.6494	78°	.9781	.2079	4.7046
34°	.5592	.8290	.6745	79°	.9816	.1908	5.1446
35°	.5736	.8192	.7002	80°	.9848	.1736	5.6713
36°	.5878	.8090	.7265	81°	.9877	.1564	6.3138
37°	.6018	.7986	.7536	82°	.9903	.1392	7.1154
38°	.6157	.7880	.7813	83°	.9925	.1219	8.1443
39°	.6293	.7771	.8098	84°	.9945	.1045	9.5144
40°	.6428	.7660	.8391	85°	.9962	.0872	11.4301
41°	.6561	.7547	.8693	86°	.9976	.0698	14.3007
42°	.6691	.7431	.9004	87°	.9986	.0523	19.0811
43°	.6820	.7314	.9325	88°	.9994	.0349	28.6363
44°	.6947	.7193	.9657	89°	.9998	.0175	57.2900
45°	.7071	.7071	1.0000	90°	1.0000	.0000	

Exercises

1. Use the table to find the numerical values of the tangents of the following angles.

    a. $62°$ **b.** $8°$ **c.** $40°$ **d.** $20°$ **e.** $45°$ **f.** $89°$

2. Use the table to find the numerical values of the sines of the angles in Exercise **1.**

3. Use the table to find the numerical values of the cosines of the angles in Exercise **1.**

4. Use the table to find the measures of the angles whose tangents have the following values.

    a. .4245   **b.** 1.3270   **c.** 7.1154
    d. .2679   **e.** 3.7321   **f.** 2.0503

5. Use the table to find the measures of the angles whose sines have the following values.

    a. .3090   **b.** .8988   **c.** .9998
    d. .3256   **e.** .1908   **f.** .9063

6. Use the table to find the measures of the angles whose cosines have the values in Exercise **5.**

7. Find the sum of the angles in the answers for Exercises **5a** and **6a, 5b** and **6b, 5c** and **6c,** etc. What do you notice?

8. In a right triangle, ABC, $\angle C = 90°$. Find the length of BC if
    a. $\angle A = 30°$ and $AB = 15''$.   **b.** $\angle A = 50°$ and $AB = 10''$.
    c. $\angle A = 50°$ and $AC = 10''$.   **d.** $\angle A = 7°$ and $AC = 60''$.

9. In a right triangle, ABC, $\angle C = 90°$. Find the length of BC if
    a. $\angle B = 86°$ and $AB = 60'$.   **b.** $\angle B = 22°$ and $AB = 7'$.
    c. $\angle A = 44°$ and $AC = 28'$.   **d.** $\angle A = 63°$ and $AC = 15'$.

10. In a right triangle, ABC, $\angle C = 90°$. Find the length of AB if
    a. $\angle A = 30°$ and $BC = 15''$.   **b.** $\angle A = 42°$ and $BC = 6'$.
    c. $\angle B = 60°$ and $BC = 8'$.   **d.** $\angle B = 60°$ and $BC = 27'$.

11. A ladder against the side of a house makes an angle of $24°$ with the house. The foot of the ladder is 8 feet from the base of the house. How long is the ladder? Give your answer to the nearest foot.

12. The chord of a circle is 20 inches long. A line joining one end of the chord with the center of the circle forms a $40°$ angle with the chord. What is the distance of the chord from the center of the circle?

ANGLES OF ELEVATION AND DEPRESSION

The angle of elevation or the angle of depression is the angle formed by an observer's line of sight and a horizontal line. When an observer on the ground looks up to the head of the statue, the angle formed with a horizontal line is called the *angle of elevation.* An observer in the head looking down forms an angle with a horizontal line called the *angle of depression.*

The Statue of Liberty stands 151 feet high. Within the statue, visitors may climb to an observation platform in the crown.

Developmental Exercises

DE—1. At a point 40 feet from the foot of a building, the angle of elevation of the top of the building is 70°. Find the height of the building correct to the nearest foot.

Solution

Let x represent the number of feet in the height of the building.

$$\tan 70° = \frac{x}{40},$$

$$2.7475 = \frac{x}{40},$$

$x = 109.9$.   The height of the building is 110′.

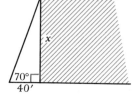

Fig. 434

DE—2. Compare the angle of elevation to the angle of depression.

Solution

$\angle 1 =$ angle of elevation, $\angle 2 =$ angle of depression. $AB \parallel CD$. Why? Since, if two parallel lines are cut by a transversal, the alternate-interior angles formed are equal, $\angle 1 = \angle 2$.

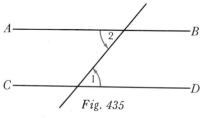

Fig. 435

DE—3. To determine the height of a tower, a transit mounted on a tripod 5 feet high is set up 60 feet from the foot of a tower. Then the angle of elevation is found to be 53°. How high is the tower? Give your answer to the nearest foot.

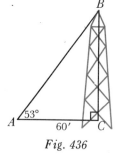

Fig. 436

Solution

When a transit mounted on a tripod is used for measuring angles, the *height of the instrument* must be taken into account.

Let x represent the number of feet in the length of BC in right triangle ABC. Then $x+5$ represents the number of feet in the height of the tower.

$$\tan 53° = \frac{x}{60},$$

$$1.3270 = \frac{x}{60},$$

$$x = 79.62.$$

$x+5 = 79.62 + 5$ or 84.62. Therefore the height of the tower is 85 ft.

Exercises

In the following exercises give the answers to the nearest foot unless otherwise indicated.

1. In $\triangle ABC$, $\angle C$ is a right angle, $a = 8''$, $b = 6''$, and $c = 10''$. Find the value of $\sin A$.

2. Two sides of a parallelogram are $12'$ and $20'$ and the included angle is $35°$. Find, correct to the nearest integer, the length of the altitude to the $20'$ side.

3. From the top of the Statue of Liberty, about 300 feet high, the angle of depression of a Staten Island ferry boat is $40°$. How far is the boat from the Statue of Liberty?

4. At a point 50 feet from the foot of a flagpole, the angle of elevation is $67°$. Find the height of the pole.

5. A surveyor measuring the height of a cliff places his transit at a point 100 feet from the foot of the cliff. The angle of elevation of the top of the cliff is found to be $52°$. If the height of the instrument is $5\frac{1}{2}$ feet, find the height of the cliff.

6. $MNOP$ is an isosceles trapezoid with base $PO = 12''$, base $MN = 20''$, and $\angle M = 63°$. Find the length of the altitude, PQ, correct to the nearest inch.

7. The base of the gable of the roof of a building is 28 feet. The height of the roof at the center is 10 feet. Find the angle at which the roof slopes. Give your answer correct to the nearest degree.

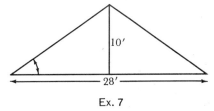

Ex. 7

Ex. 8

8. In $\odot O$, $OP \perp MN$, $\angle NOP = 48°$, and $OP = 10''$. Find the length of MN to the nearest inch.

9. A regular pentagon is inscribed in a circle whose radius is 8.0 inches. Find the distance from the center of the circle to a side of the pentagon and find the length of a side of the pentagon.

10. The angle of depression from the top of a building to a car parked 50 feet from the base of the building is 47°. Find the height of the building.

11. A railroad track slopes at an angle of 10° to the horizontal. What vertical distance does it rise in a horizontal distance of 1 mile?

12. The diagram illustrates two buildings that are 100 feet apart. From *P* the angle of elevation of point *R* is 15° and the angle of depression of point *N* is 20°. Find the height of both buildings represented by *MP* and *RN*.

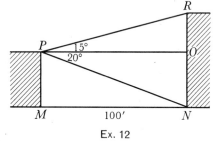

Ex. 12

13. A fence post and a utility pole both standing on level ground are represented by *DE* and *BC* respectively in the diagram. The utility pole is 30 feet high and the distance, *EC*, between the post and the pole is 10 feet. The angle of elevation is 68°. Find the height of the fence post, *DE*.

14. The angle of elevation of the top of a tree is 64° at point *G* and 54° at point *D*. *GF* = 15 feet. *D*, *G*, and *F* are in a direct line with the tree. Find the height *EF*, of the tree and distance, *DG*.

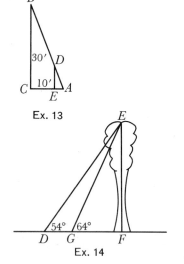

Ex. 13

Ex. 14

15. A pilot flying at an altitude of 3000 feet sighted an airport at an angle of depression of 46°. How far was he, horizontally, from the airport?

16. An object is sighted from two observation points on a building. The angle of depression of the object from one of the points is 28° and the angle of depression of the same object from the other point is 34°. If the object is 240 feet from the foot of the building, find the distance between the two observation points.

EXTEND YOUR HORIZON

Trigonometry also includes the study of the relationships existing between the functions. For example, it can readily be proved that given any right triangle with acute angle A, $\sin^2 A + \cos^2 A = 1$. [$\sin^2 A$ is another way of writing $(\sin A)^2$; it avoids the use of parentheses.] The proof is as follows:

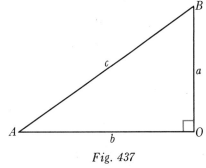

Given: Right triangle ABC,
$\qquad \angle C = 90°$.
Prove: $\sin^2 A + \cos^2 A = 1$.

Fig. 437

STATEMENTS	REASONS
1. $\triangle ABC$ is a right triangle, $\angle C = 90°$.	1. Given.
2. $a^2 + b^2 = c^2$.	2. The Pythagorean Theorem.
3. $\sin A = \dfrac{a}{c}$, or $a = c \sin A$.	3. In a right triangle the sine of an acute angle is the ratio of the length of the opposite leg to the length of the hypotenuse.
4. $\cos A = \dfrac{b}{c}$, or $b = c \cos A$.	4. In a right triangle the cosine of an acute angle is the ratio of the length of the adjacent leg to the length of the hypotenuse.
5. $a^2 = c^2 \sin^2 A$, $b^2 = c^2 \cos^2 A$.	5. Why?
6. $c^2 \sin^2 A + c^2 \cos^2 A = c^2$.	6. Substitution in Reason 2.
7. $\sin^2 A + \cos^2 A = 1$.	7. If equals are divided by equals, the quotients are equal.

Another common relationship in trigonometry is called the Law of Sines. This proposition states that the lengths of the sides of any triangle are proportional to the sines of their opposite angles, or symbolically

$$\frac{a}{\sin A} = \frac{b}{\sin B} = \frac{c}{\sin C}.$$

Examine the scalene triangle, *ABC*. By constructing a perpendicular from *C* to *AB*, two right triangles are formed.

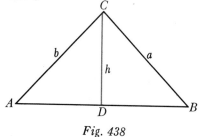

Fig. 438

By definition, $\sin A = \dfrac{h}{b}.$

$$\sin B = \dfrac{h}{a}.$$

then, $\dfrac{\sin A}{\sin B} = \dfrac{h}{b} \div \dfrac{h}{a} = \dfrac{h}{b} \times \dfrac{a}{h} = \dfrac{a}{b}.$

or $\dfrac{\sin A}{\sin B} = \dfrac{a}{b}.$

Likewise by constructing a perpendicular from *A* to *BC*, two right triangles are formed.

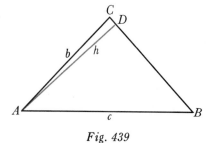

Fig. 439

By definition, $\sin B = \dfrac{h}{c}.$

$$\sin C = \dfrac{h}{b}.$$

then, $\dfrac{\sin B}{\sin C} = \dfrac{h}{c} \div \dfrac{h}{b} = \dfrac{h}{c} \times \dfrac{b}{h} = \dfrac{b}{c}.$

Using the principle of alternation, you obtain $\dfrac{b}{\sin B} = \dfrac{c}{\sin C}$.

By combining these two statements, $\dfrac{a}{\sin A} = \dfrac{b}{\sin B}$ and $\dfrac{b}{\sin B} = \dfrac{c}{\sin C}$, you have proved the Law of Sines.

$$\frac{a}{\sin A} = \frac{b}{\sin B} = \frac{c}{\sin C}.$$

There are six parts to every triangle, the three angles and the three sides. If the measures of three of the six parts are known, including one side, the measures of the remaining parts of the triangle can be computed using the trigonometric functions and relationships.

Can you solve these problems?

(*1*) In right triangle ABC, $\angle A = 45°$, $a = 10$ inches, solve for the measures of the other parts of the triangle.

(*2*) In right triangle ABC, $\angle C = 90°$, $c = 125$ rods, and $\angle A = 48°$. Determine the measures of a, b, and $\angle B$.

(*3*) Given triangle ABC with $b = 7$ feet, $\angle A = 60°$, $\angle B = 42°$, determine the measures of the unknown parts.

(*4*) Two weather bureau observers sight a weather balloon directly over a highway which extends past their stations 2500 yards apart. From the stations the angles of elevation of the balloon are $46°$ and $66°$. How high is the balloon?

CHAPTER SUMMARY

In a right triangle the ratio of the lengths of the legs depends on the size of the included angle. These ratios are

1. $\tan A = \dfrac{\text{leg opposite } \angle A}{\text{leg adjacent to } \angle A}$.   (page 510)

2. $\sin A = \dfrac{\text{leg opposite } \angle A}{\text{hypotenuse}}$.   (page 513)

3. $\cos A = \dfrac{\text{leg adjacent to } \angle A}{\text{hypotenuse}}$.   (page 515)

CHAPTER REVIEW

Vocabulary

Match the word in the left hand column with its correct definition in the right hand column.

1. Trigonometry

2. Similar Triangles

3. Hypotenuse

4. Adjacent Side

5. Opposite Side

6. Tangent A

7. Sine A

8. Cosine A

9. Angle of Depression

10. Angle of Elevation

a. In a right triangle the ratio of the length of the side adjacent to $\angle A$ to the length of the side opposite $\angle A$.

b. In a right triangle the ratio of the length of the side opposite $\angle A$ to the length of the side adjacent to $\angle A$.

c. In a right triangle the ratio of the length of the side adjacent to $\angle A$ to the length of the hypotenuse.

d. In a right triangle the ratio of the length of the side opposite $\angle A$ to the length of the hypotenuse.

e. An angle down from the line of sight.

f. An angle up from the line of sight.

g. The side opposite the right angle in a right triangle.

h. Triangles which can coincide.

i. Triangles having equal angles and the lengths of corresponding sides in proportion.

j. In a right triangle the leg next to the acute angle.

k. In a right triangle the leg across from the acute angle.

l. The branch of mathematics concerning the measurement of triangles.

Exercises

1. Using the method illustrated in Developmental Exercise **1** of The Table of Trigonometric Functions, determine the numerical values of the trigonometric functions for a 45° angle.

2. Using the same method as in Exercise **1,** determine the numerical values of the trigonometric functions for a 60° angle.

3. Using the table, check your answers in Exercises **1** and **2.**

4. Using the table, find the numerical values of the following trigonometric functions.

    a. sin 86°.   **b.** tan 32°.

    c. cos 54°.   **d.** tan 88°.

    e. sin 42°.   **f.** cos 79°.

5. Using the table, determine the measure of the angles A and B if their trigonometric functions have the following numerical values.

    a. sin $A = .9455$.   **b.** tan $B = 2.2460$.   **c.** cos $A = .0349$.

    d. sin $A = .9925$.   **e.** tan $B = .2126$.   **f.** cos $B = .5592$.

6. Using your answers in Exercise **4,** determine the numerical value of the following:

    a. cos 4°.   **b.** sin 36°.   **c.** cos 48°.   **d.** sin 11°.

7. Using your answers in Exercise **5,** determine the measure of the angles A and B if their trigonometric functions have the following numerical values.

    a. cos $A = .9455$.   **b.** sin $B = .0349$.

    c. cos $A = .9925$.   **d.** sin $B = .5592$.

8. Prove the relationships used in Exercise **6-7.**

9. From a 75 foot high fire tower in Cascade Park, a guard observes wisps of smoke. From his position the angle of depression is 13°. How far from a point directly below the observation platform is the smoke? Express your answer to the nearest tenth of a mile.

10. 300 feet from the base of a radio tower, on level ground, the angle of elevation of the top of the tower is 23°. Find the height of the tower to the nearest 10 feet.

11. When the angle of elevation of the sun is 53°, how tall is a tree if its measured shadow is 17.6 feet long?

12. When an ice boat has been driven just 3 miles northeast of its starting point, how far north has it traveled?

13. Use a sketch to show that the sine, cosine, and tangent ratios do not depend on the length of the sides of a right triangle.

14. The beam from a spotlight, on the ground, makes an angle of 62° with the ground. It illuminates the under side of a balloon which rides vertically at the end of a 150-foot wire. How far is the spotlight from the other end of the wire?

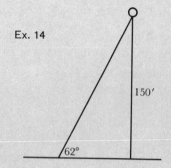

Ex. 14

150′

62°

15. A surveyor records that a new highway makes an angle of 6° with the horizon. How many feet does the highway rise with each 1000 feet of length?

16. Near a window in Jim's room, a large tree shields the window from the hot summer sun. Jim found the angle of elevation of the top of the tree from the lower edge of the window to be 36°. Then he measured the angle of depression of the base of the tree from the same point to be 27°. The base of this window is 14 feet above ground. How far is the tree from the window?

17. What width of tread should a carpenter construct in building a stairway if it is to have an inclination of 35° and each riser is to be 5 inches?

18. Using a transit 5′3″ in height, Fred measured the angle of elevation of a TV antenna as 50°. From his position to a point below the antenna was 30 feet. Compute the height of the antenna.

19. The base angles of an isosceles triangle measure 38°. The legs are 8.3 inches in length. Compute the length of the base of the triangle.

20. Compute the area of a parallelogram whose sides measure 7 inches and 10 inches with an included angle of 57°.

CHAPTER TEST

1. If $\angle X$ and $\angle Y$ are the two acute angles of a right triangle, $\cos \angle X = \sin \angle Y$. True or false? Give a reason for your answer.

2. The sides of a right triangle are 6 inches, 8 inches, and 10 inches. Express as a fraction the cosine of the smallest angle.

3. In $\triangle ABC$, $\angle C = 90°$, find the length of side a if side $b = 10$ inches and $\angle A = 42°$.

4. In $\triangle ABC$, $\angle C = 90°$, $\cos \angle A = .8660$, and $AB = 10'$. Find the measure of $\angle A$, $\angle B$, AC, and BC.

5. The diagonals of a rectangle are each 24 inches and intersect at an angle of 100°. Find, correct to the nearest integer, the lengths of the sides of the rectangle.

6. To find the distance across a swamp from A to B, a surveyor located a point, O, such that angle AOB was a right angle. By measurement, he found that distance $AO = 725$ feet, and $\angle A = 41°$. Find the length of AB correct to the nearest foot.

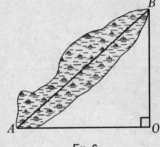

Ex. 6

7. At a given time, the angle of elevation of an airplane from a certain point on the ground is 55°. Another point on the ground directly under the plane is one-half mile from the first point where the angle of elevation was taken. How high is the plane at that time? Have your answer correct to the nearest foot.

8. From the top of a lighthouse 120 feet high, the angle of depression to a ship is 8°. How far is the ship from the base of the lighthouse? Give your answer correct to the nearest foot.

9. Find the length of a side of an isosceles triangle whose altitude measures 10 inches and base angles measure 40 degrees.

10. Some students, wishing to find the height of a tower, set up a transit 100 feet from the foot of the tower. They found that the angle of elevation to the top of the tower was 47°. If the height of the instrument was 4.7 feet, find the height of the tower.

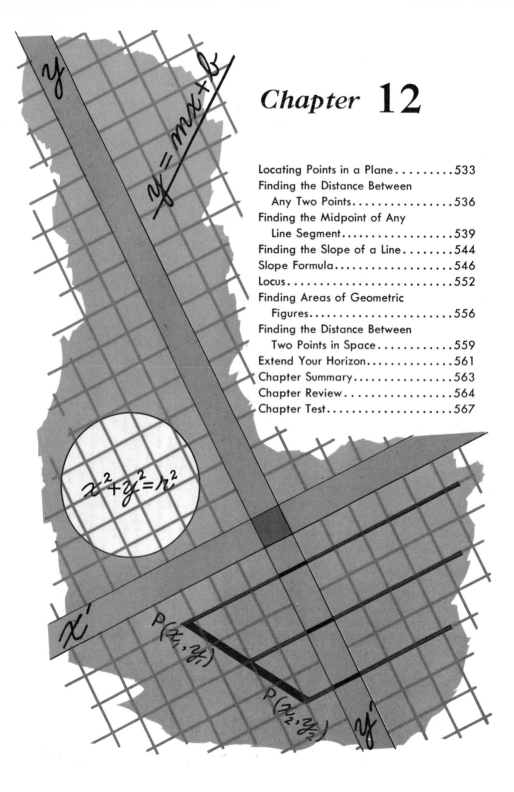

Chapter 12

COORDINATE GEOMETRY

LOCATING POINTS IN A PLANE

Coordinate Geometry is the link between geometry and mathematical analysis. It applies the language of algebra to describe various geometric relationships. In Chapter 7 you learned how a pair of ordered numbers (*coordinates*) and a pair of axes may be used to locate a point in a plane. In this chapter you will learn more about such a coordinate system.

Developmental Exercises

DE—1. Plot the points having the following coordinates: $A(2,4)$, $B(8,4)$, and $C(8,-6)$.

Solution

Draw a coordinate axis. Remember that numbers on the x-axis to the right of the origin are positive and that numbers on the x-axis to the left of the origin are negative. Numbers on the y-axis above the origin are positive and numbers on the y-axis below the origin are negative.

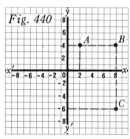

Fig. 440

The *abscissa* or x-coordinate of point A is 2 and the *ordinate* or y-coordinate of point A is 4. To plot this point proceed to the right of the origin 2 units and then up 4 units.

To plot point $B(8,4)$ count 8 units to the right of the origin and up 4 units.

To plot point $C(8,-6)$ count 8 units to the right of the origin and down 6 units.

Points A and B have the same ordinate while points B and C have the same abscissa.

Notice the following:

Two points with the same abscissa lie on a line parallel to the y-axis.
Two points with the same ordinate lie on a line parallel to the x-axis.

DE—2. Find the distance between the points **a.** A and B, and **b.** B and C in Developmental Exercise **1.**

Solution

a. By counting you find that the distance between points A and B is 6 units. This distance may also be determined from the coordinates of the points $(2,4)$ and $(8,4)$. Notice that the ordinates of these points are the same. Therefore, the distance between them is determined by the abscissas.

|| The distance between two points with the same ordinate is equal to the absolute value of the difference of their abscissas.

This distance may be represented by $|x_2-x_1|$ or $|\Delta x|$ (read delta x) if the coordinates of the two points are (x_1,y_1) and (x_2,y_1), respectively. Thus, the distance between points A and B is $|8-2|$ or 6 units.

b. By counting you can determine that the distance between points B and C is 10 units. The coordinates of the points, $B(8,4)$ and $C(8,-6)$, may also be used to determine the distance between them. Notice that the abscissas of these points are the same. Therefore, the distance between them is determined by the ordinates.

|| The distance between two points with the same abscissa is equal to the absolute value of the difference of the ordinates.

This distance may be represented by $|y_2-y_1|$ or $|\Delta y|$ (read delta y) if the coordinates of the two points are (x_1,y_1) and (x_1,y_2) respectively. Thus the distance between points B and C is $|-6-4|$ or 10 units.

DE—3. Plot $A(-3,-3)$, $B(7,-3)$, $C(3,2)$, and $D(-7,2)$. Prove that $ABCD$ is a parallelogram.

Solution

$DC \parallel XX'$ and $AB \parallel XX'$ since two points with the same ordinate lie on a line parallel to the x-axis. Therefore, $DC \parallel AB$ because two lines parallel to a third line are parallel to each other.

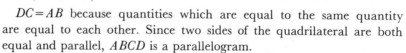

$DC=|3-(-7)|$ or 10 units.
$AB=|7-(-3)|$ or 10 units.

$DC=AB$ because quantities which are equal to the same quantity are equal to each other. Since two sides of the quadrilateral are both equal and parallel, $ABCD$ is a parallelogram.

Exercises

1. Plot the following points on graph paper:

   a. $A(3,5)$ **b.** $B(2,0)$ **c.** $C(-4,6)$ **d.** $D(7,-9)$

   e. $G(0,2)$ **f.** $I(0,-2)$ **g.** $J(8,-8)$ **h.** $K(-5,-5)$

2. In what quadrant is a point located

   a. if both coordinates are positive?

   b. if both coordinates are negative?

   c. if the abscissa is negative and the ordinate positive?

   d. if the abscissa is positive and the ordinate negative?

3. Find the distance between each of the following pairs of points:

   a. $(3,8)$ and $(11,8)$.   **b.** $(6,4)$ and $(6,9)$.

   c. $(-2,7)$ and $(6,7)$.   **d.** $(-3,-1)$ and $(-3,5)$.

4. A square whose side is 4 units has one vertex at the origin, another on the lower y-axis, and another on the x-axis to the right of the origin. Find the coordinates of the vertices.

5. Find the distance between each of the following pairs of points:

   a. $(0,c)$ and $(0,d)$.   **b.** $(a,0)$ and $(b,0)$.

   c. $(0,-c)$ and $(0,-d)$.   **d.** $(-d,c)$ and $(-b,0)$.

6. Plot the following points: $A(1,1)$, $B(7,1)$, and $C(4,10)$. Connect the points in the order given. What kind of triangle is triangle ABC? Prove your answer.

7. Draw the quadrilateral whose vertices are as follows. Name the type of quadrilateral formed.

   a. $(1,1)$, $(2,4)$, $(8,4)$, $(10,1)$

   b. $(-2,-2)$, $(-4,2)$, $(-6,-2)$, $(-4,-6)$

8. Plot $A(4,-1)$, $B(7,2)$, $C(4,5)$, and $D(1,2)$. Show that $ABCD$ is a parallelogram. Is it a special parallelogram? Justify your answer.

9. A rectangle has its center at the origin and one vertex at the point $(-2,3)$. If two sides are parallel to the y-axis, find the coordinates of the other vertices. Complete the drawing of the rectangle.

10. Plot the following points: $A(0,0)$, $B(5,-2)$, $C(10,0)$, and $D(5,2)$. Connect these points in the order given. Show that BD is the perpendicular bisector of AC. What type of quadrilateral is $ABCD$?

FINDING THE DISTANCE BETWEEN ANY TWO POINTS

In the previous lesson you found the distance between two points that lie on a line parallel to one of the axes. The following theorem enables you to find the distance between any two points located any place in a plane.

Developmental Exercises

DE—1. Prove the following theorem:

> **THEOREM 130**
>
> **The distance between any two points, $P_1(x_1,y_1)$ and $P_2(x_2,y_2)$, is $\sqrt{(x_2-x_1)^2+(y_2-y_1)^2}$.**

Solution

Given:

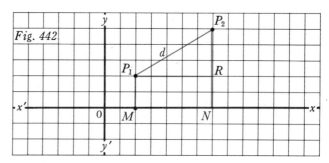

Fig. 442

Prove: $d=\sqrt{(x_2-x_1)^2+(y_2-y_1)^2}$ where d represents the distance between points P_1 and P_2.

Construction: Construct $P_1M \perp OX$, and $P_2N \perp OX$. R is the intersection of the perpendicular from P_1 to P_2N.

Proof:

As a result of the construction the coordinates of R are (x_2,y_1) and P_1P_2R is a right triangle.

$P_1R = |x_2-x_1|$, $P_2R = |y_2-y_1|$. Why?

Applying the Pythagorean Theorem you obtain

$$d^2 = (P_1R)^2 + (P_2R)^2$$

$$\text{or } d^2 = |x_2-x_1|^2 + |y_2-y_1|^2.$$

$$\text{therefore, } d = \sqrt{|x_2-x_1|^2 + |y_2-y_1|^2}.$$

Since the square of any number is a positive number, the absolute value signs are no longer necessary. Thus, the formula may be written

$$d = \sqrt{(x_2-x_1)^2+(y_2-y_1)^2}.$$

DE—2. Find the distance from point $B(4,7)$ to point $C(8,10)$.

Solution

Let the coordinates of point B be represented by (x_1,y_1).
Let the coordinates of point C be represented by (x_2,y_2).

$$x_1=4 \qquad y_1=7 \qquad x_2=8 \qquad y_2=10$$

$$d= \sqrt{(x_2-x_1)^2+(y_2-y_1)^2},$$
$$d= \sqrt{(8-4)^2+(10-7)^2},$$
$$d= \sqrt{(4)^2+(3)^2},$$
$$d= \sqrt{16+9},$$
$$d \doteq \sqrt{25},$$
$$d=5.$$

DE—3. Show that the quadrilateral which has the following points as vertices is a parallelogram: $(3,3)$, $(9,4)$, $(10,8)$, and $(4,7)$.

Solution

By means of the distance formula it can be shown that the opposite sides of the quadrilateral are equal.

To find the length of DC let point $D(4,7)$ be represented by (x_1,y_1) and point $C(10,8)$ be represented by (x_2,y_2).

$$d= \sqrt{(x_2-x_1)^2+(y_2-y_1)^2},$$
$$d= \sqrt{(10-4)^2+(8-7)^2},$$
$$d= \sqrt{(6)^2+(1)^2},$$
$$d= \sqrt{36+1},$$
$$d= \sqrt{37}.$$
$$DC= \sqrt{37}.$$

To find the length of AB, let point $A(3,3)$ be represented by (x_1,y_1) and point $B(9,4)$ be represented by (x_2,y_2).

$$d= \sqrt{(x_2-x_1)^2+(y_2-y_1)^2},$$
$$d= \sqrt{(9-3)^2+(4-3)^2},$$
$$d= \sqrt{(6)^2+(1)^2},$$
$$d= \sqrt{36+1},$$
$$d= \sqrt{37}.$$
$$AB= \sqrt{37}.$$
$$DC= \sqrt{AB}.$$

Likewise it can be shown that $AD= \sqrt{17}$ and $BC= \sqrt{17}$ so that $AD=BC$. Since the opposite sides of the quadrilateral are equal, the quadrilateral is a parallelogram.

Exercises

In the following exercises leave your answer in simplest radical form.

1. Find the distance between each of the following pairs of points.

    a. (1,2) and (7,10)   **b.** $(-6,-8)$ and $(-5,-3)$

    c. $(-4,7)$ and $(4,-8)$ **d.** $(9,-5)$ and $(-3,6)$

    e. (0,0) and $(-2,1)$ **f.** (o,a) and (b,o)

    g. (0,0) and (6,9)   **h.** $(-10,-8)$ and $(-6,12)$

2. Find the lengths of the diagonals of a quadrilateral whose vertices are $(2,-2)$, (8,2), and (2,8), and $(-5,1)$.

3. A circle whose center is the point (7,5) is tangent to the x-axis. Find the coordinates of the point of tangency.

4. The center of a circle is at point (3,4) and it passes through point (6,6). Will it also pass through point (1,7)?

5. The points (2,2), (11,2), (11,6), and (2,6) are the vertices of a rectangle. Show that the diagonals are equal.

6. The vertices of a trapezoid, $ABCD$, are $A(2,-9)$, $B(10,-5)$, $C(6,-2)$, and $D(2,-4)$. Show that $ABCD$ is an isosceles trapezoid.

7. Find the radius of the circle whose center is at the point $(-4,-6)$ and which passes through the point $(-6,-2)$.

8. A circle whose center is at the point (3,4) passes through the origin. Show that the point $(-1,1)$ lies on the circle and that the point (8,6) does not lie on the circle. Do not construct the circle.

9. The vertices of triangle ABC are $A(5,2)$, $B(-3,11)$, and $C(-7,1)$. Show that triangle ABC is isosceles.

10. Show that triangle ABC having vertices $(-2,6)$, $(7,-1)$, and (1,8) is a right triangle.

11. Find the lengths of the sides of a triangle whose vertices are $A(3,-5)$, $B(5,8)$, and $C(-4,5)$.

12. Find the perimeter of the triangle whose vertices are $(6,-3)$, $(-4,-2)$, and $(-6,-9)$.

13. Find the perimeter of the quadrilateral whose vertices are $A(-6,-2)$, $B(4,-8)$, $C(9,-2)$, and $D(-1,4)$.

14. Classify the quadrilateral in Exercise **13.** Give a reason for your answer.

15. Show that the triangle whose vertices are (1,2), (4,9), and (7,2) is isosceles.

16. Show that the triangle whose vertices are $(-7,1)$, $(1,-3)$, and (6,7) is a right triangle.

17. Show that the quadrilateral whose vertices are (1,3), (5,4), (6,8), and (2,7) is a rhombus.

18. The vertices of quadrilateral *ABCD* are the points $A(-4,3)$, $B(0,9)$, $C(-3,11)$, and $D(-7,5)$. Prove that quadrilateral *ABCD* is a rectangle.

FINDING THE MIDPOINT OF ANY LINE SEGMENT

In Figure 443 it is apparent that the midpoint of *AB* is (5,4) and the midpoint of *BC* is $(8,-1)$. These midpoints were obtained by counting. They could also have been found using the following principles.

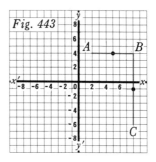

Fig. 443

If a line segment is parallel to the *x*-axis, the abscissa of its midpoint is found by averaging the abscissas of its endpoints.

$$x = \frac{x_1 + x_2}{2}$$

If a line segment is parallel to the *y*-axis, the ordinate of its midpoints is found by averaging the ordinates of its endpoints.

$$y = \frac{y_1 + y_2}{2}$$

These methods hold only for line segments parallel to an axis. In the following developmental exercises a method will be derived that can be used to find the midpoint of any line segment.

Developmental Exercises

DE—1. Prove the following theorem:

> **THEOREM 131**
>
> **The coordinates of the midpoint of any line segment from $P_1(x_1,y_1)$ to $P_2(x_2,y_2)$ are the averages of the coordinates of the endpoints.**

Given: Point M, the midpoint of P_1P_2.

Prove: The coordinates of M are $\left(\dfrac{x_1+x_2}{2}, \dfrac{y_1+y_2}{2}\right)$.

Solution

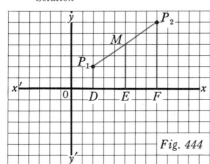

Fig. 444

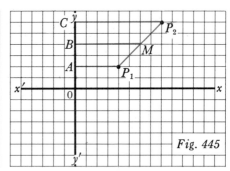

Fig. 445

The proof is in two parts. First, the proof of the abscissa using Figure 444, and second, the proof of the ordinate using Figure 445.

Construction: In Figure 444, construct P_1D, ME, and P_2F perpendicular to OX.

Proof:

STATEMENTS	REASONS
1. M is the midpoint of P_1P_2.	1. Given.
2. $P_1M = MP_2$.	2. Why?
3. $P_1D \perp OX$, $ME \perp OX$, $P_2F \perp OX$.	3. From a point outside a given line one, and only one, perpendicular can be constructed to the given line.
4. $P_1D \parallel ME \parallel P_2F$.	4. Lines perpendicular to the same line are parallel.
5. $DE = EF$.	5. If three or more parallel lines cut off equal line segments on one transversal, they cut off equal line segments on any other transversal.

6. Point D has coordinates $(x_1,0)$.
Point F has coordinates $(x_2,0)$.
Therefore point E has for its
coordinates $\left(\dfrac{x_1+x_2}{2},0\right)$.

7. Since ME is parallel to the y-axis, the abscissa of M is equal to $\dfrac{x_1+x_2}{2}$.

6. If a line segment is parallel (or on) to the x-axis, the abscissa of its midpoint is found by averaging the abscissas of its endpoints.

7. Why?

In like manner the ordinate of M can be shown to be $\dfrac{y_1+y_2}{2}$.

DE—2. Find the coordinates of the midpoint of the line segment which joins the point $B(3,5)$ and the point $C(7,-3)$.

Solution

Let (x,y) represent the coordinates of the midpoint of BC.

$$x=\frac{3+7}{2}.\qquad\qquad y=\frac{5+(-3)}{2}.$$
$$x=5.\qquad\qquad y=1.$$

$(5,1)$ are the coordinates of the midpoint of BC.

DE—3. Prove that the quadrilateral whose vertices are $A(2,2)$, $B(6,3)$, $C(8,9)$, and $D(4,8)$ is a parallelogram.

Solution

$ABCD$ is a parallelogram if the diagonals bisect each other. That is, the midpoint of AC should have the same coordinates as the midpoint of BD.

Let (x_1,y_1) represent the coordinates of the midpoint of AC.
$$x_1=\frac{2+8}{2}=5.$$
$$y_1=\frac{2+9}{2}=5\tfrac{1}{2}.$$

Therefore, $(x_1y_1)=(5,\ 5\tfrac{1}{2})$.
Let (x_2,y_2) represent the coordinates of BD.
$$x_2=\frac{4+6}{2}=5.$$
$$y_2=\frac{8+3}{2}=5\tfrac{1}{2}.$$

Therefore, $(x_2,y_2)=(5,\ 5\tfrac{1}{2})$.
Both AC and BD have the point $(5,\ 5\tfrac{1}{2})$ as their midpoint. Therefore, AC and BD bisect each other and $ABCD$ is a parallelogram.

Exercises

1. Find the coordinates of the midpoint of the line segments which join the following points:

    a. $(5,10)$, $(3,8)$ **b.** $(-3,-3)$, $(-4,-7)$

    c. $(-2,9)$, $(0,-1)$ **d.** $(3,-8)$, $(-3,8)$

    e. $(9,-5)$, $(7,-3)$ **f.** $(12,9)$, $(-2,-3)$

    g. $(6,9)$, $(0,0)$ **h.** $(8,4)$, $(6,7)$

    i. $(5,0)$, $(8,11)$ **j.** $(5,0)$, $(8,11)$

    k. $(17,8)$, $(0,0)$

2. Find the coordinates of the midpoints of the sides of a triangle whose vertices are $D(4,3)$, $E(-6,6)$, and $F(-2,-5)$.

3. Find the coordinates of the midpoints of the line segments which join the following points:

    a. $(0,0)$, $(0,d)$ **b.** $(4a,2a)$, $(a,6a)$

    c. $(3m,5n)$, $(2m,4n)$ **d.** $(-4b,2c)$, $(10b,8c)$

    e. $(0,0)$, (a,b) **f.** $(r,3s)$, $(5r,7s)$

    g. $(-2c,4b)$, $(8c,10b)$

4. Find the midpoints of the sides of a quadrilateral whose vertices are $(6,9)$, $(-5,5)$, $(-1,-2)$, and $(4,-4)$.

5. The midpoint of a line segment is $(6,6)$ and one endpoint is $(2,8)$. Find the other endpoint.

6. In trapezoid $ABCD$, M is the midpoint of side AB. The coordinates of point A are $(7,3)$ and the coordinates of M are $(-4,-8)$. Find the coordinates of point B.

7. M is the midpoint of side DF in triangle DEF. The coordinates of D are $(3,1)$ and of M $(7,4)$. Find the coordinates of point F.

8. AB is a diameter in a circle whose center is O. If the coordinates of point A are $(5,8)$ and of point $O(-2,4)$, find the coordinates of point B.

9. Find the abscissa of the midpoint of the line segment whose endpoints are $(3a,b)$, and $(-7a,3b)$.

10. RS is a diameter in a circle whose center is O. If the abscissa of point R is $6r$ and of point O is $-4r$, find the abscissa of point S. What is the length of the radius of the circle?

11. Find the coordinates of the midpoint of the line segment whose endpoints are $(4c,8d)$ and $(5c,-2d)$.

12. The points $D(-9,3)$, $E(-11,8)$, and $F(-2,3)$ are the vertices of a triangle. DM is a median to side EF. Find the coordinates of point M. What is the length of DM?

13. In a circle whose center is O, C and D are the endpoints of a diameter. Find the coordinates of point O when the coordinates of C and D are $(2r,0)$ and $(0,2s)$. Find the length of CD.

14. M is the midpoint of line segment AB. The coordinates of point M are $(-5,-2)$ and of point B are $(6,-8)$. Find the coordinates of point A. Find the length of AB.

15. The points $(1,1)$, $(9,3)$, $(11,8)$, and $(3,6)$ are the vertices of a quadrilateral. Show that its diagonals bisect each other. Classify the quadrilateral. Give a reason for your answer.

16. The points $A(2,0)$, $B(10,0)$, and $C(4,8)$ are the vertices of triangle ABC. Show that the line segment which joins the midpoints of CA and CB is equal to one-half of AB.

17. Given the quadrilateral whose vertices are $R(-6,-2)$, $S(1,2)$, $T(3,7)$, and $U(-4,3)$. Show that $RSTU$ is a parallelogram. Do the diagonals bisect each other?

18. Plot $A(-5,-1)$, $B(13,-1)$, $C(7,5)$, and $D(-3,5)$. Find the coordinates of the midpoints M and P of AD and BC respectively. Draw MP. Find the lengths of DC, MP, and AB. State the theorem that explains the relationship between the lengths of DC, MP, and AB. Does your data agree with the theorem?

19. Show that the diagonals of the quadrilateral whose vertices are $(8,-9)$, $(9,-3)$, $(4,5)$, and $(1,-3)$ do not bisect each other.

20. The points $D(-2,-1)$, $E(6,1)$, $F(10,9)$, and $G(-4,7)$ are the vertices of polygon $DEFG$. Find the coordinates of the midpoints of the sides of polygon $DEFG$. Draw the line segments joining the consecutive midpoints and prove that the resulting figure is a parallelogram.

FINDING THE SLOPE OF A LINE

The diagrams below show the inclination of a line. *The **inclination** of a line is the least angle a given line makes with the **x**-axis measured in a counterclockwise direction from the positive direction of the **x**-axis to the line.*

In Figure 446 the inclination of line AB is angle XRB.

In Figure 447 the inclination of line CD is angle XSC.

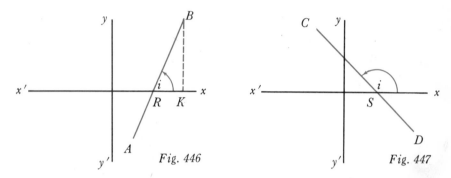

Fig. 446   Fig. 447

*The **slope of a line** is the trigonometric tangent of its inclination.* In Figure 446 the slope of $AB = \tan i = \dfrac{BK}{RK}$.

If the inclination of a line is an acute angle, the slope of the line is positive. In Figure 446 the slope of line AB is positive.

If the inclination of a line is an obtuse angle, the slope of the line is negative. In Figure 447 the slope of line CD is negative.

*If a line is parallel to the **x**-axis the slope of the line is zero.*

*If a line is parallel to the **y**-axis, the slope of the line does not exist* since division by zero yields a meaningless result. We say such a slope is undefined or does not exist.

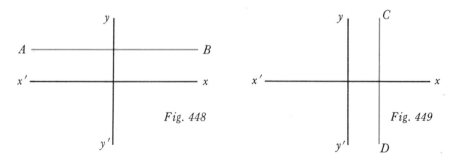

Fig. 448   Fig. 449

Exercises

1. Complete: The slope of a line is the trigonometric_____
_____.

2. The slope of a line is sometimes expressed by the formula: slope $=$
$\dfrac{\Delta y}{\Delta x}$. Explain this in the light of the definition given in Exercise **1**.

3. Express in words the formula given in Exercise **2**.

4. Classify the slopes of each of the following lines as positive, negative, zero, or undefined.

a.

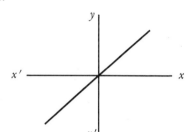

b.

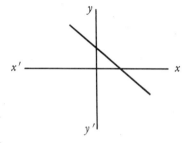

c.

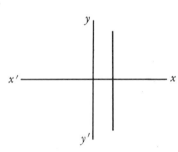

d.

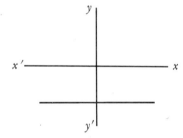

5. Determine the numerical value of the slope of the following lines.

a.

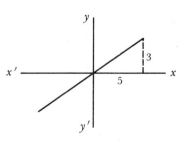

b.

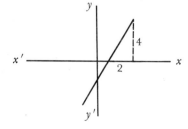

c.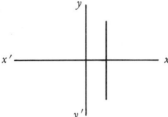

d.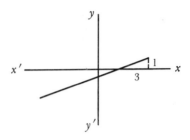

e.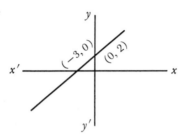

f.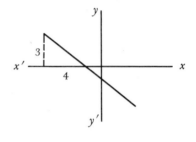

6. On rectangular coordinate paper draw the line that
   a. passes through the origin and has a slope of 2.
   b. passes through (2,0) and has a slope of 1.
   c. passes through $(0, -3)$ and has a slope of $\frac{1}{2}$.
   d. passes through (0,3) and has a slope of 0.
   e. passes through $(-2,3)$ and has a slope of $\frac{3}{2}$.
   f. passes through $(1, -1)$ and has a slope of $\frac{-3}{5}$.

SLOPE FORMULA

We will now derive a special formula for finding the slope of a line segment joining two points.

To find the slope of the line segment which joins point $A(x_1,y_1)$ and point $B(x_2,y_2)$, we will apply the tangent function.

$$\tan i = \frac{BC}{AC}.$$

$$\tan i = \frac{y_2 - y_1}{x_2 - x_1}.$$

Let m represent $\tan i$ or the slope of AB, then $m = \dfrac{y_2 - y_1}{x_2 - x_1}.$

The method for finding the slope of a line segment may be modified to find the slopes of these peaks in the Teton Mountains.

‖ *Developmental Exercises*

DE—1. Find the slope of a line whose inclination is 40°.

Solution

The slope of the line is equal to tan 40°.

Using the table of trigonometric functions, the slope of the line is .8391.

DE—2. Find the slope of the line segment which joins the points $A(3,2)$ and $B(9,5)$.

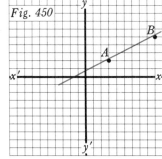

Solution

Let $A(3,2)$ be represented by (x_1, y_1) and $B(9,5)$ be represented by (x_2, y_2).

$$m = \frac{y^2 - y^1}{x_2 - x_1},$$

$$m = \frac{5-2}{9-3},$$

$$m = \frac{3}{6} \text{ or } \frac{1}{2}.$$

Fig. 450

DE—3. Prove that the points $D(2,5)$, $E(5,6)$, and $F(11,8)$ are collinear.

Solution

Assumption 48

The slopes of all line segments of the same straight line are equal.
The slope of a straight line is a constant.

Assumption 49

Three points, A, B, and C, are collinear if the slope of the line segment which joins A and B is equal to the slope of the line segment which joins B and C.

Thus, to prove that D, E, and F are collinear, show that the slope of line segment DE is equal to the slope of line segment EF.

The completion of this exercise is left to the student. Did you find the slope of both segments to be $\frac{1}{3}$?

DE—4. Prove that the line which joins the points $G(2,3)$ and $H(6,9)$ is parallel to the line which joins the points $J(7,6)$ and $K(11,12)$.

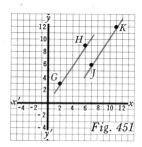

Fig. 451

Solution

Assumption 50

If two straight lines are parallel, their slopes are equal.

Assumption 51

If the slopes of two straight lines are equal, the lines are parallel.

To prove that $GH \parallel JK$, show that the slope of line segment GH is equal to the slope of line JK.

To find the slope of GH, let $G(2,3)$ be represented by (x_1,y_1) and $H(6,9)$ be represented by (x_2,y_2).

$$m = \frac{y_2 - y_1}{x_2 - x_1},$$
$$m = \frac{9-3}{6-2},$$
$$m = \frac{6}{4} \text{ or } \frac{3}{2}.$$

Now show that the slope of JK is also $\frac{3}{2}$.

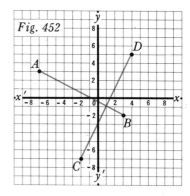

Fig. 452

DE—5. Prove that ·the line which joins the points $A(-7,3)$ and $B(3,-2)$ is perpendicular to the line which joins the points $C(-2,-7)$ and $D(4,5)$.

Solution

Assumption 52

If two straight lines are perpendicular, the slope of one line is the negative reciprocal of the slope of the other line.

If the product of two numbers is 1, one number is said to be the **reciprocal** *of the other number.* For example, $\frac{2}{3}$ is the reciprocal of $\frac{3}{2}$ because $\frac{2}{3} \times \frac{3}{2} = 1$.

If the product of two numbers is -1, *one number is said to be the* **negative reciprocal** *of the other number.* For example, $\frac{-2}{3}$ is the negative reciprocal of $\frac{3}{2}$ because $\frac{-2}{3} \times \frac{3}{2} = -1$.

Assumption 53

If the slope of one straight line is the negative reciprocal of the slope of another straight line, the lines are perpendicular to each other.

To prove that $AB \perp CD$, show that the slope of line AB is the negative reciprocal of the slope of line CD.

To find the slope of AB, let $A(-7,3)$ be represented by (x_1,y_2) and B $(3,-2)$ be represented by (x_2,y_2).

$$m = \frac{y_2 - y_1}{x_2 - x_1},$$

$$m = \frac{-2-3}{3-(-7)},$$

$$m = \frac{-5}{3+7},$$

$$m = \frac{-5}{10} \text{ or } \frac{-1}{2}.$$

It is left to the student to show that the slope of CD is the negative reciprocal of $\frac{-1}{2}$ which is $\frac{2}{1}$ or 2.

Exercises

1. Find the slope of a line whose inclination is 70°.

2. The vertices of a quadrilateral are $A(-2,4)$, $B(5,7)$, $C(1,10)$, and $D(-6,7)$. Prove that the figure is a parallelogram. (Use the method of slopes.)

3. Find the slope of the line segment which joins the two points in each of the following parts.

    a. (4,6) and (7,9)   **b.** (0,5) and (3,8)
    c. (0,0) and (10,4)   **d.** (2,5) and $(-1,6)$
    e. $(-4,7)$ and $(-2,0)$ **f.** (0,0) and $(-3,5)$
    g. (7,9) and (5,4)   **h.** $(6,-3)$ and $(8,-10)$
    i. $(0,-4)$ and $(-7,0)$ **j.** $(-5,-9)$ and (0,0)

4. Prove that the points $A(-4,-9)$, $B(8,-5)$, $C(4,-2)$, and $D(-2,-4)$ are the vertices of a trapezoid.

5. Find the slope of a line which is perpendicular to a line whose slope is: **a.** $\frac{3}{5}$, **b.** $\frac{-4}{7}$, **c.** 5, **d.** $\frac{-3}{8}$. **e.** $2\frac{1}{4}$, and **f.** .3.

6. The vertices of a quadrilateral are $R(-3,2)$, $S(4,1)$, $T(9,6)$, and $U(2,7)$. Show that the quadrilateral is a rhombus.

7. Find the slope of the line segment which joins the points $A(2,2)$ and $B(5,6)$.

8. Prove that $(-1,-2)$, (7,4), (4,8), and $(-4,2)$ are the vertices of a rectangle.

9. Complete the following statements:
    a. The slope of a line is positive if _____.
    b. The slope of a line is zero if _____.
    c. The slope of a line is negative if _____.
    d. The slopes of two straight lines are equal if _____.
    e. The slope of one line is the negative reciprocal of the slope of another line if _____.
    f. The slope of a line does not exist if _____.

10. Prove that (3,3), (6,6), (3,9), and (0,6) are the vertices of a square.

11. Prove that the points $A(2,-2)$, $B(-1,1)$, and $C(-5,5)$ are collinear.

12. Show that $\dfrac{y_2-y_1}{x_2-x_1}=\dfrac{y_1-y_2}{x_1-x_2}$.

13. Prove that the line which joins the points $A(17,5)$ and $B(-3,2)$ is parallel to the line which joins the points $C(-5,7)$ and $D(3,1)$.

14. $D(6,-8)$, $E(-2,2)$, and $F(12,0)$ are the vertices of triangle DEF. G is the midpoint of DE and H is the midpoint of DF. Show that GH is parallel to EF and $GH=\frac{1}{2}EF$.

15. Prove that the line which joins the points $A(1,3)$ and $B(11,7)$ is perpendicular to the line which joins the points $C(4,10)$ and $D(10,-5)$. Is it the perpendicular bisector?

16. The vertices of a parallelogram $ABCD$ are $A(1,-3)$, $B(10,-2)$, $C(11,y)$, and $D(2,4)$. Find the slope of AD. Express the slope of BC in terms of y and then find the value of y.

17. Find the slope of a line, if possible, which is perpendicular to a line which joins the points

    a. $(3,4)$ and $(6,9)$ **b.** $(-2,-5)$ and $(0,7)$

    c. $(1,8)$ and $(10,-6)$ **d.** $(3,4)$ and $(-5,5)$

    e. $(-3,2)$ and $(5,-2)$ **f.** $(0,0)$ and $(17,0)$

    g. $(3,2)$ and $(2,3)$ **h.** $(-3,2)$ and $(-3,-2)$

18. The point $(x, 12)$ lies on the line which passes through the points $(3,8)$ and $(-5,10)$. Find the slope of the line and then find the value of x.

19. Determine by means of slopes which of the following points are the vertices of a right triangle.

    a. $(2,7)$, $(7,11)$, $(-2,12)$ **b.** $(-4,3)$, $(2,-3)$, $(5,1)$

    c. $(-3,-3)$, $(7,-4)$, $(4,-8)$ **d.** $(-4,-2)$, $(7,-3)$, $(1,-8)$

    e. $(-1,0)$, $(8,-3)$, $(7,2)$ **f.** $(6,2)$, $(-4,3)$, $(-2,0)$

20. The vertices of quadrilateral $EFGH$ are $E(0,0)$, $F(a,-b)$, $G(a,c-b)$, and $H(o,c)$. Find the slope of HG and the slope of EF. Find the length of HG and the length of EF. Prove that $EFGH$ is a parallelogram.

LOCUS

Before we begin our study of locus in terms of rectangular coordinates, recall that a **locus** *is a line, or a set of lines, that contains all points that satisfy a given condition and contains no points which do not satisfy the given condition.* An equation of a locus is an equation which is satisfied by the coordinates of any point on the locus and is not satisfied by the coordinates of any point not on the locus. The locus of an equation contains all points and only those points whose coordinates satisfy the equation.

‖Developmental Exercises

DE—1. What is the locus of all points for which $x = 2$?

Solution

Fig. 453

The locus of all points for which $x = 2$ is a line parallel to the y-axis and 2 units to the right of it. The equation of the line is $x = 2$.

To generalize we can state:

‖ **The locus of all points whose abscissa is *a* is a line which is parallel to the y-axis. The equation of the line is $x = a$.**

DE—2. What is the locus of all points for which $y = -4$?

Solution

Fig. 454

The locus of all points for which $y = -4$ is a line parallel to the x-axis and 4 units below it. The equation of the line is $y = -4$.

‖ **The locus of points whose ordinate is *b* is a line which is parallel to the x-axis. The equation of the line is $y = b$.**

DE—3. What is the locus of all points whose ordinate is three times its abscissa?

Solution

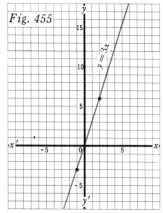

Fig. 455

The locus of all points whose ordinate is three times its abscissa is a line which passes through the origin and whose slope is 3. The equation of the line is $y = 3x$.

> The locus of all points whose ordinate is m times its abscissa is a line which passes through the origin with slope equal to m. The equation of the line is $y = mx$.

DE—4. What is the locus of all points whose ordinate is 2 less than 5 times its abscissa?

Solution

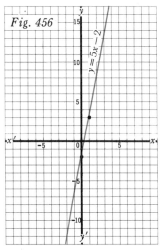

Fig. 456

The equation of the line is $y = 5x - 2$. By substituting values for x and plotting the resulting x and y coordinates of the points we observe that the line intersects the y-axis 2 units below the origin and has a slope of 5. Therefore, the locus of points whose ordinate is 2 less than 5 times its abscissa is a line whose slope is 5 and which intersects the y-axis 2 units below the origin.

> The locus of all points whose slope is constant is a line whose equation is $y = mx + b$, where m represents the slope of the line and b represents the y-intercept, the ordinate of the point at which the line intersects the y-axis.

DE—5. Write the equation of the line which passes through the point (3,4) and whose slope is $\frac{1}{2}$.

Solution

From the derivation of the slope formula in the previous lesson, it can be shown that:

> **A straight line which passes through the point $P(x_1y_1)$ and has a constant slope, m, has the equation $m = \dfrac{y - y_1}{x - x_1}$.**

Let the point (3,4) be (x_1,y_1) and the slope $\frac{1}{2}$ be m.

$$m = \frac{y - y_1}{x - x_1}.$$
$$\frac{1}{2} = \frac{y - 4}{x - 3}.$$
$$x - 3 = 2(y - 4),$$
$$x - 3 = 2y - 8,$$
$$-2y = -5.$$

DE—6. What is the locus of all points 5 units from the origin?

Solution

From our earlier study of the chapter on locus we recall that the locus of all points at a given distance from a given point is a circle whose center is the given point and whose radius is the given distance.

Therefore, the locus of all points 5 units from the origin is a circle whose center is the origin and whose radius is 5 units. To find the equation of the circle we will apply the distance formula. Let point $P(x,y)$ be any point on the circle. The coordinates of the origin are (0,0) and the distance of point P from the origin is 5.

Fig. 457

Let point $P(x,y)$ be (x_2,y_2) and point $O(0,0)$ be (x_1,y_1).
Then $d = (x_2 - x_1)^2 + (y_2 - y_1)^2$.
$$5 = (x - 0)^2 + (y - 0)^2,$$
$$5 = x^2 + y^2.$$
$25 = x^2 + y^2$ or $x^2 + y^2 = 25$ is the equation of the circle.

> **The locus of points whose distance from the origin is r is a circle whose center is the origin and whose radius is r. The equation of the circle is $x^2 + y^2 = r^2$.**

Exercises

1. a. What is the locus or points for which $x = -7$?

    b. What is the locus of points for which $y = 3$?

2. Write the equation and plot the graph of the line which is the locus of points whose ordinate is 3 more than 2 times its abscissa.

3. What is the locus of points equidistant from $y = 4$ and $y = -2$?

4. Write the equation of the line which passes through the point $(2,5)$ and whose slope is $\frac{1}{3}$.

5. What is the locus of points whose ordinate is four times its abscissa? Give a sentence answer and also write the equation.

6. What is the locus of points 8 units from the origin? Give a sentence answer and also write the equation.

7. What is the locus of points whose ordinate is equal to its abscissa? Give a sentence answer and also write the equation.

8. Find the slope and y-intercept for each of the following:

    a. $y = 5x + 2$.   **b.** $y = \frac{3}{4}x - 6$.

    c. $y = x - 8$.   **d.** $4x + y = 11$.

    e. $y = -x$.   **f.** $7y - 3x = 13$.

    g. $8x + 2y = 5$.   **h.** $3x - 2y = 7$.

9. Write the equation of a straight line through the point $(-4,1)$ perpendicular to the y-axis.

10. Give the x and y-intercepts for each of the following:

    a. $y = x + 3$.   **b.** $x + y = 8$.

    c. $y = x - 5$.   **d.** $x - y = 4$.

    e. $y = 6x + 2$.   **f.** $4x - 3y = 11$.

    g. $3x + 2y = 5$.   **h.** $3y - 3x = 5$.

11. Write the equation of a straight line passing through the point $(-3, -3)$ and parallel to the x-axis.

12. Line AB passes through the points $(0,3)$ and $(0,9)$. Point $C(0,7)$ is on line AB. Write the equation of the locus of the centers of circles which are tangent to line AB and point C.

13. Write the equation of a straight line whose slope and y-intercept are

    a. 2 and 3.   **b.** $\frac{3}{5}$ and 6.

    c. 3 and -7.   **d.** $-\frac{3}{4}$ and -2.

    e. -4 and 8.   **f.** $-\frac{7}{4}$ and 1.

14. Write the equation of the locus of points whose distance from the origin is 6. Is the point $(3,5)$ on the locus? Is the point $(-6,0)$ on the locus? Show your work.

15. Express algebraically the locus of points which are 4 units from the line $x = -3$.

16. Write the equation of the locus of the centers of circles which are tangent to both **a.** $x = -1$ and $x = -7$, **b.** $y = 3$ and $y = -9$. What are the coordinates of the center of a circle which will be tangent to the lines in both a and b? What is the length of the radius of this circle?

17. Write the equation of the locus of points equidistant from the points $(2, -6)$ and $(6,2)$.

18. What is the locus of the centers of circles which pass through the two given points $(-4, -4)$ and $(6, -8)$? Write the equation.

19. Represent graphically: **a.** the locus of points 6 units from the x-axis, and **b.** 8 units from the origin. Write the equation for the loci in parts **a** and **b**. Find the coordinates of the points of intersection of the loci.

20. a. What is the locus of points equidistant from the points $A(-1,9)$ and $B(9,3)$? **b.** What is the locus of points equidistant from the points $C(-12,2)$ and $D(-6,12)$. Express the answer to each part algebraically. Find the coordinates of the point which satisfies the conditions given in both **a** and **b**.

FINDING AREAS OF GEOMETRIC FIGURES

If necessary, before studying this lesson, review the area formulas presented in the chapter on areas of surfaces. In many cases we will be combining the areas of several geometric figures in our process of finding the area of a given polygon with reference to a given coordinate system.

Developmental Exercises

DE—1. Find the area of a parallelogram whose vertices are $A(-4,-1)$, $B(4,-1)$, $C(2,3)$ and $D(-6,3)$.

Solution

    To find the area of a parallelogram $ABCD$, find the length of the base AB and the length of the altitude CE.

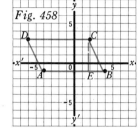

Fig. 458

$AB = |4-(-4)|$,

$AB = |4+4|$,

$AB = 8$.

$CE = 4$.

Area of $ABCD = bh$.

Area of $ABCD = 8(4)$ or 32 square units.

DE—2. Find the area of a triangle whose vertices are $A(-7, 3)$, $B(5,6)$, and $C(-5,8)$.

Solution

    To find the area of a given polygon, drop perpendiculars from the vertices of the polygon to the x-axis or to the y-axis. In this way more convenient figures are formed and then, by the process of addition or subtraction, the total area of the given polygon can be computed.

    Construct perpendicular lines through the vertices A, B, and C of the triangle to form a rectangle, $ADEF$. You must find the areas of triangles AFC, CEB, and ABD. By subtracting their total area from the area of rectangle $ADEF$ you will obtain the area of triangle ABC.

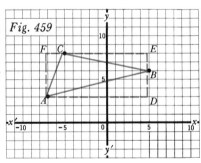

Fig. 459

Area of $\triangle ABC =$ Area of rectangle $ADEF -$ (Area of $\triangle AFC +$ Area of $\triangle CEB +$ Area of $\triangle ABD$).

Area of $\triangle ABC = 12\ (5) - \frac{1}{2}(2)\ (5) + \frac{1}{2}\ (10)\ (2) + \frac{1}{2}\ (12)\ (3)$.

Area of $\triangle ABC = 60 - (5+10+18)$.

Area of $\triangle ABC = 60 - (33)$.

Area of $\triangle ABC = 27$ square units.

Exercises

1. Find the area of a parallelogram whose vertices are $(-6,-4)$, $(6,-4)$, $(9,3)$, and $(-3,3)$.

2. Find the area under the graph of equation $y = 3x + 2$ and above the x-axis from $x = 0$ to $x = 4$.

3. Find the area of a rectangle whose vertices are $(-4,4)$, $(6,4)$, $(6,7)$, and $(-4,7)$.

4. Points $D(1,-8)$, $E(10,-8)$, $F(13,-3)$ and $G(4,-3)$ are the vertices of quadrilateral $DEFG$. What kind of quadrilateral is $DEFG$? Find the area of quadrilateral $DEFG$.

5. Find the area of a triangle whose vertices are $(0,0)$, $(0,8)$, and $(-4,3)$.

6. The coordinates of the vertices of triangle ABC are $A(3,2)$, $B(11,2)$ and $C(7,12)$. Find the length of the altitude of triangle ABC on side AB. Find the area of triangle ABC.

7. Find the area of a trapezoid whose vertices are $(2,-5)$, $(6,-2)$, $(6,-14)$, and $(2,-9)$.

8. Plot the points $D(-3,-6)$, $E(5,-2)$, and $F(3,7)$. Through point D draw lines parallel to both axes. Through point F draw a line parallel to the x-axis. Find the area of the rectangle that is formed. Draw DE, EF, and DF. Find the area of triangle DEF.

9. Find the area of a rhombus whose vertices are $(-5,2)$, $(8,2)$, $(13,14)$, and $(0,14)$. Show a check using a different formula.

10. The vertices of triangle RST are the points $R(2,3)$, $S(8,11)$, and $T(14,5)$. Find the area of triangle RST. Find the length of side RS. Find the length of the altitude from point T to side RS.

11. Find the area of a triangle whose vertices are $A(-6,6)$, $B(6,2)$, and $C(3,8)$. Show two solutions.

12. Prove that the quadrilateral whose vertices are $R(-4,-2)$, $S(4,-8)$, $T(12,-2)$, and $U(4,4)$ is a rhombus. Find the area of the rhombus.

13. The lines $x = 0$, $y = x$, $x = 6$, and $y = x + 8$ intersect to form a quadrilateral. Find the area of the quadrilateral.

14. Given points $O(0,0)$, $P(10,0)$, and $M(14,3)$, write the equation of the line through point O parallel to line MP. Write the equation of the line through point M parallel to line OP. Find the coordinates of the point of intersection of the two lines. Find the area of quadrilateral $MNOP$.

15. On the same set of axes draw the graph of each of the equations $y = 2x$, $y = x$, and $y = 8$. Find the coordinates of the vertices of the triangle whose sides are the line segments joining the points of intersection of the graphs. Find the area of this triangle.

16. The coordinates of the vertices of triangle DEF are $D(2,3)$, $E(8,9)$, and $F(12,5)$. Show that triangle DEF is a right triangle. Find the area of triangle DEF in two different ways.

FINDING THE DISTANCE BETWEEN TWO POINTS IN SPACE

In the study of plane geometry we use a pair of coordinates to locate a point in a plane. To locate a point in space we need three coordinates. We use three *mutually perpendicular planes*, the xy-plane, the xz-plane, and the yz-plane, respectively. To locate a point whose coordinates, are $(3,4,-2)$, we proceed 3 units perpendicular to, and to the right of, the yz-plane; 4 units perpendicular to, and to the left of, the xz-plane; and 2 units perpendicular to, and below, the xy-plane. Study the location of the point in Figure 460.

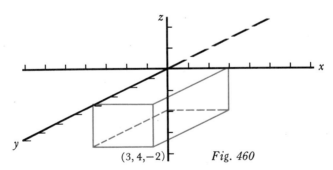

$(3,4,-2)$ *Fig. 460*

It can be proved that the distance between two points (x_1,y_1,z_1) and (x_2,y_2,z_2) in space is given by the formula,

$$d = \sqrt{(x_1 - x_2)^2 + (y_1 - y_2)^2 + (z_1 - z_2)^2}$$

Use the distance formula on the previous page to find the distance between point $A(-3,5,6)$ and point $B(2,4,-5)$.

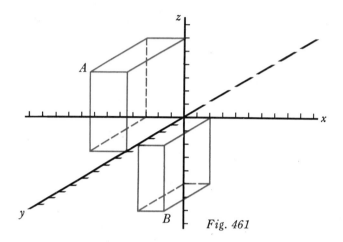

Fig. 461

Solution

Let point $A(-3, 5, 6)$ be (x_1, y_1, z_1) and point $B(2, 4, -5)$ be (x_2, y_2, z_2), then

$$x_1 = -3 \qquad\qquad y_1 = 5 \qquad\qquad z_1 = 6$$
$$x_2 = 2 \qquad\qquad y_2 = 4 \qquad\qquad z_2 = -5$$

$$d = \sqrt{(x_1-x_2)^2+(y_1-y_2)^2+(z_1-z_2)^2},$$
$$d = \sqrt{(-3-2)^2+(5-4)^2+(6-[-5])^2},$$
$$d = \sqrt{(-5)^2+(1)^2+(6+5)^2},$$
$$d = \sqrt{25+1+121},$$
$$d = \sqrt{147},$$
$$d = \sqrt{3} \cdot \sqrt{49},$$
$$d = 7\sqrt{3}.$$

Exercises

1. Plot the points $C(2,3,4)$, $D(-2,3,4)$, $E(2,-3,4)$, and $F(2,3,-4)$ by drawing three mutually perpendicular lines.

2. Find the distance between the following points:

a. $A(4,3,7)$ and $B(2,5,-6)$,

b. $C(-5,3,4)$ and $D(-6,-2,-5)$,

c. $E(1,2,3)$ and $F(-1,-2,-3)$.

CHAPTER SUMMARY

The distance between two points

1. with the same ordinate is equal to the absolute value of the difference of the abscissas.   (page 534)

2. with the same abscissa is equal to the absolute value of the difference of the ordinates.   (page 534)

3. having coordinates (x_1, y_1) and (x_2, y_2) is $\sqrt{(x_2 - x_1)^2 + (y_2 - y_1)^2}$. (page 536)

The midpoint of a line segment

1. parallel to the *x*-axis, has as its abscissa the average of the abscissas of the endpoints of the line segment.   (page 539)

2. parallel to the *y*-axis, has as its ordinate the average of the ordinates of the endpoints of the line segment.   (page 539)

3. has coordinates which are the averages of the coordinates of the endpoints.   (page 540)

The slope of a line

1. is the trigonometric tangent of its inclination.   (page 544)

2. is positive, if the inclination of the line is an acute angle. (page 544)

3. is negative if the inclination of the line is an obtuse angle. (page 544)

4. is zero if the line is parallel to the *x*-axis.   (page 544)

5. does not exist if the line is parallel to the *y*-axis.   (page 544)

6. joining two points, (x_1, y_1) and (x_2, y_2) is $\dfrac{y_2 - y_1}{x_2 - x_1}$.   (page 546)

7. is a constant.   (page 548)

If two lines

1. are parallel, their slopes are equal.   (page 548)

2. are perpendicular, the slope of one line is the negative reciprocal of the slope of the other line.   (page 549)

CHAPTER REVIEW

Vocabulary

Match the word in the left hand column with its correct definition in the right hand column.

1. Abscissa

2. Ordinate

3. Coordinates

4. Origin

5. Midpoint

6. Locus

7. Delta y (Δy)

8. $d = \sqrt{(x_2 - x_1)^2 + (y_2 - y_1)^2}$

9. Inclination of a Line

10. Slope of a Line

a. The distance between two points with the same ordinate.

b. The distance between two points with the same abscissa.

c. The trigonometric tangent of its inclination.

d. The least angle the line makes with the x-axis measured in a counterclockwise direction from the positive direction of the x-axis to the line.

e. The distance measured along the vertical axis.

f. The distance measured along the horizontal axis.

g. The point of intersection of the coordinate axis.

h. The abscissa value and the ordinate value of a point.

i. The middle point of a line segment.

j. A set of points satisfying stated conditions.

k. A set of points.

Exercises

1. Plot the following points: $R(4,6)$, $S(-7,-3)$, and $T(9,-4)$. Connect these points in the order given. What is the resulting figure?

2. Find the distance between the points $(4,1)$ and $(4,9)$ and give the coordinates of the midpoint of the line segment joining the two points.

3. Plot the points $D(-9,2)$, $E(-5,11)$, and $F(-1,2)$ and connect them with straight lines. What kind of a triangle is formed? Prove your answer.

4. Plot $A(-8,-4)$, $B(6,-4)$, $C(11,3)$, and $D(-3,3)$. Prove that $ABCD$ is a parallelogram.

5. Find the coordinates of the midpoint of the line segment which joins the point $A(-5,-4)$ and the point $B(9,4)$. Find the length of AB.

6. Show that the diagonals of the quadrilateral whose vertices are $R(-6,2)$, $S(-1,4)$, $T(0,12)$ and $U(-5,10)$ bisect each other. Classify the quadrilateral.

7. Find the distance from point $A(-9,-7)$ to point $B(-3,1)$. Find the midpoint of the line joining these two points.

8. Find the lengths of the sides of a triangle whose vertices are $D(-4,2)$, $E(3,10)$, and $F(5,-5)$. Leave your answer in simplest radical form.

9. Plot $A(-2,-2)$, $B(2,0)$, and $C(-4,4)$. Find the length of MN, the line segment joining the midpoints of AC and BC. Compare the length of MN with the length of AB. What theorem is illustrated in this problem?

10. Plot $A(-9,-1)$, $B(9,-2)$, and $C(-3,7)$. Show that triangle ABC is a right triangle.

11. Find the slope of a line whose angle of inclination is $50°$.

12. Prove that the points $A(-2,12)$, $B(1,10)$, and $C(7,6)$ are collinear.

13. Find the slope of the line segment which joins the points $C(-6,8)$ and $D(4,-2)$.

14. On rectangular coordinate paper draw the line that

   a. passes through the origin and has a slope of -1.

   b. passes through $(3,-2)$ and has a slope of 2.

   c. passes through $(3,0)$ and has a slope of $\frac{1}{2}$.

   d. passes through $(-2,-2)$ and has a slope of 0.

15. Prove that the line which joins the points $D(2,1)$ and $E(12,5)$ is parallel to the line which joins the points $F(4,4)$ and $G(14,8)$.

16. Prove that the line which joins the points $R(-8,2)$ and $S(-2,10)$ is perpendicular to the line which joins the points $T(-9,9)$ and $U(7,-3)$.

17. What is the locus of points for which $x=-3$?

18. What is the locus of points for which $y=5$?

19. What is the locus of points whose ordinate is five times its abscissa?

20. What is the locus of points whose ordinate is 4 less than 3 times its abscissa?

21. Write the equation of the line which passes through the point $(-5,3)$ and whose slope is $\frac{1}{4}$.

22. What is the locus of points 6 units from the origin?

23. Find the area of a parallelogram whose vertices are $D(-2,-8)$, $E(-2,4)$, $F(-7,7)$, and $G(-7,-5)$.

24. Find the area of a triangle whose vertices are $R(-6,3)$, $S(4,11)$, and $T(9,5)$. Show two solutions.

25. On the same set of axes draw the graph of each of the equations $x=-3$, $y=-x$, and $y=-4x$. Find the coordinates of the vertices of the triangle whose sides are the line segments joining the points of intersection of the graphs. Find the area of this triangle.

26. The vertices of a triangle are $D(0,0)$, $E(b,0)$, and $F(x,y)$. How is the area affected if

   a. x is doubled and b and y are constant.

   b. b is doubled and x and y are constant.

   c. b and y are doubled and x is constant.

CHAPTER TEST

1. Plot the points $A(-5,4)$, $B(7,-1)$, and $C(1,8)$. Show that triangle ABC is a right triangle.

2. Prove that the quadrilateral formed by joining the consecutive midpoints of the quadrilateral whose vertices are $(1,3)$, $(5,1)$, $(9,7)$, and $(3,9)$ is a parallelogram.

3. Show that the quadrilateral whose vertices are $A(4,-10)$, $B(10,-4)$, $C(4,2)$, and $D(-2,-4)$ is equilateral. Show that the diagonals of this quadrilateral are equal. What type of quadrilateral is this?

4. Find the slope of the line which passes through the points $R(2,8)$ and $S(10,4)$. If point $T(-2,y)$ lies on this line, find the value of y.

5. Prove that the points $D(2,3)$, $E(8,9)$, and $F(11,12)$ are collinear.

6. The vertices of a triangle are $D(2,9)$, $E(10,3)$, and $F(-2,2)$. Find the area of triangle DEF. Find the length of side DE. Find the length of the altitude from point F to side DE.

7. Find the distance between the points $(-6,3)$ and $(4,3)$ and give the coordinates of the midpoint of the line segment joining the two points.

8. Prove that the line which joins the points $A(-5,5)$ and $B(4,2)$ is perpendicular to the line which joins the points $C(5,5)$ and $D(1,-7)$.

9. What is the locus of points 9 units from the origin? Give a sentence answer and also write the equation.

10. Write the equation of the line which passes through the point $(9,6)$ and whose slope is $\frac{1}{3}$.

TABLE OF SQUARE ROOTS

N	$\sqrt{N}$	N	$\sqrt{N}$	N	$\sqrt{N}$	N	$\sqrt{N}$	N	$\sqrt{N}$
1	1.000	51	7.141	101	10.050	151	12.288	201	14.177
2	1.414	52	7.211	102	10.100	152	12.329	202	14.213
3	1.732	53	7.280	103	10.149	153	12.369	203	14.248
4	2.000	54	7.348	104	10.198	154	12.410	204	14.283
5	2.236	55	7.416	105	10.247	155	12.450	205	14.318
6	2.449	56	7.483	106	10.296	156	12.490	206	14.353
7	2.646	57	7.550	107	10.344	157	12.530	207	14.387
8	2.828	58	7.616	108	10.392	158	12.570	208	14.422
9	3.000	59	7.681	109	10.440	159	12.610	209	14.457
10	3.162	60	7.746	110	10.488	160	12.649	210	14.491
11	3.317	61	7.810	111	10.536	161	12.689	211	14.526
12	3.464	62	7.874	112	10.583	162	12.728	212	14.560
13	3.606	63	7.937	113	10.630	163	12.767	213	14.595
14	3.742	64	8.000	114	10.677	164	12.806	214	14.629
15	3.873	65	8.062	115	10.724	165	12.845	215	14.663
16	4.000	66	8.124	116	10.770	166	12.884	216	14.697
17	4.123	67	8.185	117	10.817	167	12.923	217	14.731
18	4.243	68	8.246	118	10.863	168	12.961	218	14.765
19	4.359	69	8.307	119	10.909	169	13.000	219	14.799
20	4.472	70	8.367	120	10.954	170	13.038	220	14.832
21	4.583	71	8.426	121	11.000	171	13.077	221	14.866
22	4.690	72	8.485	122	11.045	172	13.115	222	14.900
23	4.796	73	8.544	123	11.091	173	13.153	223	14.933
24	4.899	74	8.602	124	11.136	174	13.191	224	14.967
25	5.000	75	8.660	125	11.180	175	13.229	225	15.000
26	5.099	76	8.718	126	11.225	176	13.266	226	15.033
27	5.196	77	8.775	127	11.269	177	13.304	227	15.067
28	5.292	78	8.832	128	11.314	178	13.342	228	15.100
29	5.385	79	8.888	129	11.358	179	13.379	229	15.133
30	5.477	80	8.944	130	11.402	180	13.416	230	15.166
31	5.568	81	9.000	131	11.446	181	13.454	231	15.199
32	5.657	82	9.055	132	11.489	182	13.491	232	15.232
33	5.745	83	9.110	133	11.533	183	13.528	233	15.264
34	5.831	84	9.165	134	11.576	184	13.565	234	15.297
35	5.916	85	9.220	135	11.619	185	13.601	235	15.330
36	6.000	86	9.274	136	11.662	186	13.638	236	15.362
37	6.083	87	9.327	137	11.705	187	13.675	237	15.395
38	6.164	88	9.381	138	11.747	188	13.711	238	15.427
39	6.245	89	9.434	139	11.790	189	13.748	239	15.460
40	6.325	90	9.487	140	11.832	190	13.784	240	15.492
41	6.403	91	9.539	141	11.874	191	13.820	241	15.524
42	6.481	92	9.592	142	11.916	192	13.856	242	15.556
43	6.557	93	9.644	143	11.958	193	13.892	243	15.588
44	6.633	94	9.695	144	12.000	194	13.928	244	15.620
45	6.708	95	9.747	145	12.042	195	13.964	245	15.652
46	6.782	96	9.798	146	12.083	196	14.000	246	15.684
47	6.856	97	9.849	147	12.124	197	14.036	247	15.716
48	6.928	98	9.899	148	12.166	198	14.071	248	15.748
49	7.000	99	9.950	149	12.207	199	14.107	249	15.780
50	7.071	100	10.000	150	12.247	200	14.142	250	15.811

N	√N	N	√N	N	√N	N	√N	N	√N
251	15.843	301	17.349	351	18.735	401	20.025	451	21.237
252	15.875	302	17.378	352	18.762	402	20.450	452	21.260
253	15.906	303	17.407	353	18.788	403	20.075	453	21.284
254	15.937	304	17.436	354	18.815	404	20.100	454	21.307
255	15.969	305	17.464	355	18.841	405	20.125	455	21.331
256	16.000	306	17.493	356	18.868	406	20.149	456	21.354
257	16.031	307	17.521	357	18.894	407	20.174	457	21.378
258	16.062	308	17.550	358	18.921	408	20.199	458	21.401
259	16.093	309	17.578	359	18.947	409	20.224	459	21.424
260	16.125	310	17.607	360	18.974	410	20.248	460	21.448
261	16.155	311	17.635	361	19.000	411	20.273	461	21.471
262	16.186	312	17.664	362	19.026	412	20.298	462	21.494
263	16.217	313	17.692	363	19.053	413	20.322	463	21.517
264	16.248	314	17.720	364	19.079	414	20.347	464	21.541
265	16.279	315	17.748	365	19.105	415	20.372	465	21.564
266	16.310	316	17.776	366	19.131	416	20.396	466	21.587
267	16.340	317	17.804	367	19.157	417	20.421	467	21.610
268	16.371	318	17.833	368	19.183	418	20.445	468	21.633
269	16.401	319	17.861	369	19.209	419	20.469	469	21.656
270	16.432	320	17.889	370	19.235	420	20.494	470	21.679
271	16.462	321	17.916	371	19.261	421	20.518	471	21.703
272	16.492	322	17.944	372	19.287	422	20.543	472	21.726
273	16.523	323	17.972	373	19.313	423	20.567	473	21.749
274	16.553	324	18.000	374	19.339	424	20.591	474	21.772
275	16.583	325	18.028	375	19.365	425	20.616	475	21.794
276	16.613	326	18.055	376	19.391	426	20.640	476	21.817
277	16.643	327	18.083	377	19.416	427	20.664	477	21.840
278	16.673	328	18.111	378	19.442	428	20.688	478	21.863
279	16.703	329	18.138	379	19.468	429	20.712	479	21.886
280	16.733	330	18.166	380	19.494	430	20.736	480	21.909
281	16.763	331	18.193	381	19.519	431	20.761	481	21.932
282	16.793	332	18.221	382	19.545	432	20.785	482	21.954
283	16.823	333	18.248	383	19.570	433	20.809	483	21.977
284	16.852	334	18.276	384	19.596	434	20.833	484	22.000
285	16.882	335	18.303	385	19.621	435	20.857	485	22.023
286	16.912	336	18.330	386	19.647	436	20.881	486	22.045
287	16.941	337	18.358	387	19.672	437	20.905	487	22.068
288	16.971	338	18.385	388	19.698	438	20.928	488	22.091
289	17.000	339	18.412	389	19.723	439	20.952	489	22.113
290	17.029	340	18.439	390	19.748	440	20.976	490	22.136
291	17.059	341	18.466	391	19.774	441	21.000	491	22.159
292	17.088	342	18.493	392	19.799	442	21.024	492	22.181
293	17.117	343	18.520	393	19.824	443	21.048	493	22.204
294	17.146	344	18.547	394	19.849	444	21.071	494	22.226
295	17.176	345	18.574	395	19.875	445	21.095	495	22.249
296	17.205	346	18.601	396	19.900	446	21.119	496	22.271
297	17.234	347	18.628	397	19.925	447	21.142	497	22.294
298	17.263	348	18.655	398	19.950	448	21.166	498	22.316
299	17.292	349	18.682	399	19.975	449	21.190	499	22.338
300	17.321	350	18.708	400	20.000	450	21.213	500	22.361

GLOSSARY-INDEX